To chery!

RAY HODGSON

HEARTBREAK
IN THE HIMALAYAS

based on a true story

So blessed to
meet you !.

Enjoy
God bless
Dr Ray

First published by Busybird Publishing 2019
Copyright © 2018 Ray Hodgson

ISBN 978-1-925830-54-5

Cover design: Busybird Publishing
Layout and typesetting: Busybird Publishing
Editor: Laura McCluskey

Busybird Publishing
2/118 Para Road
Montmorency, Victoria
Australia 3094

www.busybird.com.au

Dedication

For Tamika and Eloise, who inspire me every waking day.

Drama in Theatre: Part I

Camp 3, Mid-Western Nepal
Day #3. 6:30pm, Operating Theatre

It will be dark soon. The power is sure to go out at any minute and we'll have no light. To have any chance of completing this operation we'll need the hand-held torches.

This is our fifth and final operation for the day. Our team of volunteers must be as weary as I am. For the past two hours we've been operating on a woman named Dilli. Dilli is 28 years old, and a mother of four young children. Like almost all of our patients, she suffers from severe genital prolapse. We've only known Dilli for the 48 hours leading up to her surgery today, but during this time she's won enormous respect from our surgical team with her resilience and grace in the face of her dreadful affliction.

Four years earlier, Dilli's bladder, bowel and uterus burst through her vaginal entrance and sat painfully between her upper thighs. She has been incontinent of urine every day now for three years. Sexual intercourse has been impossible. A year ago, ulcers appeared over the mass of prolapsed tissue, and in recent months the ulcers have often become infected.

We can fix this woman. We can get rid of this fetid mass and put her bladder and bowel back where they belong. We can take away her chronic pain and stop her incontinence. We can restore her sexual function. We can restore her dignity.

We just need more light …

6:52pm

The lights go out.

Ah, the Nepalese electrical grid-sharing system – on days like these it seems to deliberately challenge our surgical camps.

Our team members find every conceivable source of light to shine into our deep, dark operating field. They struggle to find the best angle to hold the battery-powered lights. These lights are getting dim. Despite months of planning we usually neglect one thing or another on our camps. This time it's the torch batteries. How could we miss that?

As the light gradually fades, it's a race against time to finish this operation. This is becoming dangerous. There is bleeding – there is always some bleeding – but this is heavier than usual, and in the dimming light I struggle to see the source of the blood loss. In a desperate effort to improve my view of the convoluted web of blood vessels and nerves and ligaments, I ask for immediate suction to quickly clear the blood from the area. But I'm reminded that the suction machine also relies on electrical power; we will have no suction until the power returns, and this will be at least another hour. Swabs will have to do.

We continue to apply pressure and mop up the blood in an effort to find the source of this bleeding. An hour ago we ran out of standard surgical swabs. We've improvised with pieces of drapes that our resourceful nurses have cut into small squares.

Despite every effort, things go from bad to worse as the volume of blood loss escalates. It becomes clear that the situation is now critical. Dilli's blood pressure begins to fall in response. At home we would transfuse this woman immediately, but here we work with limited facilities. The nearest blood bank is in Pokhara – nine hours away. The theatre team are silent as they grasp the gravity of the situation. We are now at crisis point.

We use our hands to apply pressure to the general area of bleeding. This settles the blood loss temporarily, long enough to allow us to catch our breath, to think.

'What is this woman's blood type?' I ask.

Mack, our anaesthetist replies. 'B Positive. But, Ray, you know we have no blood bank.'

B Positive is an uncommon blood group. I realise that our chances of finding a match are even smaller.

'Alright,' I say, my heart in my mouth, 'who else in this room has the blood type B Positive?'

Fazi, a junior Nepalese doctor with a soft, gentle voice says, 'I am blood type B Positive.'

'Have you been screened recently for HIV and hepatitis B and C?'

'I have, and I am negative for these viruses.'

'Then I need to ask for a very big gift from you. We need you to donate a litre of your blood to transfuse directly into this woman. It will possibly save her life.'

Fazi does not hesitate; she appears proud that she can play a crucial part in helping this woman. Our team quickly arrange another table in theatre next to our bleeding patient, and Fazi lays down next to her. Within 10 minutes, precious, whole blood is flowing from Fazi to Dilli. We have a reprieve.

Paul – our ever-reliable theatre aid – remembers that his mobile phone still has some charge. He moves to an area above my right shoulder, points his phone towards the operating field, and turns on the torch function. Light – gorgeous, dazzling, radiant light!

We quickly see the haemorrhaging pelvic vessels and suture these tightly to arrest the bleeding. After another 30 minutes we complete this demanding operation.

Despite the struggles and the near disaster during the surgery, Dilli will recover completely.

The team have been fantastic. The conditions here are really challenging. Our camp is on the edge of a mountain in the foothills of the spectacular Himalayas. And it's cold – really cold – and it will get even colder when that sun disappears in a few minutes. But no one in the team complains. It's something I notice on each of the camps we have run to date: the harsher the conditions, the greater the resilience, and the stronger the bond between the team members. A wonderful camaraderie develops with these volunteer adventures.

Is it the shared burden? Is it the simple joy we all get from making a difference to the abysmal lives of these underprivileged women? I guess it's a combination of the two.

At dinner tonight we'll all crowd together in the Dining Hall to suck in every bit of heat from the ridiculously small potbelly stove that will do its best to warm our cold, weary bodies. And like nearly every night here, we'll be exhausted, but content.

And yet...

After dinner as we all sit there huddled together, I watch that tiny stove as it struggles with the impossible task of heating the huge room to anything near a comfortable temperature. But this will never happen; the natural elements are far too overpowering for this pintsized potbelly.

As I stare into the small flames, the stove takes on a bizarre, distorted human form. I know this stove. I know its twisted, writhing face. And I understand the reasons it squirms and spits and contorts. We are brothers, this stove and I. We both struggle in grossly one-sided battles. The number of women enduring appallingly poor health in Nepal is immense. Despite the valiant attempts of our organisation, I wonder if we can really make a major difference to the overwhelming numbers of women suffering in this beautiful, desperate country.

*

Most of the team have gone off to bed. The only two team members who remain in the room are Louise and I, and we sit together in the dim, flickering light of the dying embers. Shadows dance off the walls of the Dining Hall, bringing the room alive as if all of the volunteers were still here, animated but silent.

Louise is a midwife, a registered nurse, a leader in our team, and a wonderfully wise and loyal friend. 'Okay, Ray,' she says. 'Want to tell me what's bothering you?'

I give an uneasy sigh. 'We're not making inroads, Lu Lu. There is so much prolapse here. I know it's only our first camp in this part of Nepal, but we're not even scratching the surface.'

'But, Ray, you know there's only so much we can do. We're treating as many women as we possibly can each day, and we're transforming their lives.'

The problem is that when we leave this camp we'll also leave behind hundreds of women we've been unable to treat. There's simply nowhere near enough time or resources to treat the enormous numbers of women suffering from genital prolapse in this country.

We want to feel like we've made a big difference here – we all do. But on our final day here when we're packing up to leave, I know it will be just like the end of our other camps: there'll be so many untreated women with faces of forlorn hope. And just like the other camps, their wretched looks will weigh on us, long after we've returned home. We all get the joy and fulfilment from improving the lives of the women we treat, but too often this is eclipsed by the despair of the women we can't help.

'Lu Lu,' I say, 'it's not only that. We nearly lost a patient today. This is *elective* surgery; this is not emergency surgery. What went wrong today with Dilli was almost fatal, and it was entirely preventable. Obviously I take responsibility for the near miss, but we've got to do everything we can to make sure these mistakes never happen again. Batteries – can you believe it? Batteries, for God's sake!'

Louise begins to speak, but I cut her off – I'm on a roll now.

'I get the buzz, too, Lu Lu; I get that sense of exhilaration when we manage to fix these women who've suffered so much. But whenever I look at the bigger picture I feel we're not really helping at all. How many women do we treat on each of these camps – 40 or 50? By the time we return to this part of Nepal next year there'll be at least another hundred women here with prolapse. We're going backwards. There has to be another way.'

Louise responds in her reassuring style. 'Ray, you're way too hard on yourself. It's wrong to overlook the colossal effects we're having on so many women. Most of these women were destitute before we came along. Just think how many women would still be suffering if we weren't running these camps.'

But Louise's words of encouragement sound distant, and I sense in her that she, too, has some doubts. Even though our days are full and our resources are stretched, we can surely do more, and do it better.

What is Genital Prolapse?

It's a lot to expect from the pelvis of any woman: support all those pelvic organs – uterus, bowel, and bladder – with nothing more than a few slender muscles and ligaments and some thin strips of connective tissue. This is the job of the pelvic floor – hold those organs in place, stop them from falling down – and do this, year after year, despite of the forces of gravity, coughing, laughing and lifting. Then add to this the concept that these delicate supporting tissues must also cope with the weight of a full-term pregnancy and the ravages of childbirth. It's no wonder these structures wear and tear, and in so many women, eventually fail. When this happens, the pelvic organs slip down from their normal position and protrude into the vagina. This is genital prolapse.

If the prolapse progresses, the organs protrude beyond the vaginal entrance and present as a lump between the thighs. It's these more severe forms of prolapse that we see by the thousands in our surgery camps in Nepal.

Symptoms of Genital Prolapse:
Early stages

So many women are unaware of the early stages of prolapse. They're often surprised to learn of their prolapse when it's discovered during a routine pelvic examination or a Cervical Screening Test. The pelvic organs are bulging into the vaginal canal but there is nothing visible at the vaginal entrance.

Other women with early stage prolapse describe a sensation of heaviness or an ache in the vagina or lower back, particularly towards the end of the day or after prolonged standing. Some women experience urinary problems like the sense of urgency, hesitancy, or incontinence. Others can't completely empty their bowel.

Later stages

This was Dilli's disorder before her surgery with us, and this is the disorder of the large majority of women who present to our camps; organs plunge through the vaginal opening and sit, often painfully, between the woman's thighs. Uterus, bowel, or bladder – but often all three organs – protrude through the vagina.

This area of the body is so emotionally sensitive that even in an educated woman, deformities like these are really disturbing. But in rural Nepal, where the large majority of women have a very limited understanding of anatomy and medical disorders, the grief of severe prolapse can be harrowing.

In these later stages of prolapse, activities like walking and working lead to more intense cramping pain. And yet, most women living in rural Nepal are farm workers; their lives revolve around heavy, physical work. With the severe forms of prolapse, bladder and bowel symptoms can be debilitating. In many, it's not possible to empty the bladder or bowel until the lump is pushed back with the hand or some other object. So many of the women we see leak urine or faeces continually. If the prolapsed tissues become infected, the woman will develop a foul-smelling discharge.

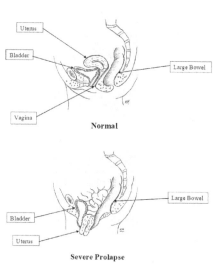

Normal

Severe Prolapse

Sexual intercourse may be possible if the prolapsed organs are pushed back into the vaginal canal, but even if this is achieved, intercourse will often be distressingly painful. In many women with these more severe forms of prolapse, intercourse is impossible.

Treatment of Genital Prolapse

The secret is to tackle the problem in its very early stages, or better yet, prevent prolapse from occurring in the first place. If it's detected early enough, we can usually prevent the pelvic organs from falling further into the vaginal canal and beyond. In these early stages, it's all about lifestyle.

In the West, most women are aware of the importance of pelvic floor exercises. Those seeking treatment for early stage prolapse will be advised to avoid heavy lifting and constipation, and to brace their pelvic floor with any strenuous activities. But in developing countries most women are ignorant of these really important lifestyle changes. And even if these women do receive advice, the chances of them taking this on board are remote.

In moderately advanced stages of prolapse, a pessary can often be inserted into the vagina to assist in the support of the pelvic organs. A vaginal pessary is a small device, usually in the shape of a ring. Many women use pessaries to successfully support their prolapsing tissues, and they'll often experience some relief of their bladder or bowel problems. However it's fairly common for the device to simply fall out. In others the pessary leads to vaginal irritation or infection. In elderly, postmenopausal women, the thin tissues of the vaginal wall are prone to ulceration from the pessary. In some cases, complications have included impaction or entrapment of the pessary, bowel and bladder fistulas, and rarely, bowel perforation and sepsis.[1]

In all cases the pessary must be changed every three to six months to detect early ulceration and to prevent entrapment of the device. The initial insertion and the regular checkups usually require medically-trained personnel.

In severe forms of prolapse where pelvic organs have fallen well past the vaginal opening, surgery is usually necessary. This may involve a 'vaginal repair' where the damaged pelvic floor ligaments are tightened, or a partial or total hysterectomy, where the cervix or entire uterus is removed through the vagina.

Surgical Rounds

Day #4. 7:00am, Postoperative Ward

Our five women from yesterday's surgery all seem to be doing really well. Thankfully, this includes Dilli, who waves to us as we enter the ward. Our two official interpreters are not available this morning, so one of the local nurses, Sangina, has joined our ward round to help out with translation. Sangina has a limited English vocabulary, but she's keen to do the best she can.

On the first day following surgery, most women have some pelvic pains, but we ask Sangina to explain to them that this discomfort will be temporary. As usual, the painkillers we prescribe are highly effective – most of these women have never been exposed to any form of narcotic. As a result, we simply don't see drug tolerance in this part of the world.

Further up the ward we see the postoperative patients from the surgery our team performed two and three days ago. It's always so gratifying to see this group of women walking around the ward fairly freely. Some are beginning to smile – expressions we haven't seen for the whole time they've been at the camp. They don't speak our language, and when we're without interpreters, the women communicate with their dark, brown sugar eyes. When we first meet these women a day or two before surgery, their eyes are full of fear and sadness. Two or three days following the surgery the same eyes radiate wonder and joy, and sometimes exhilaration. This is probably the most rewarding and uplifting part of each camp. That hideous, painful lump that has often been present for many years, that deformity that has caused so much shame – it's gone now. The bladder no longer leaks uncontrollably. And most importantly: they've recovered their self-respect and dignity.

But something's wrong with Anjula. Anjula is a shy, 26-year old woman who underwent the surgical correction of her advanced genital prolapse three days ago. Her surgery went well at the time, but now she sits alone and silent. As we approach her, she lifts her head. Her eyes don't show the joy or glee of the others – instead they're filled with tears.

'*Didi**,' I say, 'are you in pain?'

Sangina translates my question.

Anjula looks down towards the floor and shakes her head quickly.

'Then what upsets you?' I ask. I look to Sangina, who doesn't appear to understand my question, so I rephrase.

'Why sadness?'

Sangina translates my simpler question, and repeats Anjula's answer to me in English.

'Dr Ray, *Didi* no pain. *Didi* happy. She cry for happy.'

Then, as is if to ease our own fears of disappointment, Anjula stands and hugs each one of us surgical team members. It's so unusual to see people hugging in this part of the world. Public displays of affection are so rare in rural Nepal, even between husband and wife, and we're caught off guard. I look across to see my own team members' eyes welling up with tears. This ward round has turned in to a blubbering mess!

But as I stand back and look more closely into Anjula's eyes, I begin to wonder if there is more to her tears than simple joy. Although her eyes are moist, they do not sparkle; I'm sure there's a sadness in there. Despite her smiles and hugs, something seems to be troubling this lovely woman. And it frustrates me that right now we can't explore this further.

*

---

* *Didi* is a common Nepali word that's used to address an older or a younger sister, but it's also a friendly term used to refer to other women roughly in your generation

Generally, most postoperative patients would be able to go home on the third or fourth day following surgery. This is the routine in Australia, and most Western countries; a few days following prolapse surgery women are advised to return home to rest for the next four to six weeks.

This is so not the case in rural Nepal. The return trip home is a walk, which can often take days. Roads don't exist in most parts of this country, and walking tracks involve a great deal of physically demanding climbs and descents.

Once the women reach their homes, many are expected (and often compelled) to return to heavy physical work, and even sexual intercourse well before their surgical wounds have healed. When women fail to rest adequately following their surgery it's far more common for them to develop recurrent prolapse and other complications. To protect our postoperative patients from problems like these, we've learned that it's safer to keep most of them in our small hospital for a week or more following their surgery.

7:45am, Preliminary Assessment Clinic.

So many women are here already. It's daunting to see hundreds of people queuing at the clinic registration point, but I reassure myself that many of these people are not here for treatment. Most women are with friends for support. In some cases four or five friends have joined the woman on her walk from her village to our camp. There are a few men among the large crowd – presumably the husbands of some of the women who queue.

I check the clinic register to see that 150 women have enlisted today in the hope that they might be cured of their various ailments. Some arrived the evening before and have camped overnight in the cold, harsh conditions. It's slow, often tedious work to sift through the medical problems of these despairing women. And this would be almost impossible without the help of our tireless interpreters, and the two Nepalese doctors we've employed to assist us with this camp. Frustratingly there are so many dialects among the queuing women, even in this relatively small area of Nepal, and this makes the job of interpreting really challenging at times.

A number of women who turn up to the camp don't suffer with prolapse, but instead have heard of a 'Free Women's Health Camp' and assume that we're here to treat all female medical disorders. Many have aches and pains and pelvic infections, and with our limited supplies we do our best to treat these conditions.

Most women dress in brightly coloured saris and shawls, and this gives the first impression that they're reasonably well off. But we know by now that the vast majority of these women are impoverished, and that they depend on the demanding work of subsistence farming for their livelihood. Mid- and Far-Western Nepal suffer from protracted food deficit, and despite national and international food aid programs, the region is plagued by chronic malnutrition, particularly of mothers and children. The bright garments the women wear are often the only full set of clothes they own. Most don't even possess underwear.

As usual, severe genital prolapse is rife again today. The suffering of these dejected women is heart-wrenching. We try our best to remain detached as we examine one severely affected woman after another. Many have inserted everyday items into the vagina in a desperate effort to keep their falling organs at bay. During the pelvic examination we remove stones, bark, dried mud and other objects that, in many cases, seem to have been inside for months. The vibrant clothes of so many of the prolapse patients reek of the unmistakeable odour of stale urine.

Did we really complain of the cold conditions last night when we had the luxury of clean clothes and warm blankets? Once again, I remind myself that it's a simple quirk of fate that I was born in Australia, a country that is, by world standards, so very affluent.

After a little less than two hours of medical assessment and triage we've whittled down the initial group of around 150 general patients to 62 with symptomatic genital prolapse. Perhaps half of these will be suitable for conservative treatment with a ring pessary, but we must be very carefully selective with this group. With every woman who is fitted with a pessary there must be no doubt in our minds that she'll return regularly, either to our medical post or another where she can be seen by health workers who are familiar with vaginal pessary management. At the beginning of each camp we spend considerable time with each of our interpreters, stressing the importance of precise translation of the women's medical problems and our proposed treatments. This includes getting across accurate advice to every woman who receives a pessary. Our two official interpreters for this camp, Gamika and Nabin both appear adept, but there are still times I'm fearful that the woman with her new pessary may be lost in the follow-up.

From our large group today we now have 29 women with prolapse that is so severe a ring pessary can't hold back the uterus and other pelvic organs; surgery is the only effective means of treatment in this group. Unfortunately, as with the women in all camps, many of this severe prolapse group suffer with additional medical problems that make it too hazardous for them to undergo surgery in such a remote area. Many have a productive chronic cough – a result of their exposure to the smoke from their cooking, or local cigarettes. In some, the cough produces specks of blood, and in these women we suspect tuberculosis, or lung cancer. In this isolated corner of the world, at this moment in time, there is nothing we can do for these hapless women.

In other women we find various forms of congenital heart disease – conditions that in our own country would usually be treated with surgery in infancy. There is virtually no prospect of these women ever undergoing such surgery. Once again, we're reminded of our own good fortune.

Of the 150 women who presented to our camp today, nine will benefit from surgical correction of their severe genital prolapse, as they appear medically suitable to undergo the rigours of this surgery. Today we'll run a few screening tests on these women to confirm they're medically fit. All being well, they'll then be ready to undergo surgery tomorrow.

Our next problem is that each day we only have time (and energy) to carry out five operations, six if we're lucky. What do we do with the three or four women who will miss out on their surgery tomorrow? We can postpone their operations until the following day, but by this time we will have accumulated several other women requiring surgery; there may not even be time on that day.

We can't simply send these women home and ask them to return for treatment in a few weeks or months – our surgical team are unlikely to return to this part of Nepal for another 12 months. On top of this, many women here have walked for days (and in considerable discomfort) to reach our camp. Every one of us on the camp wants to treat as many women as possible, but we realise that in a few weeks' time when this camp ends, a number of bitterly disappointed women with severe forms of genital prolapse will remain. As with every surgical camp we run, this will sour our departure.

Even though it's really fulfilling to treat severe forms of genital prolapse in Nepal, at this stage our work is a drop in the ocean of this pervasive disease. In a country where there are vast numbers of women suffering with severe genital prolapse, it was short-sighted and even naïve to think we could make inroads by operating on a handful of women each day for a three- or four-week volunteer camp every few months.

Part of our strategy is to train as many local Nepalese surgeons as possible to allow them to continue this work when we leave each camp, but this has become more challenging than we'd expected. Our two local doctors with this camp, Fazi and Laya, are general doctors from Pokhara. Neither has an interest in performing surgery, and they've come along simply to help out with general medical care. Two other general surgeons from Kathmandu were supposed to be here to undergo surgical training with our team, but it's the fourth day of the camp, and neither has arrived.

A Curious Encounter

9:30am

While we've been assessing the hordes of women this morning in the Preliminary Assessment Clinic, our theatre nursing team have been setting up for today's surgery. Our path from the clinic to our operating theatre is a pleasant five-minute stroll along a narrow track through paddies brimming with tall green rice stubble. I'm glad the theatre is set away from the clinic, because the morning walk gives us a chance to clear our minds and prepare ourselves for the surgical day in store.

Our anaesthetist for this camp, Mack, walks with me through the lush highland fields. As we breathe in the bracing mountain air, we take in the shifting scenes that surround us. Today our path is carpeted with thousands of golden-red leaves that have been recently cast away in the late autumn air. For all their gaiety and splendour, the leaves are fragile as they crunch under our stodging feet.

Mack's attention has also been drawn to the colourful display. 'Poetry, Ray, poetry,' he says as he stares at our striking trail. 'Not for the *ears*. Poetry for the *eyes*.'

We both look up to the source of the fallen leaves. Several poplar trees soar above the bristling paddies. They stand tall and proud, their arms extended as if to protect the delicate life below. Most of their changing leaves remain attached to the branches as the hulking tree bodies sway almost imperceptibly in the cool mountain breeze.

I stoop down and pick up one of the fragile tangerine leaves. The leaf has the shape of a heart with fine serrated sides. As I admire its elegant beauty, I run my finger along its uneven edge. There is a sudden sharp pain, and I'm surprised to see that the leaf has cut deeply into my finger to draw bright blood.

Mack looks at the bleeding cut. 'There's love, right there,' he says. 'Beautiful, gentle, but sometimes oh-so-painful.'

'Quite the philosopher today, Mack,' I say as I apply pressure to the bleeding, and we continue our stroll along the theatre path.

As we approach the operating theatre we're confronted by a Nepalese man I've not seen before. The man is squatting on the edge of the path ahead of us, and I assume he's a local farmer tending to his crops of rice. But as we get closer the man jumps up and faces us. Most Nepalese men are short by Western standards, but this man is one of the shortest I've seen. He has no obvious features of dwarfism or other skeletal disorder; his limbs and body appear in proportion. The man is clearly an adult – his face suggests he is at least 50 years old. It's as if he just stopped growing far too soon.

The man has in his hands a timber crate the size of a large suitcase. He places the crate on the ground between himself and us, and then stands on the container. Once he's steadied himself he stares at me with eyes that are grey and piercing. Despite the boost from his crate, the man's eye line remains several centimetres below mine. His grey-white hair is long and scraggly, with some tied loosely back in an untidy ponytail. Mack and I have stopped a metre in front of this curious man on his crate and I have no idea what is happening or what will happen next.

Then, in silence, the man steps down and moves his crate closer to me. The container is now almost touching my toes. As Mack and I stand there, bewildered, the man climbs back onto the crate and again stares into my eyes. His stare is penetrating, his frown deep in concentration as if he's trying to read something in my eyes. Initially I'm simply bemused at this bizarre confrontation, but as this peculiar man's eyes take on a wild, fanatical look, I begin to feel quite unsettled.

Mack breaks the silence. 'Friend of yours, Ray?' he jokes. 'Seems to like you a lot.'

'Ah, not exactly my type, Mack.'

Finally the strange little man begins to speak. His words are in Nepali, the delivery rich and strong. As his powerful address progresses, the volume and vigour increase. After 20 or 30 seconds he is almost shouting, with a passion that matches the fervour of his face. I have no idea what he is saying, and I can't work out if he is angry or simply excited. He continues his incomprehensible rant, and then grabs my left hand. He places my hand in both of his and squeezes firmly. I'm surprised at the strength of a person so small.

The man's eyes close and, while squeezing my hand between his two, he moves my arm slowly to the sky and then to the ground. His bellowing is even louder now. He repeats these movements two or three times before letting go of my hand and becoming silent again. He steps off his crate, picks it up, and then, as if nothing at all had happened, walks past Mack and me towards the clinic.

'Some interesting customs they have here, Mack.'

'What on earth do you make of all that?' he asks.

'I'm not sure if that was a blessing or a curse. This land never ceases to intrigue me.'

Amused and baffled by the morning's unexpected theatrics, Mack and I resume our short walk to the operating theatre and begin our surgery for the day.

Part of me desperately wants to learn the meaning of this bizarre encounter with this peculiar, haunting man; it wants to understand his hysterical tirade and solve this morning's mystery. But another part of me wants to remain ignorant, to allow the contemplation of this puzzling confrontation to linger. There is a charm, an allure to mystery, and mystery remains a captivating part of this seductive country.

There is a battle between the desire for discovering truth, and the desire for preserving wonder. And throughout this battle – reality versus imagination – it is our curiosity that will usually tip the contest in favour of facts. And yet, once the mystery is solved and replaced with knowledge, those delicious elements of charm and allure are lost. These are the inevitable casualties of our fundamental desire to know.

Sixty-Second Summary

7:40 pm, Dining Hall

It's been a good day. Our surgery team treated five cases of severe prolapse, and unlike yesterday, today was all smooth sailing. Paul managed to procure a box of torch batteries from a trekking store a few kilometres from our camp and a large package of surgical swabs arrived from Pokhara this morning. As it turned out we didn't even need the torches today as there were no power outages. But we've learnt our lesson, so in future operating lists we'll be prepared for disruptions like these.

There's a buzz in the air of the Dining Hall tonight; we all share a buoyant mood and there's lots of laughter over a few drinks while we wait for our dinner to arrive. This is usually everyone's favourite time of the day, when we can sit back and relax after a long, fulfilling day's work.

Cheering and applause suddenly erupt from the volunteers, and I look up to see the kitchen hands have burst into the Dining Hall. They're proudly carrying our favourite treat: spicy poppadoms. There are only one or two evenings of each camp when these exquisite little delicacies are available to us, and this simple, delicious surprise adds to the effervescence of the night.

During the evenings around the dinner table, we've made it a ritual that each team member gives an account about something that was significant to him or her during that day. We call this the Sixty-Second Summary. We take it in turns as each volunteer is given the floor to present his or her observations. There are seven of us on this camp and tonight, as with nearly all nights, there are laughs and wisecracks from the floor as each of us delivers the brief reflection.

The most common Sixty-Second Summary is a recount of the heartwarming reactions of the women following their surgery. Sometimes the account is about an interesting local that the volunteer has met earlier in the day, or the discovery of an unusual custom.

Jayne, our gifted theatre nurse stands and talks about her adjustment to the conditions in the camp. Tonight, and on almost all nights, Jayne wears her thick red scarf. The old scarf looks crudely knitted with chunky woolen yarn. It's wrapped twice around her tiny neck, and both ends drape down her legs to almost reach the floor.

'This is my first trip,' Jayne says, 'and I've gotta say, I struggled during the first few days here. I'm so used to having everything we need in theatres back home in Queensland – all the swabs and sutures and instruments and stuff. But where we work here we've got so little, and we run out of things, like, often. I've gotta be honest – it freaked me out a bit at first. I'm so used to being in control. But now, today for the first time, I kind of really enjoy having to make things up as we go along, having to improvise and that. It's like a big adventure, but at the same time I know we're doing all this good. I feel like a pig in mud.'

'You should wash more often, Jayne!' one of the crowd yells out.

'Did you say "pig in mud" or "pig in blood"?' from another.

There are a few predictable 'oink' noises as Jayne realises she's left herself open for the rowdy insults. But she and all of the volunteers laugh at the banter. She sits down with a huge, happy grin.

It's Norman's turn. Norman is a quietly spoken general assistant on our team. Back in Australia, he works as an industrial engineer in a company that produces soft drinks and, like all our volunteers, he's joined our team to help out in any way he can. Norman is stone-faced, and every time he speaks he is serious and restrained. He stands, and turns to Jayne.

'Before I start my sixty seconds, I want to say to you, Jayne that as a theatre scrub nurse, you are the most well-organised, um …competent, um …resourceful pig in mud I have ever known!'

The room erupts with more oinks and snorts and raucous laughter.

Finally, it's my turn for the Sixty-Second spiel. It's difficult because by now the group is in such a jovial mood. They clearly want more material to laugh at, but tonight, what I have to say is more solemn. As I stand, I realise that I will probably break this jubilant air.

'This camp is going really well, even though we nearly lost a patient yesterday. It's so uplifting to see everyone getting on so well together. And I'm especially glad to see everyone's looking after our dirty little piggy here,' I say, turning to Jayne. A few more oinks and snorts break out. 'But more seriously, Louise and I spoke last night. Yeah, we're helping a fair number of women here. In the scheme of things, we're making a small difference. And Louise is right – we should all be proud of that. But in this land of massive genital prolapse, I want you all to pause for a moment.'

I pause myself now, and catching each volunteer's eye in turn, I make sure I have everyone's full attention.

'Rather than just making a *minor* difference, how could we make a *major* difference? What else can we do to really tackle this whole …this …pandemic of prolapse, and turn it on its head? Think about this tonight. Think about this as you're all lying in your beds, in those precious moments before you fall off to sleep. Think about this. We're only a small organisation right now, but one day we'll be really big. Along the way, what can we do so that instead of helping only 40 or 50 women every few months, we help hundreds – no – even that won't be enough. Let's think bigger than that – how can we help *thousands* of women at a time?'

I'm surprised at how quickly the mood does change. I don't want to be a killjoy, and perhaps I could have found a better time to raise my brooding questions. My eye catches Louise's, and she gives me a subtle nod with a wry smile. She understands, and I'm sure she's now feeling the same strange combination of satisfaction and discontent as I am.

The Shame of Genital Prolapse

Australians for Women's Health run prolapse camps in Nepal a few times each year. The village communities learn of the upcoming camps through local radio and by word of mouth from Community Health Workers. Even though large numbers of women turn up to our surgical camps for treatment, there are countless others with advanced prolapse who do not attend. During their time in hospital our patients tell us that many of their friends and relatives suffer severe genital prolapse, but are too ashamed or too fearful to attend the camps.

In many rural areas of Nepal women suffering from genital prolapse are considered impure. Once they reveal their problem to those around them they're often demeaned and shamed by their husbands, their family, and their community. A 'culture of silence' and *laaj* (shame about reproductive health) restricts women from talking about genital problems and pregnancy complications.[2,3,4] In Western Nepal almost a third of Nepalese women with severe prolapse tell no one of their condition. In most cases they keep their prolapse a secret because they're 'embarrassed'.[5] Many of the patients we interview in our surgical camps think that prolapse is a 'normal' condition.

The woman's shame, or ignorance, or fear of condemnation results in delays in contacting healthcare workers until her prolapse has reached the most advanced stages.[3,6] Many of our patients have experienced the pain of severe genital prolapse for years before reporting their problem to a nurse or doctor. During these years of silence about their secret disability, it becomes increasingly more difficult for women to carry out their daily work as their pelvic pain progresses.

For Nepalese women, these effects can prove disastrous for their personal lives since much of their worth in society derives from their ability to successfully reproduce, maintain households, and contribute an income. Many of the afflicted women tell us that their family and friends accuse them of laziness, and that they chasten them for working too little during this extremely difficult time.[7,8]

Among the patriarchal convictions of rural Nepal there is a widespread belief among women and men that a wife should not refuse to have intercourse with her husband. Amnesty International reviews and other studies in rural Nepal report that when women do express a reluctance to have sexual intercourse, many sustain emotional and physical abuse from their husbands.[8,9,10]

In Nepal a large proportion of women suffering with genital prolapse suffer considerable pain during intercourse. Among the women with genital prolapse, United Nations studies found that more than one third of women reported having intercourse with their husband 'unwillingly'.[11] Many women view this type of sexual abuse as 'normal' and 'something that women have to bear'. And yet any sexual act without full, free consent of both parties is defined as rape, and marital rape is criminalised under Nepalese law.[12] In rural Nepal in 2002, only 9% of women and girls had heard about the law of marital rape.[13] And those who had say it made no difference in their ability to say 'no' to their husbands.[14] Women rarely file complaints about domestic violence for 'fear of stigma, lack of resources or legal literacy, lack of safe shelter and other support services, dependence on male relatives to access the legal system, and fear of repercussions, including further abuse'.[15]

Boys and Girls

Day #5. 7:45am, Hospital Path.

After a hearty breakfast our team of seven set off towards our hospital to begin our day's work. Our path follows a deep, slow-flowing stream as it curves its way through the leafy foothills of our camp. Eventually the path widens as we pass through farmland with several small huts that serve as homes.

As with most mornings, a number of young boys run through the fields, yelling and laughing and chasing each other. They're kicking around one of their makeshift soccer balls that they've somehow forged from cardboard scraps. Their breezy antics remind me of the preadolescent boys at home in Australia. When they spot our team today, they stop their game and approach us. A boy of around 10 years addresses us.

'You are American?'

Paul answers, 'No. We are from Australia.'

Each of the boys appears confused.

'Australia,' Paul repeats. 'You know, kangaroos.' He places his hands under his chin and begins to hop like a kangaroo.

'Ahhh,' the boys say, nodding and smiling. 'KanGARoo! KanGARoo!'

They all begin to mimic Paul and hop around with their own impressions of the famous Australian symbol.

The first boy speaks again. 'You play football with us, now?'

'I'm sorry,' Paul replies, 'we can't play with you. We have important work to do in the hospital.'

The boys screw their faces in disappointment, but quickly skip away and return to their eager games.

As we continue our walk to the hospital Jayne says, 'We only ever see the boys playing. So when do the girls get to play then?'

'I haven't seen any girls playing,' says Louise. 'Have you noticed that? All the boys are out having fun, while their sisters always seem to be hard at work with their never-ending chores.'

'I guess it's a cultural thing,' I say. 'It's gotta be intensely frustrating for the girls though.'

'I've spoken to some of the girls here,' says Louise. 'Do you know what they say?'

'I imagine they say that it's cruel and unfair.'

'Come and I'll show you how they express themselves, Ray.'

Ahead of us in an open field, three young girls stoop down, their backs towards us. They appear to be collecting firewood. Louise and I leave our group and walk towards them.

'Watch,' Louise says to me. 'This will be so depressing. *Namaste!*'

Each of the girls freezes in her hunched pose. The middle girl slowly curls her head towards us. Her dark eyes seem too wide for her tiny face. '*Namaste,*' she whispers before looking away.

The three girls slowly stand and move towards each other before turning their bodies in our direction. The other two girls glance at Louise and me, and quickly sink their eyes to the ground. All three appear to be 13 or 14 years old.

'There is no need to be afraid,' Louise says tenderly. 'We are friends.'

But even with these gentle words of reassurance, the girls are silent. They move in closer to one another, their heads still bowed and arms firmly by their sides.

'Do you speak English?' Louise asks.

It's a few moments before the middle girl answers, 'Yes,' she whispers, 'We learn at school.'

'You girls all work so hard,' Louise continues, 'but your brothers just play games. Does this not upset you?'

There is no response from the girls. Their expressions remain low and fixed. Eventually the middle girl glances up again and I catch her eye.

'What is your name?' I ask her.

'Laxmi,' she says softly.

'*Namaste*, Laxmi. My name is Dr Ray, and this is Louise. Our team are here for a few weeks to treat people who are sick. It's lovely to meet you all, and I hope we can see you again soon.'

There is the softest of nods from Laxmi, before she cowers once more. Her two friends remain frozen. Louise and I look across to each other and shake our heads. We turn and walk back towards the hospital path.

'That went well,' I say to Louise. 'We totally won those girls over.'

'We've been here for five days now, Ray. Every young girl I've spoken to is so painfully shy. At least these girls today stayed put when we tried to speak to them. Sometimes they're so timid, they simply run away.'

We understand the concept of 'stranger danger' and its importance in the safety education of children, and we're working in a part of the world where the scourge of child trafficking is a major issue. But it's really disheartening to see these enormous gender disparities entrenched at such an early age.

Jumari

8:20am, Preoperative Assessment Clinic

It's another typical, frenetic morning of prolapse screening as we try to establish some sort of order to the clinic. The women talk and shout in small and large groups as they push ahead for their chance to be assessed. The concept of 'single file' and 'one at a time' is foreign to so many in this part of the world. Louise and Norman do their best to control the crush of the restless crowd. As they coax back the advance of one fold of women, another fold slips in behind them. And as I watch our volunteers' exasperation with this impossible task, I let out a guilty laugh.

I cast my eyes around the masses of people, and my attention is drawn to a young woman who sits alone at the edge of the throng. Her shoulders are slumped and she stares ahead, motionless. She doesn't join the push towards the clinic entrance, and I suspect she may simply be a support person for someone else in the crowd. We continue our screening for another hour or so until the numbers of waiting women have dwindled to only a handful. I decide to leave the final few patients to be assessed by the Fazi and Laya.

As I step outside it's heartening to see that the courtyard is now nearly deserted. But I'm surprised to see that the young, lone woman is still here. She remains hunched and detached. I'm about to walk over to her when I see Louise and the interpreter, Gamika, approaching the woman from the other side of the yard. Louise squats down in front of the woman and begins a conversation. After a few moments

Louise looks up in my direction. She and the young woman stand and then walk hand-in-hand towards me. Gamika follows closely.

'Dr Ray,' Louise says, 'This is Jumari. It sounds like she has some dreadful prolapse. She's walked here alone from her village, and it's taken her three days to get here.'

'*Namaste*, Jumari,' I say. 'It's very brave of you to come so far alone.'

Gamika translates, but there is no response from Jumari. I notice for the first time that she is shaking. I'm not sure if the tremor is due to agitation or a fever, or some other cause.

'We may be able to help you,' I continue. 'Would you mind if we examine you?'

Jumari's eyes are wide and frightened. She trembles as she walks slowly into the clinic while Gamika waits outside. Inside the clinic, I'm now aware of a dreadful odour coming from beneath Jumari's stained clothes. On the examination couch she lifts her sari to reveal a most repulsive sight. Between this young woman's legs sits a mass of rotting tissue that I can only assume is grossly infected prolapse.

Louise and I both impulsively put a hand to our nose and grimace. In all of my years as a gynaecologist I cannot remember a more revolting sight. We look at each other, eyes wide in alarm.

'We need to admit this lady,' I say. 'Right now.'

'Of course,' Louise replies, 'but what are we going to do?'

'The first thing we'll need to do is get this horrible infection under control. Let's get the nurses to clean this up. She'll need saline washes every couple of hours. And let's do some bloods, make sure this infection hasn't spread.'

'And she'll have surgery?'

'Eventually, yes, but there's no way we can operate like this; if we begin cutting into this tissue too soon we'll make things worse. She would never heal.'

I look back to Jumari's face. She stares straight ahead again with no obvious emotion.

'What do you think she's thinking, Ray?'

'Impossible to say. Let's find out as much as we can about her. Can you get Gamika and take a really thorough history? Explain to her that we'll take care of her.'

'Antibiotics?'

'Absolutely. Once you explain what's going on, could you put in an IV line? I'll write up some intravenous antibiotics.'

'Ray. Will we fix this?'

I pause for a moment to think. 'I don't even know what we're dealing with here, Lu Lu. I'm guessing this is a complete prolapse that's all distorted from severe infection. But right now I can't be sure this is not some sort of advanced cancer. Let's not build up her hopes too much right now.'

Just How Common
is Genital Prolapse?

In Nepal it's *really* common. Genital prolapse is the leading cause of morbidity in rural and remote areas of Nepal.[16] It's estimated that over 25-35% of rural Nepalese women are suffering from prolapse[17], and in some districts the prevalence has been shown to be as high as 44.5%.[18] By comparison, the prevalence of genital prolapse in Australia is only around 8-9%[19], and most of these cases are treated in the early stages.

The most commonly quoted survey estimating the prevalence of genital prolapse in Nepal is a United Nations study that showed approximately 600,000 women suffer with the condition. According to this survey, one third of these women are 'in urgent need of surgery'.[20] This figure is alarming enough, but this study almost certainly underestimates the true prevalence of genital prolapse in the country, as the survey only included women of reproductive age (15-49 years). Large numbers of women 50 years of age and over also suffer with severe forms of prolapse.

The distinctive feature of prolapse in Nepal is that the condition has a major impact on *younger* women. In Australia and other Western countries, the majority of genital prolapse occurs in postmenopausal women. The average age of those seeking treatment for prolapse in the West is 61-62 years.[21,22] In Nepal however, prolapse usually appears far earlier in life. In some studies, nearly half of the women with prolapse are younger than 29 years of age.[23] 14% of cases occur before the age of 20.[24]

On average, Nepalese women suffer with their symptoms for at least seven years before seeking medical assistance.[6] By this time the condition has usually progressed to a stage where the only chance of cure is with pelvic floor surgery. Nearly half of all Nepalese women suffering with genital prolapse never receive any treatment.[6]

Poppy

Our surgical camps would be virtually impossible without the solid support of the local Nepalese people. They help us in so many ways with our day-to-day activities. Before each camp begins we make contact with Nepalese families from the local villages, and hire some of them to assist us for the three or so weeks of the camp. Some are employed to help us with our work in the hospital – transporting patients, maintaining the ward and operating theatre, and so on. Others are employed to take care of our daily domestic needs – cooking, cleaning, and washing our clothes. The Nepalese families always appear really pleased to see us; it's clear that the wages they draw from their work with us during those few weeks of the camp are a welcome supplement to their meagre annual incomes.

Almost all of the domestic workers are female, mothers and their daughters. Some of the girls are as young as 11 or 12 years. It's inspiring to watch these tireless, hardworking young people in action, but even though we admire these children, our feelings are mixed with pangs of guilt. The girls get up before dawn and throw themselves into a mountain of chores. They sweep, and clean and scrub, collect wood for the fire, and help prepare breakfast – all before they begin their walk to school.

And in the afternoon when they return from school, they get back into their domestic work, and continue on until well into the evening. Day after day they do this, and to date we haven't heard a single word of complaint.

Day 6#. 6:40 am, Dining Hall.

Our team are all enjoying our usual breakfast of roti and vegetable curry. While we prepare ourselves for the challenging day ahead we practise our very basic Nepalese vocabulary. One of the young helpers – a girl of 12 or 13 years of age – places a pot of tea on the table in front of me.

I look up at her and say, 'We would like some *cheesle tute*, please.'

This is my flimsy Nepalese attempt to ask for *cold milk*. I anticipate the typical tacit response we get from the domestic workers, and that this young girl will simply return in a few minutes, mute, with the milk for my tea. But instead she looks at me and holds my gaze. Can this be happening? A young, rural, Nepalese girl is looking at me in the eye and staring me down.

'I will get cold milk,' she says eventually, 'but is not *"cheesle tute"*. Is *cheeso dute*. You must say *cheeso dute*.'

I smile and say, '*Cheeso dute*'.

Without any hint of a smile herself, she whisks away to fetch my milk. I am astounded.

When the girl returns a little later with my milk, I study her face more closely. It's a pale, chubby little face, sprinkled sparingly with freckles. Her dark, round eyes hold the innocence you'd expect in a child of this age, but there is something else in there, something other than the captivating candour of innocence. These eyes contain the distinctive seeds of confidence.

'What is your name, spirited Nepalese girl?' I ask.

'My name is Ganuradha Shresthra. But because your Nepali words are so bad, you call me Poppy.'

I laugh. 'I'm so glad we can call you Poppy, because you're right – we have no hope of remembering your other name.'

I pour the milk into my tea while Poppy clears some metal plates from the table. 'Why have we not seen you here before, Poppy?'

'Perhaps, Dr Ray, you do not look so properly. I was here also on first day.'

Man – she even knows my name. She has stopped clearing plates and stares again with those entrancing eyes.

'I am sorry that I didn't notice you before, Poppy. Do you enjoy working here?'

'Yes, Dr Ray. I am happy to be working here. It is much better working in eating room than in washing room.'

'And why do you like working here in the "eating room"?'

'In eating room, I talk English. I make my English better.'

'Why do you wish to make your English better?'

'In Nepal, people who do not speak good English are poor; people who speak good English are not poor.'

I look around the breakfast table at the perplexed faces of the other volunteers who witness this strange and totally unexpected conversation. And although my team members do not utter a word, I can see that they, too, realise we're dealing with a very special girl.

For the rest of the day, I dwell on this intriguing conversation with Poppy and her self-confident manner. Here we are again, in another remote area of Nepal, with all its infuriating, patriarchal ways. And here is a young girl, surrounded by gender discrimination and domination; a girl who, despite this repression, somehow develops self-confidence and poise. And on top of all of that she is keen to learn. I smile as I realise that if one girl like Poppy can develop this disposition and spirit, there is so much hope for other young women in this country.

But none of us could have had any idea of the suffering and tragedy that was in store for this fascinating, bourgeoning young girl.

Dilli and Jumari's Progress

The cornerstone to ethical conduct in surgical management involves informed consent prior to treatment, and open disclosure following treatment. This principle applies equally to patients in the West and to those in developing countries.

When surgery is recommended for any patient, it's essential that she understands the risks of the procedure and any adverse events that do occur. In the West, even at the best of times this interaction between doctor and patient can be demanding. But when you throw in the language and cultural barriers of an area like remote Nepal, this encounter often becomes extremely challenging. Every Nepalese patient contemplating the surgical correction of her prolapse is given a thorough verbal explanation of her condition, the proposed treatment, and the risks and likely benefits. In more recent camps we've added descriptive diagrams and illustrations to help provide a greater depth of understanding.

Day #7. 7:30 am, Postoperative Ward

The near disaster we had two days earlier with Dilli's surgery was clearly an adverse event, and now that she appears to be able to mentally focus, I realise it's time to sit down with her and provide full, honest, open disclosure of the complications of her surgery.

We complete our ward rounds, and at my request the nursing staff take Dilli to a small, empty assessment room adjacent to the postoperative ward. I choose Gamika to join me for translating duties once again as she has a warm, gentle manner that seems to put many of the women at ease during discussions. However, despite my confidence in Gamika's interpreting skills, I know this conversation with Dilli is going to be difficult.

The three of us sit around a small timber table in the stark assessment room.

'How are you doing, Dilli?' I ask through Gamika.

Dilli looks pale and exhausted. Her expression is stolid, so difficult to read. She speaks in her soft, mellow tone, and Gamika translates.

'This lady say she is tired and she has some pain near her bottom, but this pain is not as bad as yesterday.'

'This pain will settle over the next couple of days,' I reply. 'Dilli, I must explain something else to you. This is very important.' I pause for Gamika to translate. Better to talk in short bursts to allow more accurate delivery.

Dilli looks at me quizzically now.

'Your operation was a success in the end,' I say, 'but during the surgery you had some serious complications.'

So much of me does not want to explain this to Dilli. If this open disclosure process goes poorly, once she returns to her village she is will almost certainly relate her near death incident to other women who suffer from severe genital prolapse. When they hear of Dilli's experience, I know they'll be discouraged from attending the camp and undertaking corrective surgery themselves.

As I sit there, waiting for translations back and forth, a battle rages in my head – to tell or not to tell. Perhaps I'm better off playing this down. If Dilli thinks that she merely had a little extra bleeding during the surgery and we simply topped her up with a little blood of one of her countrymen, no big drama – she is more likely to return home with only a glowing report of her surgical cure. When others hear of her success they will be more likely to seek help and be cured themselves. But this woman has a right to know the precise details of her complications, and it's her decision to use that information, not mine ... But if I tell her everything, other women may suffer unnecessarily ...

Back and forth, back and forth, the silent argument oscillates in my head. An extended rally in a torturous game of tennis.

But as this rally progresses, some important words slowly return to me from years earlier. During the early part of my surgical training in

Australia, one of my favourite and most inspiring teachers, Professor Brian Spurrett said to me on a number of occasions, 'Nothing trumps full, honest, open disclosure, Ray. Nothing.'

Those simple, guiding words reverberate in my head. 'Nothing trumps full, honest, open disclosure. Nothing.'

There is silence in the room as I realise both Dilli and Gamika are staring at me in anticipation, waiting for my next comment.

'Dilli, during your operation you lost a lot more blood than is normal. You became very unwell. At one stage we feared that you might not survive the surgery.'

I pause for the translated words to have their effect. Again I try to read Dilli's expression. More quizzical looks. She says nothing.

'Dilli. I don't mean to frighten you, but during your operation you almost died. The only way we could save your life was to give you some blood from one of the other doctors.'

I wait in trepidation for her response. I wait for the shock and anger and tears. But as I watch Dilli's face, her expression is far from agitated or distressed. Instead, her face slowly softens and develops a look that is almost serene.

'A doctor gave me his blood?' she asks.

'Yes, Dilli. It was a female doctor. It was necessary to save you'

'This doctor must love me.'

Her remark is so unexpected it brings a tear to my eye – such an innocent, grateful, bewildering remark. And then this delightful woman utters some words that will stay with me for the rest of my life.

'Doctor. Before I come here I am very sad. I not work and I not be wife for my husband. My husband not want me. If this is Dilli, many times I feel I not want life. Here, in hospital, maybe I nearly die. But I do not die, and here everybody does good to me. Everybody helps me. You people make me better. My sickness gone, and now I am very happy.'

I am lost for words. The three of sit there in silence as broad, beaming smiles gradually fill the faces of both Dilli and Gamika. It is one of those strange, bittersweet moments where you feel both joy and sadness simultaneously. Eventually I begin to smile too, but still I can think of no words to respond. And even if I could, I doubt very much they would find it past the rapidly growing lump in my throat.

*

The local nurses have done an impressive job cleaning Jumari's grossly infected tissues, but it's clear there are some large, angry ulcers over most of the inflamed mass. Now that most of the sludge has been washed away, it's more obvious that Jumari does have severe genital prolapse. But the ulcers are far deeper and broader than we've seen with prolapsed organs in any other women, including Dilli. It's still not clear whether this severe infection has developed simply as a result of the prolapse being exposed to the elements, or if a cancer is present and infection has developed secondary to that. If this turns out to be advanced cancer that has invaded into the surrounding flesh, we'll have no hope of curing this disease.

At home we would take biopsies of this suspicious tissue and arrange pathology to give us the diagnosis. This branch of pathology – histology – is where the biopsied tissue is prepared and then analysed under a microscope. There's no chance of this happening here – our pathology tests on camp are only basic, and they don't include histology.

I decide instead that we will continue to treat Jumari conservatively for the time being. If, with continued cleansing and antibiotics, the ulcers gradually heal, this will strongly suggest that there is no cancer present. If this is the case, we should be able to operate on Jumari and fix her distressing problem.

Louise joins me at the bedside to give me a report on Jumari's background.

'It's just disgusting,' Louise says.

'Yeah, but already a lot better than yesterday, don't you think?'

'No, not the infection. I mean this poor girl's *story* is disgusting. And she *is* only a girl – she's only just turned 20.'

'What else did you learn?' I ask.

Louise holds Jumari's hand now as she speaks. She gives her a soft, warm smile. 'This poor, poor girl has had only one child, Ray, a little girl who died a few hours after birth. That was three years ago. It was a vaginal birth, but it sounds like the labour went on for days. She noticed something coming down between her legs not long after the baby was born. It got more and more painful and smelly as the months and years went on. She worked on a farm with her husband – well, she used to. And it got to a stage with the pain that she just couldn't work anymore. But this is the worst bit – I know this sort of thing happens, but I was just flabbergasted when Gamika told me this: Jumari's husband eventually got sick of her – she couldn't work, and she couldn't have sex, so he just kicked her out of home. Kicked her out, for Christ's sake!'

My heart sinks further with this news. This does happen to quite a few women. Most Nepalese men are supportive of their wives who suffer with genital prolapse, but tragically there are many men who desert them. Making things even worse, the parents of the abandoned wife often won't take her back to her original home. When a woman is thrown out of the husband's home it is a shame on her family.

'We fix,' Louise says as she smiles again at Jumari. 'We fix.'

'No, Lu Lu. We can't say that. We can't promise we'll fix this. We'll do our best, but we can't promise we'll be able to cure her.'

'I'm sorry. I just want to reassure the poor thing.'

Our camp will run for another two weeks. During this time Jumari's deep ulcers will need to improve markedly for us to be able to safely operate to correct her prolapse.

Norman

Day #7. 7:10pm, Dining Hall

Norman has asked to see me before dinner for a chat. I welcome that because I try to spend some one-on-one time with each volunteer at least once during each camp. This is Norman's first camp, and I'm interested in his thoughts.

I don't know much about Norman, other than his career back home. Among the medical camp volunteers, it's useful to have one or two with expertise in areas other than medicine or nursing. There are always maintenance issues within the dilapidated buildings and the outdated medical equipment we have at our disposal. Non-medical volunteers like Norman and Paul are really helpful with the upkeep and repairs. And they're invaluable to us with their activities in and around the hospital. They help us with patient transport (usually this is literally carrying the women from one area of the hospital to another), they sterilise our instruments, procure supplies, and during busy pre-op assessment mornings, manage crowd control. Perhaps equally importantly, non-medical assistants add a broader range of personalities and conversation to our otherwise purely medical group of volunteers.

I walk into the already crowded Dining Hall and spot Norman in deep conversation with Louise. Norman is such a large-framed man, with wild curly hair and a soft, amiable face. He doesn't appear to have shaved since the camp began and he's now produced a full set of red whiskers. As he towers over Louise with his cumbersome frame, he reminds me of a big, cuddly teddy bear.

At this time of the evening, dinner is usually half an hour away. The volunteers are standing around, drinks in hand as they discuss the day's various highlights. Norman looks up and spots me; he excuses himself from Louise and calls me over to sit with him at a small bench separate from our main dining table. He looks so ungainly as he lowers his lumbering body onto the tiny seat.

'Hi, Norman,' I say. 'How's it all going?'

'Ray,' he replies, 'I need to tell you – this camp is so good. I volunteered because I wanted to contribute. Even though I'm not a doctor or a nurse or anything, I feel like I'm helping in my small way. I was hoping that this experience would be fulfilling, and I haven't been let down.'

'I'm really glad to hear you saying that, Norman,' I say. 'You understand that you and Paul are a crucial part of the team here.'

'Thank you for saying that,' Norman continues. 'I've been thinking about what you asked us a couple of nights back.'

'Ah. About how we can make a bigger difference?'

'Yes. About how we could maybe help large numbers of these Nepalese women.' Norman looks deep in thought as he takes another sip of his beer-lemonade shandy.

'I'm all ears,' I say.

'Bearings. The answer is bearings,' Norman opens the palms of his large hands and points them upwards. He speaks as if he's solved an elementary puzzle.

'Can't say I'm following you yet, Norman.'

'Bearings, Ray. The unsung heroes of the rotary motion world. There's your answer, right there.'

'Norman, you're starting to scare me.'

'Bearings. Metal bearings. These break down, too, just like the women here. Well, their uteruses, or whatever.'

'I'm still listening, Norman. But I'm struggling to see a connection here.'

'OK. I spend most of my working life at the Mega Beammi soft drink plant. Our factory is the biggest in the southern hemisphere. We produce 1,200 bottles or cans of soft drink every minute. You can probably imagine how highly automated the plant is. Sometimes I stare out of the window in my office to the factory floor and the thousands of sugar drinks that we make every day. I look at the obesity epidemic in our country, and then I look at the under-nutrition in this country. How crazy is that?'

'It's one of a number of outrageous contradictions,' I say.

'Anyway, it's all about productivity and output. Our managers are always on to us about efficiency and getting as many of those crates of drink off the assembly line every hour. Downtime is the enemy.'

I have not seen Norman so passionate before. He's normally so quiet and reserved. I'm still struggling to see how his experiences are connected with our work here in Nepal, but he's so enthusiastic about his factory I choose not to interrupt his lively spiel.

'Of course, there are inevitably downtimes when we introduce a new flavour or a new product; the management team kind of accept that. But God help us when the assembly line breaks down and production stops unexpectedly. With even the smallest of delays, the company can lose thousands of dollars in lost production and overtime. That's usually where I come in with my engineering skills. And Ray, do you know the commonest cause for breakdown of the assembly line?'

'Ah, I'm going to guess bearings.'

'Yes, sir. You better believe it.' Norman is on fire now.

'And your job is to fix the broken bearings.'

'No, no, no. If that's all I did our plant would be breaking down every few days. Production numbers would be miserably low, and I would be out of a job. My job is to work out *why* the bearings have failed, to get to the bottom of the problem, and make sure it doesn't happen again.'

'So, Norman – why do bearings fail?'

'Well, there are so many causes. The problem might be with the raw materials used in their construction, or the manufacturing of the bearings. The design may be wrong for their precise purpose. The installation may have been faulty. It may be an operations problem – the weight of the bottles or the cans might be too great, or the speed or the rollers, or the temperature, or humidity ... there are so many possible causes here. Proper maintenance is crucial, too – you know, lubricating the bearings, cleaning them, and so forth.'

Norman is speaking so quickly. This is such a strange transformation from his usual slow, almost monotonic speech pattern.

'Let me tell you about a situation we had towards the end of last year,' he continues. 'In the space of two months, we had six separate container conveyer breakdowns – a breakdown almost every week. Management were livid. I was flat out trying to find the cause. I went through the whole system with a fine-toothed comb. And then I went over it again. A few times I spent the whole night in that plant analysing, reanalysing. I could see the problem was that the bearings were overheating. You see, once you get to a tipping point with heat, it doesn't matter how much lubricant you add to the bearings, the oil film becomes too thin to prevent metal-to-metal contact. Friction and heat builds up, and this leads to seizure of the machinery.

'This overheating thing is such a well-recognised problem, we've got all sorts of techniques to ward off bearing damage. Our technicians use things like thermography, and shaft-voltage testing and so forth to spot the problems early on, to detect any overheating before this tipping point is reached. You know, before things get out of hand. But none of these techniques was giving us the information early enough to allow us to jump in and protect the bearings. With enough warning, with enough notice, we can change the lubricant to one that's more effective at higher temperatures – but we weren't getting the warnings until it was too late.

'So what had changed to cause this breakdown in our system? Why weren't our early detection frameworks working anymore? They had served us well for the previous four years. That's when we first introduced our inverters. You know, the ones that save on energy costs.'

I'm doing my best to keep up with Norman, but thermography? Inverters? I'm struggling now, and I'm sure the confusion is showing on my face.

He continues. 'I did a program analysis on every one of our diagnostic networks. Eventually, I opened up the shaft-voltage platform, and low and behold – there it was. Can you believe this? Someone had programmed in figures for a totally different system. It was human error. But Ray, I went further than that. I found the technician who messed up the programming. She's normally such a reliable worker, so why did she make such a glaring mistake? I sat down with her and we talked. I didn't want to punish her or anything, but I needed to know why she made her blunder. I found out she's a single mum, and she's having all sorts of hassles with one of her teenage kids. Anyway, she's getting things sorted now and we've corrected the problem. So now we're right back to our extremely efficient best.'

As I watch Norman now – the new Norman, the excitable Norman – as I listen to him deliver his expansive story, I finally realise the connection.

'With all due respect, Ray,' Norman says, 'your work with the women here is inspirational. But at the moment you're only fixing the bearings as they break. If you really want to make a "major" difference, you need to work out *why* these women are getting their horrible prolapses, and stop the problem at its source.'

I'm blown away. Such a wonderful analogy. And embarrassingly, so damned obvious. Norman takes another sip of his shandy. He has a satisfied look on his wide, furry face now; he's clearly pleased with his clever narrative. And so he should be.

More Lessons in Nepali

7:30pm, Dining Hall

Our team are all seated at our large table after another long, satisfying day in the operating theatre. Most of the group are in a lively discussion about the trekking in Nepal. A few of the volunteers are planning to trek parts of the iconic Annapurna mountain range once they've finished their time here at the camp.

I'm sitting next to Mack who's enjoying an *Everest* beer while we chat about his plans for the next several years. Mack has been an anaesthetist for nearly 40 years. He's been a widower for the past eight of these, and now faces the prospect of retirement from his hospital in Melbourne.

'It's not something I regale at all, Ray,' he says with his broad Scottish brogue. 'Retire? What am I going to do then? Spend more quality time at my wife's grave?'

There is no self-pity in his words. His tone is more in keeping of a staunch, resolute man who wants to contribute as much as he can to the medical world. I have enormous respect for Mack. He's outstanding at his craft, and he has a heart of gold. With his thick white hair, and his groomed, equally white moustache, he could pass for a retired army officer, and just as easily, a warm, benevolent uncle.

'Mack,' I say, 'you know you'll always be welcome on our camps.'

'That's very kind of you, Ray,' he replies. 'And I'd love to volunteer as often as I can. But as you know, I still need to pay the bills.'

Costs for the volunteers on our camps are minimal, as accommodation and meals are very cheap in this part of the world.

The main expenses for each trip are the airfares. But for the duration of each camp, team members do forego their weekly income from their jobs back home.

Poppy is on duty again this evening, delivering our plates and serving our dinner. She works quickly and efficiently tonight without talking to any us, or even making eye contact. I notice a blue, sparkling bangle that sits tightly on her thin wrist. When she's not holding food or plates, she touches the bangle repeatedly, as if for some form of comfort.

After we finish our meal and our plates are cleared, Poppy approaches the table and stops in front of Mack and me. She's wearing a jacket that's at least two sizes too large for her. '*Pani*,' she says.

I don't understand, and I simply look at her and open my palms.

'*Pani*,' she repeats.

I take a guess at what she means. 'Pain? You're in pain?'

Poppy shakes her head and raises her dark eyes to the ceiling in mock disgust. '*Pani*,' she says again, and I realise she's pointing to my glass of water that sits in front of me on the table.

'Oh, I see,' I reply. 'Glass. *Pani* means glass.'

More slow shaking of her head. 'Water. *Pani* is *water*,' she says firmly. And then a heavy sigh to suggest I'm a very poor student of her native language.

I look across to Mack and back to Poppy, feeling guilty that I don't know this basic Nepali word. I decide to try to improve her faith in me, and point to the milk in the small jug to my right.

'*Cheeso dute*,' I say proudly, nodding.

'Two words, Dr Ray – you have long way to go.'

'But, three words if you include *pani*. And clearly, I'm only concentrating on the drinks section at the moment.'

For the first time, I see Poppy smile. And with the smile – dimples. Deep, hollow, mischievous dimples. They fight for attention with those sporadic freckles.

Mack notices the charming little dents, too. 'Poppy has dimples!' he shouts.

Someone else yells, 'Oh no! She's gonna break even more boys' hearts now.'

Poppy's plump little face flushes as she realises the room's attention is now drawn to her. She makes a quick exit from the room, and we all look at each other with expressions that suggest we're less guilty than we should be for making her feel so uncomfortable.

'She reminds me so much of my own daughter at the same age,' I say to Mack.

'Resolute young women are not so rare at home,' Mack replies. 'It's so strange to see that here though.'

'It's the same at the other camps. Louise has noticed this, too. We struggle to even get a few words out of most girls. It's not a language thing – most of the children understand at least basic English.'

Mack swallows the last of his beer. 'Why do you think Poppy's so different to the other girls then? How is it that she's got so much … grit?'

'Absolutely no idea, Mack. And right now, it intrigues me.'

We finish our main meal, and Poppy returns to the Dining Hall to collect our plates. Now she's wearing a wide-brimmed hat that largely obscures her face, and a long grey scarf that drags across the floor as she walks. There is a spring in her step now, and when she does occasionally raise her head to look in the direction of Mack and me, she has the hint of another smile.

As she walks along the length of the long table, volunteers yell out to her again.

'Poppy!'

'She's back!'

'Don't cover up that sweet, freckly face, Little One.'

'You know, Mack,' I say, 'I think Poppy is enjoying this banter.'

'I'm sure you're right.' Mack replies. 'And where is she getting all of these clothes from?'

'She does work in the laundry sometimes. Maybe she nicks them from there.'

When Poppy approaches each of the volunteers at the table they eagerly point to various items and ask for the translation. *Spoon, fork, plate, table, chair,* and so on. Poppy responds immediately by naming the objects in Nepali. The volunteers repeat the Nepali words until she's satisfied with their pronunciation.

After some time of this impromptu language lesson, Poppy walks over and stands in front of Mack and me once again. She makes sure all of the others at the table have her attention, and then, beaming her innocent smile, she points to me and says, '*Ghámar*'.

All of the volunteers repeat after her, '*Ghámar*'.

'*Ghámar*,' she says louder, and again, louder still, the volunteers yell '*Ghámar*'.

'Okay, Poppy,' I say, 'I give in. *Ghámar* – what does this mean?'

The table is silent as they wait for Poppy's response.

'Dr. Ray,' she says. '*Ghámar* in Nepali – this means *loser*!'

There's wild cheering and applause from every volunteer in the room, and from Poppy, an embarrassed, mischievous grin.

I laugh heartily with the crowd, and turn to Mack. 'Isn't she simply sensational?'

Mack is smiling. 'Implausible.'

*

Poppy features strongly in our Sixty-Second Summaries tonight; her performance is the highlight of most people's reflections, and I'm no different.

'I find it fascinating,' I say when it's my turn, 'that I have to travel half the way around the world to this far-flung, forgotten backwater, to learn from a 12-year-old girl that I'm a loser.'

There's more laughing and cheering from the team as they begin chanting, '*Ghámar, Ghámar, Ghámar*.'

As I sit down after my summary I notice Poppy has returned once again, and is standing next to my chair. She's removed the sunhat, and with both hands clutches the cumbersome headpiece tightly to her chest.

'Dr Ray,' she says, 'I please need to speak with you.'

She seems sad or disappointed, and her tone is almost despondent. I wonder to myself: is she genuinely troubled, or is she simply pretending to appear unhappy to lure me into her trap before she cleverly pranks me once more.

'Dr Ray,' she continues in her solemn tone, eyes on the floor, 'I think maybe I insult you with dinnertime tonight. But I have special surprise.'

Before I can reassure her that she has in no way insulted me, Poppy lowers the hat from her chest to reveal in its crown a bounty of poppadoms. 'I steal these from kitchen for you. I know Dr Ray love poppadoms.'

'Poppy, you are amazing,' I say, shaking my head. Mack laughs next to me.

'You must understand, Poppy,' I continue, 'that you did not insult me at all.'

She looks up from the floor. 'But I make everybody laugh at Dr Ray. I am so sorry for making rudeness.'

'I thought your teasing was very, very funny! This is the sort of humour we love in our country.'

Louise joins us. 'Poppy, where on earth did you get all those poppadoms from? No, wait – don't tell me. I don't want to know.'

Poppy offers Louise one of the delicacies from her hat, and as she reaches to accept one Louise says, 'Hey, now I understand why they call you Poppy. It's because you manage to find all the supplies of poppadoms, right?'

'That would be unfairly restrictive,' says Mack. 'Poppy manages to acquire lots of other things besides poppadoms. Have you noticed her clothing range?'

'How could you miss that?' Louise replies. 'In fact, that's the reason I wanted to speak to you, Poppy. When you finish working here tonight, Jayne and I want to see you about something.'

'Okay,' Poppy says hesitantly.

'Oh, don't worry – it's nothing bad. In fact, I think you'll find it lots of fun. Nice bangle, by the way.'

Poppy gently touches the bright trinket that decorates her tiny wrist. 'This is very special bangle,' she says. 'It comes from my mother.' Poppy points to some small Sanskrit writing between coloured glass inserts. 'This is my mother's name.'

'It's beautiful, Poppy,' Louise says. 'Would you mind if I tried it on?'

'I am sorry, Miss Louise.' Poppy pulls the bangle along her wrist, firmly towards her hand. 'This bangle – much too tight to ever come free.'

Poppy's Home

Day #8. 6:15pm

I'm really keen to learn more about Poppy. Why is she so different to the other girls her age? How did she develop this apparent composure and self-assurance? Are there other Nepalese girls in this part of the world with similar certitude? Do any others have the same appetite for knowledge?

I decide to visit her family, and I learn from our interpreters that her family home is a few hundred metres from our camp. As soon as we finish surgery for the day I approach our interpreter for the day, Nabin, who kindly agrees to take me to the home.

In the slanted golden sunlight of late afternoon, Nabin and I set off along a rocky, winding path. We pass several mud houses scattered along the lush hillside. Young, inquisitive children peek at us from the safety of their doorways, but when I catch their eye most quickly retreat into the safety of their homes.

While I try to concentrate to avoid slipping and stumbling on the precarious path, three agile young boys overtake us, giggling as they skip from rock to rock. Despite the moisture on the surface of the rocks, the boys are effortlessly steady in their nimble bare feet.

Small, stone shacks sit behind a number of the homes. I recognise these as latrines – outhouses – separate to the main structure of the home. It's encouraging to see so many toilets in this region. Despite spirited efforts from the Nepalese Government and a number of NGOs, in rural Nepal the majority of households continue to use bush or open fields for defaecation.[25,26] Open defaecation is a major cause of water and food contamination, and this leads to diarrhoeal diseases causing severe stunting and many childhood deaths.[27,28] The humble toilet is possibly the most important contributor to improved human health in history.[29]

Further along the path we cross a shallow stream. On the banks of the stream sits a grey stone structure – a collection of granite rocks arranged to form the shape of a large cube. A solid slab on the surface creates the image of a small table. A large bronze bell hangs from one side of the structure. Fine threads of some sort of cloth hang from branches of the trees overhead.

I choose to solve this puzzle immediately. 'OK, Nabin, can you explain to me what is going on here?'

'*Naga*,' Nabin replies. '*Naga* is serpent spirit, sir. This spirit comes here to this water. These rocks make altar.' He points to the bell and the strands of material above. 'Gifts here make serpent spirits pleased.'

'What do these serpent spirits do then, Nabin? Do they attack people if they are not pleased?'

'No, sir. Serpent spirits make water. Water important for farms, for life. Pleased *Naga* make rain. Not pleased *Naga* make drought, sometimes flood.'

As we continue our walk, I reflect on the powers of mythology in this extraordinary land. So why do these mythologies exist? And what is their value?

I guess the answer is that they explain the unexplainable; they satisfy our need to understand the natural world. And yet at the same time they seem to retain the delightful aura of mystery. There's no doubt that myths encourage a shared set of values that express themselves in this intriguing culture.[30] In this way they serve the crucial purpose of uniting these disparate people.

We reach a single-storey structure that Nabin is fairly sure is Poppy's family home. Like many of the buildings in this area, the dwelling is built with mud and chaff blocks that have been partially painted the colour of ochre. The edges of many of the blocks have worn or broken, but somehow the building still stands. The roof is thatched and overhangs the entrance where a dark-skinned Nepalese man sits, smoking a *bidi*. His face is impassive, detached. The lines on his face suggest he is in his mid-forties, but I suspect he may be several years younger than this – such is the premature ageing in the rural areas of this country.

As we approach the home, the man stands and acknowledges us with a subtle nod of his head. We return the nod and add the traditional Nepali greeting, *Namaste*.

I ask Nabin to ask the man if this is where Poppy lives. He responds to Nabin in Nepali that he has not heard of anybody with this name. At this stalemate, I look from the man to Nabin, and back again. Both men are silent now, and appear puzzled. I wonder if Poppy only uses her real name at home. Nabin must have the same thought, because he then asks if this is the home of Ganuradha Shresthra. The man nods.

'You are the father then?' asks Nabin.

'No. I am father's brother.'

'We wish to meet Ganuradha's parents,' explains Nabin.

'The father is home soon; the mother is dead.'

With this comment, Nabin and I both look at each other and raise our eyebrows in surprise. We then turn to the man, each with the palms of our hands together in front of our faces, our heads bowed in an attempt to indicate both respect and apology.

Poppy's uncle does not appear offended. He tells us his name is Suntil and then offers us a smoke of his *bidi*. When we politely refuse he invites us into the family home to wait.

Although the light outside is fading, as we enter the small single room home my eyes squint as I try to adjust to the darkness inside. The acrid fumes of the open fire stove are almost overpowering. Minimal light comes from two small square holes that serve as windows at the back of the dwelling. A middle-aged woman sits cross-legged in front of the fire, slowly stirring a large pot of fluid. We acknowledge each other with a hushed, *Namaste*.

As my eyes gradually accommodate to the poor light I take in more of the surroundings. There are a few cooking pots and plates, and a small pile of wood next to the stove. Frayed blankets and mats lay scattered on the clay floor. Dozens of corn cobs hang from the ceiling, presumably to dry before being ground into flour. And other than the four of us, there appears to be nothing else in the entire room. I remind myself that this single, stark room is their entire home.

This dim, smoke-filled chamber, devoid of any furniture or creature comforts – this is the shared bedroom, kitchen, and living room for probably two families. There is no electricity, no running water, and no privacy.

After a few minutes, the cross-legged woman presents cups of tea to Nabin and me. I assume the woman is Suntil's wife, but there are no introductions, and I'm unsure whether it's impolite to ask about their relationship. Suntil and Nabin are deep in conversation in Nepali as I look around the room to absorb some of this culture, this brutally primitive standard of living.

How many people actually live here? I can count six blankets, most of which are stained with what appears to be ash. No mattresses, no pillows. Two small books are partially hidden by one of the blankets; presumably these are Poppy's schoolbooks. How on earth does she read in this miserable light? And when would she even find time to read when she works such long hours? On nights like this, when she works in our Dining Hall, Poppy wouldn't be home for at least another couple of hours.

I stand up to stretch my legs, and spot a jagged shape in the corner of the room. I walk over to find another small collection of logs. But these are quite different to the small pile next to the fire. These logs are old and twisted, their offshoots gnarled and craggy. It's clear they've been collected from the limbs of ancient trees.

Suntil and Nabin continue their discussion. The cross-legged woman continues to stir her mysterious liquid. And all seem oblivious to the pungent smoke, as it swirls around the gloomy, stifling room.

The door opens and another dark-skinned Nepalese man enters the room. The man is a slightly older version of Suntil, and once his eyes adjust to the light, a look of confusion unfurls on his face. Suntil speaks softly in Nepali to the man, and then to Nabin.

Nabin turns to me. 'Dr. Ray, this is Uttam. Uttam is father of Poppy.'

Nabin and I press our palms together and salute Poppy's father with a *Namaste*. As Uttam returns our greetings I study him more closely. His hands and nails are caked in red dirt. His face is wistful and jaded, as if resigned to a life of hardship. A faded *tika* stains the deep lines of his forehead.

Nabin explains who I am and that I wish to talk to him about his daughter. A conversation then unfolds between Uttam and me, with Nabin continuing as our intermediary.

'My daughter is in trouble?' Uttam asks. His expression remains weary and depleted, with no obvious look of concern.

Nabin explains that Poppy is fine and not in any trouble.

'You and your team come to village to help the sick women?' Uttam asks.

'Yes,' I reply, 'there are many women in this country who are in very great need of medical help.'

'You leave your own country to come here, work here?' He pauses, then adds, 'You are good people. Your rebirth will be high place.'

I take this to mean all our team will receive good karma in our next life. This is reassuring. While the large majority of Nepalese are described as Hindus, in many areas of the country the predominant religion is an amalgamation of Hindu and Buddhist beliefs and practices. In this remote region of Nepal, the doctrine of animism is added to the rich religious blend. All of these belief systems and their combinations have in common the concept of reincarnation as a fundamental tenet.

Uttam looks at the large pot on the open fire. 'You will please join our family for dinner tonight?' he asks.

I'm keen to accept Uttam's invitation and I talk directly to Nabin now. 'Do you mind staying for the meal to continue this translation?' Nabin nods and smiles warmly, and I add, 'We will need to get a message to the rest of my team that I won't be joining them until after dinner.'

When Nabin explains the situation, Uttam says he will get his son to relay the message. The four of us men – Uttam, Suntil, Nabin, and I – all sit cross-legged on the floor. The woman stands and distributes metal plates to each of us. I realise that Nabin and I have still not spoken to the woman.

When she hands me my plate I finally say, 'We have not yet been introduced. My name is Dr. Ray.'

Nabin translates, but before she can respond Uttam says, 'This *didi* is Gorham. She is wife of Suntil.'

Gorham and I salute each other with another *Namaste*. She otherwise remains silent as she continues to serve us.

Uttam speaks again as Nabin translates. 'What is it you wish to ask of my daughter?' he asks.

'Uttam,' I begin, 'may I first ask about your life here, and the rest of your family?'

Through Nabin I learn from Uttam that his son is sixteen years of age. Poppy is almost thirteen. These are his only two children. Uttam's wife, Poppy's mother, died as a result of complications from childbirth.

As Uttam and I speak and Nabin translates, Gorham fishes out various pieces of food from the liquid she's been stirring since we arrived, and sets them on our plates. From the one pot we receive rice, a vegetable I recognise as seriously overcooked spinach, and another substance that appears to be some form of meat.

Goat? Mutton? ... Yak?

The door to the home opens again and an adolescent boy enters the room. He's introduced to Nabin and me as Nerum, the son of Uttam. Nerum has a young, handsome face, and unruly black hair. He is already taller than his father. He acknowledges us and begins to speak in English. 'Good evening, sirs,' he says. 'Welcome to our home. We are most thankful for work you do in hospital.'

'We get enormous pleasure by being able to help,' I reply. 'We are very thankful to be invited into your home.'

Nerum begins to sit down, but stands again as Uttam speaks to him firmly. Nerum gives a brief look of disappointment before he turns and leaves the room. Nabin explains to me that Uttam has directed his son to walk to our camp and deliver the message to my team members. I protest that I could have delivered the message myself.

'You are guest in home here,' Uttam replies. 'Boy is young with much strength.'

I learn from Uttam that his son attends Intermediate Secondary School and that he is doing well in his classes. Uttam expects him to eventually study at a tertiary level and to one day have a well-paid job.

'Nerum will need to leave village to work in big town. Earn big wealth to help family here.'

Gorham has now given all four of us a full plate of food, but her own plate is empty. Uttam, Suntil, and Nabin all commence eating. As is the custom in these parts of the world, they use their right hand to gather each bite of food.

I turn to Gorham. 'You are not going to join us?'

While I wait for Nabin to translate, Gorham looks coyly to the floor, but Nabin responds to my question himself. 'It is tradition that woman eats only when rest of family has finished their meal.'

I remind myself that I must respect the customs of the community in which we find ourselves, and uneasily I begin to eat my own meal. Mimicking the other men in the room I use my right hand to work my way through the rice and the listless spinach. When I get to the foodstuff that vaguely resembles some form of meat, I inhale deeply and close my eyes before biting into the peculiar substance. The texture is firm – very firm in fact – much like gristle or cartilage; the taste reminds me of soap.

Bravely I chew, and chew, and do my best to reduce the material to a consistency and a size that I can make some sort of attempt at swallowing. But I struggle with this battle. Looking across to my three male companions I marvel that they can appear to so effortlessly eat this local food.

Suntil looks at me, and I force a smile in an attempt to hide my advancing distress with the food that now torments my mouth. I look across to Gorham, who sits in silence, her plate still empty, and think, *Ten minutes ago, I pitied you for missing out on this meal; now I totally envy you.*

When I finally manage to empty my mouth of the disturbing food, I continue conversation with Uttam.

'What are your plans for Poppy? Will she also be going to secondary school, and university?'

Uttam does not appear pleased with this question. 'This child is very much problem,' he replies. 'Always in trouble. Not respecting father. Too much school not good for girls. If daughter too clever, no chance for husband. Best for daughter to be working in home.'

My heart sinks to the depths of my stomach. This vibrant, spirited child, who right now is the shining light among the girls in this region, so full of promise and potential, destined simply to languish in a life of domestic duties?

How do I play this? How do I respond? How do I walk this fine line between respect for local cultural traditions on the one side, and on the other – promotion of civil liberty, gender equity, and of – let's face it – human rights? My impulsive reaction right at this moment is to condemn Uttam and his oppressive, archaic idea, to use every moral and practical argument I know to stress the glaring error of his belief and to put this right. Poppy needs support, as do all of the girls and women in this corner of the world, but how do we provide this? What is the most effective approach?

I stare at Uttam, hoping my disgust of his repressive, deluded opinion is not conspicuous on my face. As difficult as it was a little earlier to conceal my distress with the unpalatable food, this new mask is even more challenging to wear. But something inside does hold me back from an onslaught at Uttam's outrageous, patriarchal stance. Instead of launching a passionate argument against his views, I bite my tongue and decide on a measured, calmer approach.

'Uttam,' I say, 'is your main wish to have a happy and healthy family?'

'Of course,' he replies, 'this is wish for every person.'

'How do you know that further education for Poppy will not lead to a happier and healthier family?'

Uttam pauses in thought after Nabin translates this sentence, so I push on with my line of questions.

'If Poppy was to progress her education and reach university, get a well-paid job – just like you expect Nerum to do – would it not be possible for her to support the family here, too?'

Uttam's pause continues a little longer before he replies with a barrage of words.

'This not way of our people,' he begins. There is more intensity in his voice now and his eyes flash with indignation. 'In this community, man leave village to work, not woman. Woman must stay home, have children, make food. This always our people. This – our life.'

I catch Nabin's eye and note a look of disquiet, almost guilt. It's clear my translator has some understanding of my frustration right now. But I realise that if I have any chance of altering Uttam's opinion, it will not be tonight. For there to be any possibility of a softening of his beliefs and principles, I must get to know him more, and allow him to know and trust me. And this will take time.

When we finish eating Uttam stands and, in a firm voice, says, '*Rakshi.*'

I know this word. *Rakshi* is a traditional Nepalese spirit, and it's really potent. The drink is usually homemade from millet or rice. It is as popular among Nepalese as vodka is with Russians.

Gorham reaches over and picks up a strange-shaped container that appears to be made of clay. The vessel is tall and thin, with a long, curved spout. It looks like a very stretched teapot that's missing its handle. Gorham pours a clear liquid from the long jug into several small clay cups that Uttam passes around to each of us men.

Before I drink, I look to my hosts, expecting them to say something like, 'Cheers,' or the Nepali equivalent, but no words are spoken as the men simply begin drinking the liquor. Tentatively, I take a small sip and swallow. It's no surprise that the fluid sears my mouth and throat, and it continues to burn all the way down to my stomach – it feels like I'm swallowing some sort of acid. But within a short time the sensation changes to something more pleasant. The piercing fire is replaced with a hot, rich velvet. Perhaps next time I visit Uttam I can wash down Gorham's distressing food with some of this mouth-numbing liquor.

I look across to the other men. Uttam and Suntil have already finished their cups and they're demanding more. Gorham quickly fills their cups again, but it's no surprise that she does not drink herself. Nabin sips his drink slowly with a pace that is closer to mine. I'm struggling to finish my first cup of Rakshi when Uttam and his brother begin their third. They gulp down the liquor with a pace that intrigues me.

Nabin and Uttam are now deep in discussion, but I have no understanding of their conversation.

Eventually I finish my *rakshi* and politely refuse a refill. I stand and thank Uttam and his family for their hospitality and their mouthwatering food and drink. As Nabin and I are about to leave, Nerum enters the room.

'Nerum,' I say, 'thank you so much for relaying the message to my team. I am sorry you could not join us for the meal.'

'Sir,' Nerum replies, 'it was honour to assist you. Perhaps next time you come, I join you?'

'Yes,' I say, looking at Nabin, 'we would love to come again, and you must join us when we do return.'

Nabin nods once again and speaks to Uttam and Suntil. Suntil responds. It's the first time he has spoken to me since his brother arrived.

Nabin translates once more. 'Dr Ray, you and Nabin welcome to come to home anytime.'

More *Namaste* salutes to Suntil and Gorham as we make our way to the door. Uttam escorts Nabin and me outside where it is now pitch black, and utterly cold. I realise only now how the open fire in the room we have just left has kept the home so comfortably warm. Perhaps it was worthwhile enduring the pungent fumes.

As Uttam farewells us and retreats into the warmth of his home, Nabin and I stand together and look out into the unwelcoming darkness.

'Nabin,' I say, 'how on Earth are we going to find our way back to our camp when we can't see our hands in front of us?' But before Nabin can respond, Uttam reappears with a burning flame torch.

'Please take,' Uttam says. 'Bring back, whenever. No problem.'

The flame torch provides a surprising amount of light, and heat for that matter. As Nabin and I set off to return to our camp, we walk in silence for a few minutes as I struggle to process so much information from the past hour or so.

'Nabin,' I say eventually. 'Uttam feels that women should stay at home, cook and clean, and spit out babies. Do you think most of the men in this region feel this way about women?'

Nabin does not reply immediately, and when I catch his face in the dancing light of the flame torch, he looks deep in thought.

'Dr Ray,' he finally responds, 'as you know I am from near this village.' Nabin pauses again as he appears to choose his words carefully. 'Dr. Ray, I would say most men here feel same as Uttam, yes. But I think some men changing now, slowly.'

There is some hope in Nabin's answer, but I wonder to myself if he's simply trying to make me feel less troubled? Is it because he feels guilty about the way women are treated here? It's difficult to read.

I also wonder about Nerum and his thoughts as a 16-year old. Does he embrace the same gender discrimination as his father and others in his father's generation? Gorham – so painfully silent all evening, and she wasn't allowed to eat until we all had finished. This was not simply a matter of serving others before she could serve herself. These were men finishing their meals before she could have some of their leftovers. And Suntil – he was so talkative before Uttam arrived, but after that, he barely said a word. What is going on here?

A New Challenge

Day #9. Very early morning, Bedroom.

In the depths of a deep sleep and dreaming about – of all things – surgery in Nepal. Inside the operating theatre the ancient suction machine is playing up again. It groans and thuds in protest as we push it harder and harder to clear the meddlesome fluids from our operative field. The thumping sounds are louder and wilder now, and as I look in pity at the struggling machine, it shakes more fiercely with each thud. I'm sure that at any moment it will rupture its shell and collapse into an exhausted pile of waste metal and smoke.

Slowly, I awaken to realise that the thuds are in fact knocks at my bedroom door. I check my watch – it's 4:15 am. The knocks are quite loud now.

'Dr Ray! Dr Ray!'

Groggily I get up into the freezing room and pull open the door. I'm greeted by the distressed faces of Guna and Mani, two of the local Nepalese nurses.

'Dr Ray, we are so sorry to disturb you,' Guna exclaims. 'You must come. The baby will die!'

'Baby? What baby?' I was not even aware we had a baby at this camp. The distraught nurses ignore my question, and instead implore me to come with them immediately. Hastily, I throw on some warmer clothes and follow the nurses at an impressive pace down the stairs and along the hospital path to the operating theatre building.

Waiting outside the entrance are three or four Nepalese men I have not seen before. Guna and Mani race straight past them and into the building. I follow them inside.

In the cramped, dimly lit anaesthetic room attached to the operating theatre there are several other women in the corner of the room. The only person I recognise among them is Jyoti, the local midwife attached to a nearby Health Post. There are murmurs and the occasional soft whimper coming from the small crowd of women.

As I approach them I see the source of their attention; a petite woman, heavily pregnant, lays on her back on the examination bed. Her knees are bent and apart – the typical position for the second stage of labour when the woman would normally be pushing. Only this woman is not pushing; she appears to be unconscious, or perhaps worse.

I call to Jyoti, who has a look of fear on her face I have not seen before. 'A quick rundown, please.'

'Dr Ray, this lady has been in labour at home for nearly three days now. The baby is stuck. The mother is exhausted.'

I ask for more light and quickly assess the woman. Although she does not respond to my questions, she is not fully unconscious – she does react to pain when I squeeze her fingertips firmly.

'Her obs?' I ask Jyoti.

'BP 90 on 50. Heart rate 85. Respiratory rate 38 and shallow. No temperature.'

'The baby?'

'Alive. Heart rate 190 to 200.'

'Guna,' I say as calmly as possible, 'I want you to wake up some other members of our team. We need these people to help us urgently. The anaesthetist, Dr. Mack, our resident doctor, Steph, our nurses, Louise and Jayne, and one of our general hands, Paul. Can you do that for me?'

I give Guna their bedroom numbers and watch her run out the theatre building door.

'Mani, we also need the pathology technician, Suman. Do you know his home? I want you to get one of the men outside to run to his home and ask him to join us immediately.' Before I can finish my sentence, Mani is running towards the theatre exit.

'Jyoti, please take this woman's blood pressure and pulse every 10 minutes, and check the heart rate of the baby after every contraction. Call these measurements out to me every time you take them.'

As quickly as I can, I try to insert a cannula into a vein in the arm of this failing woman. Unfortunately, she's so very dehydrated that her veins have collapsed, which makes them extremely difficult to find. As a result, I struggle with the cannulation, a task that is normally so simple.

'Jyoti,' I say. I can hear the urgency in my voice, 'I need more information. First baby?'

'Yes, Dr Ray.'

'Antenatal care?'

Jyoti speaks in Nepali to one of the other women in the group.

'Dr Ray,' she says, pointing to a white-haired woman whose face hangs in wrinkled folds, 'this lady here is Traditional Birth Attendant. She is seeing this patient in pregnancy and labour. The patient did not come to hospital for any checkups.'

Traditional Birth Attendants remain common in rural and remote Nepal. They have no formal training, but are trusted by most families to care for the pregnancy. Although these Birth Attendants mean well and their hearts are usually in the right place, there have been many distressing stories over the years of mismanagement of pregnancies.

'She let this woman labour for three days? Why on earth has she left it so …?' But before I complete the sentence, I realise this is not the time for such questions. I continue to assess this semi-conscious woman and her distressed baby. Her heart, chest, and abdomen appear to be normal. There is no obvious internal bleeding or infection. Other than her greatly reduced level of consciousness and her extreme dehydration, I can find nothing wrong.

'Has she been eating or drinking over the past three days?' I ask Jyoti.

'On first day, a little, yes. But next two days – nothing, Dr Ray. Not even water.'

'You have assessed the baby's liquor?'

'Very dark,' replies Jyoti. 'Like old meconium. No bad smell.'

'Blood loss?'

'Only very light bleeding, Dr Ray.'

At that moment Mack arrives, out of breath.

'Mack, thank goodness you're here. A very sick mother, semi-conscious. In labour at home for three days, severely dehydrated and possibly septic. Buggered if I can get this drip in – can you do that while I give you more details?'

Mack glides over, and within seconds he has the cannula inserted into the back of the pregnant woman's hand.

'You made that look so easy,' I say to him, 'just to make me look bad, didn't you?'

'You do that really well without my help,' Mack says dryly as he applies surgical tape to the cannula site.

'Ouch,' I say. 'No obvious blood loss, Mack, overt or concealed. Baby on board, appears near full-term, severe fetal distress. Could you take blood for haemoglobin, electrolytes, sugar level, and blood group?'

'Now you're starting to sound like an anaesthetist, Dr Ray.'

'How embarrassing,' I say, 'I'm clearly letting my standards slip. By the way, Mack – have I told you how pretty you look first thing in the morning?'

Mack grins his trademark lopsided smile. 'Have I told you how poor your eyesight is first thing in the morning?' he says. 'Do you think there's anything else going on with this lady?'

'I'm sure her electrolyte levels will be insane. Can't rule out an embolus or something cardiac – we've got so little to go on. I'm hoping like hell she'll respond to the IV fluids. I don't hold out much hope for the baby – God knows how long it's been distressed in there.'

'Have you got a plan?' Mack asks.

'Assuming we can stabilise mum, we need to do a caesar ASAP. Are you in?'

'I'm with you, brother. Let's see how she responds to the saline. I'll start some antibiotics too, just in case.'

As we connect the tubing to the cannula and begin to run intravenous fluids, the rest of the team arrive.

'Oh. Thanks for coming,' Mack says to them with gentle sarcasm. 'Putting on your makeup, were you?'

'That was just Paul,' Louise replies. 'The rest of us girls had to wait for him.'

We quickly fill in the team on the situation to hand, and I say to them, 'I know we're here in this country to fix nasty prolapses, but right now we've been thrown a new challenge. If this woman responds to the resuscitation we will need to do a caesarean section tonight.'

'I'm not sure we have the equipment for a caesarean,' says Jayne.

I look at her and give her my best impression of a fatherly smile. 'Jayne, you know we'll make do. We always make do.'

Over the next hour, we resuscitate the debilitated woman with intravenous fluids and corrections to her electrolyte levels. Encouragingly, the mother is now making random movements on the small bed, and she begins to groan through some of the continuing contractions. The baby is still alive, however, the heart rate remains worryingly fast. I look across to Steph, our resident doctor from Australia. Her face is troubled.

'Tell me what's on your mind, Steph,' I say.

'Dr. Ray,' she says, 'I don't want to be rude, but this baby has been distressed since we got here, and very likely well before that. Why didn't we do a caesarean section an hour ago?'

'It's a very reasonable question, Steph. By waiting like we have, we do risk losing the baby, or causing severe neurological problems. But if we were to perform a caesarean section on a woman who is very unstable, the stresses of this sort of surgery would put her life at risk, as well. If we jump in too soon we might end up with the loss of two lives.'

'I understand what you're saying,' she replies, 'it's just so hard to stand here and think that the baby might not be getting enough blood supply and oxygen to survive.'

'I know, and it still bothers me. But this is a really important principle in obstetrics – and in anaesthetics too, for that matter.' I turn to Mack who is reading the portable oxygen monitor. 'Mack, do you agree?'

'Wholeheartedly,' Mack replies. 'In fact, if you'd asked me to give an anaesthetic to this woman in the state she was in when she first arrived, you and I may have had our first fight, Ray.'

Ten minutes later the pregnant woman now appears to have some awareness of her situation and surroundings. Jyoti acts a translator as I explain that we are all here to help her. She gets verbal consent from the woman for us to put a needle in her back to take away the pain and to deliver her baby through a cut in her abdomen.

Mack inserts the spinal block and once it's effective we carry the woman from the anaesthetic room into the operating theatre. Jayne has managed to find a range of assorted medical instruments, and Paul has sterilised these in our primitive autoclave machine. I look down at the strange array of surgical forceps and fasteners. Most of them are foreign, and appear quite ancient. I presume that over the years various volunteer groups have donated these to the small hospital here. They're nothing like the instruments we'd use for a caesarean section.

As I try to work out ways we can use the strange equipment before us, I glance up and catch Jayne's eye. She tilts her head to the side and says nothing. I'm sure she reads my mind. How in the world are we going to do this?

I smile – unconvincingly, I'm sure. 'Just think of this as another adventure, Jayne.'

As we finally commence the caesarean section, the air in the theatre is thick with tension. The outlook for mum is good, as she's responded so well to the resuscitation with fluids and electrolytes, but the baby's outlook is precarious. Within the uterus, the baby's heart rate has been too fast for a long time now, and over the last 15 minutes or so it has shown more concerning signs, slowing after each contraction.

With the mother's abdomen open, we work our way towards the uterus and its perilous contents. I glance up to see the angst on the faces of Steph and Louise; they know that when this baby is born in a few minutes' time, it may not survive the immediate aftermath. Despite the peculiar choice of instruments, the procedure begins without complication. Eventually, we deliver a scrawny little boy who is pale and very limp. Although there is a feeble heart beat, the baby does not breathe.

I look at the helpless creature now – finally free from the treacherous home of his struggling mother. He is a lifeless rag doll lying inert in my single, gloved hand. With little hope now, I lay him on a small table that Mack has prepared for the resuscitation. He and Louise stand ready for the baby's immediate care.

'Okay, Mack,' I say. 'Give him everything you've got.'

While Steph and I continue with the surgery to close the uterus and abdomen, Mack and Louise do all they can to encourage the critically-ill newborn boy to breathe. As we expect, there is so very little neonatal equipment available here, but Louise has managed to find a small resuscitation mask. Using a bag and this mask, she and Mack dispense precious air to the tiny boy's lungs while the rest of the team look on in trepidation.

The new mother's consciousness and clarity appear to be improving by the minute. She has turned her head to watch the valiant attempts to save her baby's life. Jyoti sits by her head, explaining the activities that, to this woman must appear not just outlandish, but extremely distressing. To my surprise, I see a look of calm resignation on the mother's face. As we apply the final sutures to her abdomen, I suspect that, despite Jyoti's commentary and explanation, this woman does not grasp the gravity of the situation. Perhaps her mental state has not improved as much as I had thought.

I glance over to the resuscitation table and the lifeless baby once again. Still nothing; still no other signs of life ... But now I see something that has not been present before. There are small jerking movements in the little boy's arms. There, again – slight shudders. Stronger now, and legs, too. These are not seizures – this would be a very poor prognostic sign – they are simple tremors, which in this context are hopeful. He is now flailing his limbs – a definite positive sign. Now I see his tiny chest move, and this movement fights the rhythm of the bag pumping air to his lungs. There are no cries from the little guy, though, at least none we can hear.

We have finished the caesarean now, and after a quick *Namaste* to the new mother, I go to the baby to assist with the resuscitation. The small table is surrounded by several of the theatre staff.

'What are your thoughts, Mack?' I ask as I squeeze in beside the table.

'We seem to be winning with this wee one, Ray,' Mack replies. 'It didn't look so grand at first.'

'Just hold off with the bagging for a moment,' I say.

I lift the small mask from the little boy's face and we watch for his response. Within a few seconds – a feeble cry. And now another, and another, louder than before. I ask two of the theatre staff to move aside so that mum can see her baby as he makes the most wonderful sound on Earth.

7:30am, Postoperative Ward.

The mother has named her little boy Riddihman, which we learn means 'possessed of good fortune'. Baby Riddi, as he has quickly become known, is quite a hit in our ward full of adults; we're not used to a patient so young or so tiny in these parts. It's only a few hours since his challenging birth, and he remains stable at this stage. He's lying in a small timber cot under as many blankets as we dared pile on top of him, and he looks both serene and fragile. We have no paediatric equipment to provide continuous monitoring, no incubator to protect against the cold ambient temperature, and no mechanical means of ventilation, should this be required. As a result, we've arranged a roster for the local nursing staff to provide continuous one-on-one observation and care for the little miracle boy.

Riddi weighed in at just under 2000 grams, and at this stage his observations are relatively normal for a small baby who was clearly stressed for such a long time. An intravenous drip runs into a delicate vein in his left arm, and we administer regular antibiotics to guard against potentially disastrous systemic infection. Postoperative ward patients provide a continuous stream of visitors for the tiny baby. From the other side of the ward, our volunteer team watch on warmly as the faces of each of the women light up at the sight of the tiny, defenseless newborn boy.

We have transferred the mother to a bed next to her celebrated baby, and she now sleeps deeply, unaware of the stir her child has created in the ward. Her observations also remain stable, and once we can confirm her kidney function has not been seriously affected by her earlier severe dehydration, her outlook is positive.

Despite baby Riddi's prolonged period of reduced oxygen during his mother's protracted and arduous labour, his outlook is also very bright. Even though we have no sophisticated medical instruments to assess Riddi's brain and its function, his clinical signs suggest he has suffered no long-term damage. His reflexes and muscle tone are normal, and he suckles and feeds like any normal baby. Even though he's been through an extremely tough entry into the world, he has survived this ordeal with no apparent damage.

Among the spate of visitors to the ward this morning, I'm surprised to see Poppy among Riddi's admirers. As she peers over the side of the cot, Poppy's face takes on the same lucent glow of the other adoring women.

After a minute or two, Poppy looks up from the cot to see Louise, Steph, and me across the room. She walks over to us, and to no one in particular she says, 'This baby nearly die last night?'

Louise answers, 'Yes, Poppy. It was touch and go for a long while there. For mum, too.'

Poppy looks at each of us in turn. 'You all must feel so much happiness to save baby's life. And mother.'

'Oh, Poppy,' Louise replies, 'it is just wonderful. It's so hard to put into words.' Louise pumps her chest with a clenched fist. 'In here – you just feel so thrilled.'

'In Nepali,' Poppy says, 'we have special words for this feeling. We say *bhitra pracura*. This means inside body we feel rich.'

We all smile at Poppy's phrase, and I make a mental note to remember this one. *Bhitra pracura* – I have a strong feeling this will come in handy during our camps.

A Walk to School

Day #10. 8:00am.

It's our day off. We set aside one day each week for rest and recreation. This gives all of the team a chance to catch our breath and recharge our batteries. Most of the volunteers decide that after breakfast they'll walk to the local village and visit the markets. It's a sunny day so we all decide to have our breakfast at the tables in the courtyard outside the Dining Hall. Despite the sunshine, there is no warmth in the rays; this is the way of the sun in these parts. We all need to rug up against the cool morning, but it's well worth the effort. Although it's chilly, the rich colours that radiate from the hills that surround us are striking. A morning cloud obscures some of the distant, snowcapped peaks. But even this cloud soon retreats in some form of celestial submission to the grand beauty of this glorious Himalayan day.

After a leisurely breakfast we check in on our patients in the surgical ward. There are so many postoperative patients by now, particularly as most are staying in the hospital for several days following their surgery, until such time that they have the strength to confront their long treks home. By this stage of the camp there are far too few beds for the numbers of patients, so we limit bed use to those women who have more recently undergone surgery. Those who have reached their fourth or fifth postoperative day are relegated to sleep on blankets or towels spread out on the floor of the ward. These women do not protest, and there is no resentment in their demeanor. I suspect many have never slept in a standard bed, and the majority of these probably feel more at ease on the ward floor.

It's reassuring that there are no significant postoperative problems today. Even baby Riddi looks in great shape. Jumari continues to slowly improve. The ulcers invading her prolapse are less angry today, but they remain very deep. It's comforting to see Jumari gaining some confidence as she watches some of the other victims of prolapse recover from their surgery.

By 9:00am we've finished the ward round and we're ready to enjoy the day. I tell our volunteers that I won't be joining them on their trip to the markets, as I've chosen instead to spend the day at Poppy's school.

'Is the school far?' Jayne asks. 'I'd like to come, too, if that's okay.'

'You'd be very welcome,' I reply, pleased. 'It can't be far away because the children walk to and from the school each day. I've decided follow them there and back.'

Jayne grins in response. She wears her famous red scarf again today. It seems to follow her everywhere now. I'm sure she'd wear it into the operating theatre if it could somehow be sterilised.

I consider taking along one of our interpreters to help us with communication but decide instead to give both interpreters the day off, too. I'm hopeful the teachers and the students can provide all of our translating needs.

Jayne and I pack a light lunch and some bottled water into our backpacks and join the rest of the volunteer group. In the bright sunshine we all head off in high spirits towards the main trail that bisects our mountain village. The trail leads south to the village and its markets, and north towards the school. Once we reach the trail Jayne and I say our goodbyes to the rest of the group and we set off with several children in the direction of the school.

'Have a lovely day at school, kiddies,' Louise yells, teasing us in the sickly sweet manner of an overbearing mother.

Mack chips in with the same parental tone. 'Be nice to your teachers, now.'

The real school children who have joined us seem a little confused with these taunts, but at the same time excited to have us accompany them on the walk. I approach one of the children called Milu, an underweight young boy of around ten.

'How long will this walk take us?' I ask.

'Not long,' he replies before skipping away to join his school friends.

After a few minutes the trail narrows and we all walk single file through rocky fields and lush gorges. The children often run ahead, chasing each other eagerly, and then racing back to us. The path widens each time we pass through the small villages on our way. At every village a few more children join our group on the walk to school. After about thirty minutes our numbers have increased to about twenty. I'm wondering how much further this walk can be.

Almost every person we pass greets Jayne and me with a warm smile and a *Namaste*. As yet on this trip we've not seen people from any other country. I imagine there are trekkers who occasionally hike these remote paths, but I suspect we're largely a novelty to these kindhearted, gentle people. Our work in the hospital is so consuming we don't get many opportunities to see the Nepalese carrying out their day-to-day activities, but today we observe them tending their rice paddies and herding their mules and water buffaloes.

I begin to understand why visitors to the rural areas of this country are so charmed by these graceful people. They don't appear rushed or impatient with their tasks; there is a calmness about them, a serenity. The contrast with our own frenetic world is vast and absurd.

Occasionally we're joined by local women carrying *dokos* – large, cone-shaped woven baskets used to transport a range of different loads – firewood, food, and sometimes people. The *doko* rests against the carrier's back and is supported by a headband worn around the forehead and running under the base of the basket. Despite the often heavy loads, these women usually keep pace with us.

When we spot one *doko*-carrying woman who strains with the weight of a large haul of wood, Jayne whispers to me, 'Did you see that, Dr Ray – prolapse in evolution. I guess she'll be on our operating list next year.'

Sadly, Jayne may well be right.

At one particular village we notice a group of 15 or 20 adults all crowding around the timber portico of someone's home. When we approach the crowd we soon see the centre of attraction is a television that is screening what appears to be a Bollywood movie. We haven't seen a television since we arrived in this region several days ago. For most of the fascinated audience it's perhaps the first television they have ever seen. The viewers appear entranced with either the television or the show; they hardly notice us foreigners who have come to observe them.

A dozen questions immediately spring to my mind. How does a television make its way to this isolated, remote corner of the world? Who pays for this? Where does the electricity come from? And perhaps most importantly of all – how will this electronic cultural invasion affect the ancient traditions of these remote people? We already see smatterings of Western influence in this region – discarded plastic wrappers litter some of the ravines, the occasional villager wears a designer logo T-shirt.

As we recommence our walk, I think to myself: the ancient rhythms of life here will inevitably change. The reality is that our organisation is here to precipitate some of these changes. We want the health of these people to improve; we want greater equity in health and in opportunity. Is it too idealistic to wish for a world where the only Western influences here are positive, while the serenity of these people and the seductive charms and traditions of this area remain intact?

The path narrows once more as we round a steep, ragged mountain edge with a precipitous drop to a fast-flowing river below. The chasm looks to be about 50 or 60 metres. There is, of course, no safety rail to grasp. And to remind us of our fate should we lose our balance and fall, some of the small rocks and slate beneath our feet slip and tumble ominously down the sheer cliff face to the rushing water below.

I turn to Jayne, who is directly behind me. 'Nothing like a relaxing way to spend your day off, eh, Piggy?'

Jayne looks pale as she concentrates on each careful step. 'These children walk this … this *nightmare* every day?'

'Well, twice a day on school days, I guess. Do you think they're playing some sort of practical joke on us? Maybe this is the scenic route.'

'"Not long"?' Jayne is indignant now. 'Did that little boy really say this walk was "not long"? Is *notlong* some Nepali word that means, like, forever? We've been trekking for 45 minutes now. Yes – *trekking* – this is no longer a walk, Dr Ray; this is officially a *trek*.'

'Glad to see you're enjoying yourself so much, Miss Piggy. Imagine how bored you'd be by now if instead of being here, you were wandering around some dull little marketplace.'

I hear a soft grunt from Jayne, and as I turn my head to glance at her I'm sure I see the subtle bulge of her bottom lip. The ends of Jayne's red scarf have become quite stained now as they trail along our mountain path.

'I think your scarf needs another revolution or two around your neck, Jayne,' I say. 'Not a good place to trip over, here.'

We stop to rest for a few moments.

'Gee,' says Jayne, 'You almost sound like you care. So touching.'

'Not you I'm worried about, Jayne. If we lose you, we've suddenly got a serious dent in our surgery program.'

'Bastard!' Jayne exclaims. She re-wraps the scarf around her thin neck. The ends now reach mid-calf.

'So, what is it about that scarf?' I ask. 'Looks like you've had it for a while.'

'Family heirloom,' Jayne says, 'I'm totally attached to this thing. Had it since I was a child.' She runs her fingers slowly through the coarse woolen threads. 'There are lots of pictures at home with my mum wearing this scarf when she was a child. She gave it to me on my tenth birthday. My great-grandmother knitted this, like in the Stone Age. It's been passed down three generations now.'

'Sounds like it's your prized possession,' I say.

Jayne holds one of the ends of her scarf in both hands now. She stares wistfully at the material. 'You know, Dr Ray, this probably sounds silly, but I often think it's a bit like that slogan for that Swiss watch company – "you never actually own this scarf; you merely look after it for the next generation".'

We continue our walk, and ahead I see a long, narrow suspension footbridge that crosses the deep gorge. It's clear we'll be crossing the bridge soon.

'Oh, great!' I say with genuine enthusiasm. 'I've always wanted to cross on one of those.'

Jayne stops in her tracks. 'You are kidding me! That looks so ridiculously dangerous. You're actually enjoying this? You are a sick man, Dr Ray. This is officially a trek, and you are officially sick. You are going down in my Sixty-Second Summary tonight. You are going down. Big time.'

The bridge spans the gorge at one of its narrowest points. The slender, arching walkway appears to be about 30 or 40 metres across.

It's clear the children love this part of the journey. They run back and forth along the footbridge, laughing, and swing the structure from side to side as they go. Thankfully, the cables supporting the deck appear to be made of iron rather than rope. I'm aware that in some areas of remote Nepal primary rope suspension bridges are still prevalent. The only ropes present on our bridge are the handrails that are supported from separate anchors at each side of the gorge.

It takes a lot of coaxing before Jayne will cross the bridge. Quite reasonably she refuses to begin her crossing until the children promise they will no longer swing the cables. From the other side of the gorge they watch and laugh and tease Jayne as she takes one slow, trembling step after another. After several insufferable minutes she finally reaches the other side and falls melodramatically into the arms of two of the cheering children.

We continue our walk/trek over several more rocky outcrops, and round a bend in the trail. Suddenly, a magnificent vista opens up before us. Massive, imposing, timeless mountains soar upwards; white and grey piercing monoliths dominate the horizon from east to west as far as we can see – a titanic, jagged, white-clad ridge. Jayne and I stop, mouths agape, awestruck at the sublime, rugged beauty.

The children seem oblivious to the glorious panorama. They walk and run and skip ahead. It's difficult to imagine that anyone would ever lose fascination in such a spectacular sight, but I guess this is a consequence when the setting is your backyard, the view an almost daily display. Jayne and I don't want to continue our journey just yet. We both want to soak up this mystical grandeur. Together we stand there, and let the transcendence of the Himalayas tower over us.

After a few minutes, shouts from the children break our spell and reluctantly we saunter ahead to join them. It's been over an hour since we began this trip, and although I'm completely absorbed in the journey, I'm astounded at its distance and the challenges along its course. I marvel that these students tackle this journey to and from school.

'Hey, Milu,' I say, 'is this the only way to reach your school?'

Milu looks at me, confused. I rephrase and move my hand along the direction of our path as I speak. 'You walk this way, every day?'

'Every day to school this way, yes, sir.'

'Milu, you see these mountains here?' (How on earth could you miss them? Even so, I point loosely at the imperious range.) 'Do you know where they came from?'

I know the answer to this question, as any student of basic geography does. The Himalayas formed (and are still forming) from the tectonic uplift resulting from the collision of the Indian plate and the Eurasian plate, blah, blah, blah. But again I consider that it may be better not knowing facts like these. This knowledge takes away some of the ethereal mystery of these extraordinary natural phenomena. 'So, Milu. Why are these mountains here?'

Milu does not hesitate with his reply. 'Long time ago, angry, giant monsters fighting. Destroy many things. Monsters stop fighting and sleep now.'

There is no uncertainty or mockery in his voice. His eyes are earnest; Milu has complete faith in his story. And as I look once again at the massive, jagged shapes before us, they are indeed the spines of vast slumbering giants, their blankets thick and white. I like Milu's explanation one thousand times more than my own.

'And Milu, what will happen if the giant monsters wake up?'

Milu gives me a look that is both solemn and penetrating. His voice is now strangely haunting. 'This will be very, very bad, sir. Many people will die.'

On hearing these sober, foreboding words from the mouth of a child so young, Jayne and I turn to look at each other. We do not speak, but I can see in the depths of her widening eyes, the spectral chill that is the very reflection of my own.

Liz

We continue along this fascinating trail, and we're almost at the top of yet another hill on our protracted journey when the children ahead of us yell, 'We are here! Dr Ray, Sister Piggy, we are here!' They run ahead now, apparently eager to meet up with their other school friends.

Jayne and I walk to the hilltop ourselves and stand silent for some time, taking in the next scene before us. The school is a sad and dilapidated two storey stone structure that clings desperately to the hillside scree. Many of the stones on the walls of the building seem to have long ago given up hope, and fallen to the ground. Most of the fallen stones have surrendered to the vines and other vegetation that surround the ramshackle building. Forlorn second storey windows stare down at us in hopeless despair. The structure reminds me of a very old, and very neglected farmhouse that would more fittingly be empty, abandoned.

Jayne and I slowly stroll the final fifty metres towards the depressing school building. Closer now, we can hear the sounds of the classroom activity. A single voice – Nepali, the deep tones of a male adult – no doubt one of the teachers. And then, as one, the voices of many children, repeating the words of the adult. Again the same phrase from the adult, again the echo from the children. The melodic chanting continues for several minutes, and I find myself drifting back to my own childhood and the memories of my own early school days. For a moment I am one of the young children in the crowded classroom, dutifully reciting my teacher's lines. Warmly I think how quaint it is that some things don't ever seem to change.

Jayne and I walk over to the side of the old building where several steps suggest its entrance. We're almost at the steps when we're confronted by a most repulsive stench.

'Oh my God!' Jayne exclaims, her hand to her nostrils. 'That is disgusting. Do you think it would be impolite to vomit right now?'

'Probably not your best way to greet people, no. Do you think you could hold off with that vomit for a tad?'

The pungent smell appears to be coming from a small timber shed adjacent to the entranceway. Attached to the outside of the shed is a mouldy sign with large Sanskrit writing. These particular sacred Hindu words are some of the very few I've come to recognise in this country, and it's no surprise to learn that they declare this shed to be the toilet block. The structure is so close to the main school building and its stench so hostile, I can't help wondering why it had not been installed in a more remote location.

Jayne and I stand on the entrance steps now, both holding our breath to avoid the sickening smell. The cadence of repetition from schoolroom voices suddenly stops and is replaced by aggressive, abusive shouting. It seems to be the voice of the same adult, the one I have assumed to be the teacher. But now, for some reason he is clearly enraged. Jayne gives a troubled frown and we proceed tentatively up the steps to the corridor.

'Do you think maybe that teacher just caught a whiff of that sewer smell?' Jayne asks.

'It certainly would make me that angry if I thought one of my students made a smell like that,' I reply. 'Maybe we should wait until this class is finished before we introduce ourselves.'

There are two classrooms on this first level, each accessed from the corridor that Jayne and I are now wandering. The heated commotion is coming from the room ahead and to our right. The classroom to our left is empty, so we decide to explore. The stark, airless room reflects the depressing appearance of the building's façade. At the front of the room there is a large blackboard with several unrecognisable Sanskrit words written in white chalk. All of the walls are bare except for the area above the blackboard which displays a small, dusty map of Nepal. Most of the timber desks have attached bench seats – another memory of school days long past. One of the desks at the front of the room is propped up with two large stones to support an absent leg.

As Jayne and I begin to inspect the cheerless room, the shouting from the room across the corridor settles, and once again we hear the soothing tones of students reciting the words of their teacher. There are several tattered textbooks scattered over a long, thin table at the front of the room. A few of the books are written in English, and I pick up one and flick through its pages. Some of the information is so clearly out of date; the 'USSR' is referred to a number of times, and French currency is referred to as 'francs'. I show the references to Jayne, who looks on with sad amusement.

'The only mistake I can see,' she says, 'is that they've called this a book of current affairs. If they'd only called it a history book, everything would be okay.'

A voice suddenly comes from the other end of the classroom. 'I see you find our library entertaining.'

Jayne and I are both startled. It's the voice of a woman, foreign – American, I think. Standing in the doorway is a tall, slim lady, hands on hips in indignation.

'Quite the opposite,' I reply, gathering myself. 'We were both thinking how sad it is that the children here have such outdated textbooks.'

The woman looks to be early forties and wears a bright pink headscarf that clashes with strands of red hair that have worked their way loose from the garish material.

'Who are you, and what do you want?' she asks, but now there is no anger in her voice. The words are blunt, yet her tone is more suggestive of uncertainty, confusion.

'I'm so sorry,' I say. 'My name is Ray, and this is Jayne. We're part of an Australian humanitarian aid organisation. We provide surgical treatment in a village an hour or so from here.'

'Oh. That explains ... a bit,' the American stranger responds. 'I don't mean to be rude, but how is it that you are here in my school?'

'This is our day off – our R and R day,' I reply. 'Jayne and I decided we'd like to visit the school that some of the children from our village attend. We couldn't really phone ahead or anything, so we simply joined some of the children on their way to school this morning, on their *trek*.'

I look at Jayne for acknowledgment as I say the word '*trek*'. She nods with a frown.

'We didn't want to interrupt any teaching, so we thought we'd introduce ourselves between classes.'

The woman simply stares at us, her mouth half open as if she's about to speak, but no words come forth.

'*Your* school,' I continue, 'Did you say *your* school? You are a teacher here?'

The woman gives a reluctant smile. 'My name is Liz,' she says. 'Yes, I am a teacher here. I'm a volunteer on a three-month stint. I'm sorry if I appeared a bit aggressive. It's just that I get a little spooked sometimes.'

Jayne pipes in. 'We're the ones who should apologise. We just rocked up here, unannounced. You're from the States? Or Canada?'

'The States. San Francisco. I've been here a little over a month now. This … experience really has been such an eye opener.'

Jayne and I join Liz at the front of the room now, and we shake her hand warmly.

'I've got to say one thing,' Liz says, clearly relaxed now. 'It's lovely to be able to have a conversation that kind of flows. It's been so long now. The other teachers here speak some English, but it's fairly limited. I mean you both have pretty weird accents and all, but at least we can understand each other easily.'

'You came from the States alone?' I ask, 'to such a remote area, for three months? And by the way, you're the one with the weird accent. Right now you're outnumbered, two to one.'

'You win, this time,' she says. 'I know that must seem strange, me coming here alone and all. My friends back home said much the same. This is my bit to give back something to the world. We're very privileged where I come from.'

'You sound like our medical volunteers,' I say, 'only we all have each other to share our stimulating conversations. It's never really a one-man band.'

'Are we interrupting your classes?' asks Jayne. 'Shouldn't you get back?'

Liz gives a short laugh. 'You make it sound like we have some sort of a structure here. I wish. I can't tell you how painfully disorganised the system is. I want to change things, I want to improve them. There is so much that could be done. But I'm a lone voice in the vast wilderness out here.'

'When you have time we're very keen to have a long chat with you,' I say. 'There are so many questions we want to ask you.'

'Let's see,' Liz says, stroking her chin and looking upwards, somewhere above my head, 'I could fit you in for a long chat, in say, about … now?' She smiles again, more broadly this time.

Liz returns to her upstairs class briefly to tell the children that they can play outside for a while, and soon we hear the gleeful clamour and hurried footsteps of excited children as they make their way down two levels to the grassy surrounds below.

An Education in Schooling

While Jayne and I wait for Liz to return to the classroom, I begin reading through a Year 9 textbook, *Health, Population and Environment*. Turning to the section *Teenage Health*, my slim hopes of finding more contemporary information are quickly shattered when I see the scant material is also hopelessly out of date.

Jayne and I decide to wait outside. We walk out to the school corridor to the top of the steps and look back over the toilet shed. The foul odour is less offensive than earlier – could we be becoming acclimatised so soon? From this vantage point we can see over the top of the toilet shed and the final part of the trail we followed to the school. There are several large, shining squares on the roof of the shed. These squares have all the hallmarks of solar panels. Solar panels? Out here? Surely not. But as I study them more closely, they are unmistakably solar panels. Among the primitive setting of the school and its shabby, antiquated contents, this seems even more incongruous than the television we saw earlier in the day in the small, remote village.

Beyond the fetid shed we can see many of the children, recently freed from the confines of their classroom. They play and frolic with all of the vigour of youngsters of any country. Even the girls in this group seem to have lost their shyness and inhibitions. But something about the numbers is not right.

'Jayne,' I say, 'what do you notice about these children?'

Jayne looks out at the thirty or so children below us. 'They're certainly wild and excitable like most kids.' And then she looks again, more closely. 'There don't seem to be many girls there.'

Spot on. I can count only six girls among the group. Poppy is not among them. I fiercely hope this is not reflective of the overall sex ratio of primary school children. But there's something else that is not right. These six girls – four in one area and two in another – talk and play only with each other; they don't interact with any of the boys.

Liz returns after a few minutes and the three of us re-enter the empty classroom and sit down together. I'm eager to learn so much.

'Where do I start?' I begin. 'How do you survive out here? Where do you live?'

Liz inhales deeply. 'I've been put up – billeted, if you like – in the home of a gorgeous family, local people, about 15 minutes' walk from here. I've been teaching in the States for quite a few years, and I love it. But I thought I'd try to do a bit in part of the world that's really struggling. My marriage ended, my children are independent now, so I thought – why not?' Liz's face becomes more troubled now. 'I signed up to a volunteer organization called *Edvol*. Sounds like a painkiller, right? My God, what a disaster that was. *Edvol* basically organised the whole thing. Don't get me started on them.'

'OK,' I say, 'Tell us about the education system here in this part of Nepal.'

'Well,' Liz sighs, 'as you would know, this is mostly a primary school, of sorts, with a bit of lower secondary. There are 84 students enrolled here, in classes 1 to 8. We have four local teachers, supposedly four, anyway – all men. Five teachers, if you include me. But so many times the men are not here. I've been here now for almost six weeks, and there hasn't been one day during that time that all four have turned up. And even when they are here, so often they simply don't teach. They just don't seem motivated. One of the teachers, Manish – he arrived at school the other day and said he refused to teach that day because he was too tired after the journey to school that morning. Can you believe that? Too tired – so he just smoked and drank tea all day.

'But it's not just the lack of teaching, it's *how* they teach that's a problem. It's like teaching from fifty years ago. Rote learning. Punishment if they get it wrong. The poor little mites can't think for themselves. In most parts of the world it's so well accepted now that children need to be given the opportunity to make mistakes, and to recognise them so they can correct the errors themselves. But here, this school is a factory – and a really inefficient factory. And it produces little automatons. The children can't develop a critical mind; there is no individual thought process.'

I feel embarrassingly naïve now. Here I was, only a short time ago, feeling some sense of comfort listening to the reiteration of rote learning we heard from the classroom across the hall.

'Liz,' I begin, 'I don't quite understand. This rote learning we've been hearing in the other classroom. This is what my school friends and I grew up with, and yet we turned out okay.'

Jayne jumps in here. 'You might think you turned out okay, Dr Ray, but really that's a matter of opinion.'

'Oh, there is a limited role for this parrot learning,' Liz replies, 'Alphabets, multiplication tables, music scores, and so forth. But here it *dominates* the learning process. These children can remember lots of things, but they don't understand them. The rest of the world has moved on. In this day and age computers can recite information in a millisecond. What the world needs are people who can interpret the information and apply it.'

'And the yelling from across the hall?' I ask.

'Janma. He's the other teacher here today. I have to give him some credit, because at least he turns up on most days. But I've got to tell you, his style of teaching – well, it infuriates me. Every day it's rote learning, rote learning, one thing after another. The yelling you heard was probably his response to one of the children making a mistake. That's his way, but it's so wrong. Mistakes are such a crucial part of learning. Children need to be supported and nurtured through their mistakes, not screamed at and humiliated.'

'Have you told him this?' I ask. 'Have you told him there are better ways to teach?'

'Oh, I've spoken to all the teachers here. Can you imagine the response? A woman in this part of the world telling men how to do their job? They shake their heads and smile smugly as if I have no idea what I'm talking about.'

'These gender issues, this sexism stuff – I guess it spills out onto the female students, too?' Jayne asks.

'Jayne, this is such a massive area. So many girls are absent from school. Some never come. Lots of parents think that their daughter is more valuable to them at home than at school. The older they get, the more likely their parents will want them to stay at home, helping out with chores and things. Some parents think – what's the point of educating a daughter? She will only leave home one day and provide for the husband's parents. It's like, she'll just become another family's asset. On the other hand, if we can educate our son he will travel, get a good job, and support us when we grow old.'

I think to myself gloomily, these are precisely the views that Uttam expressed a few days back.

'The ones who do make it to school,' Jayne asks, 'are there gender issues once they get here?'

'Oh, Jayne. You've got no idea.' Liz pulls at the loose stands of her hair. 'There are so very, very few female teachers in these rural areas. When I sit in on the other classes here – the classes with male teachers – the boys seem to get all the attention; the girls are virtually ignored by the teachers. It's like the male teachers don't value the girls' abilities.

'In the first few days here I sat at the back of some of the classes and just watched in horror. I watched this primitive teaching and all of its cruel discrimination. I bit my tongue so hard one time, it actually bled. Right now, if you're a child in this region, you have such an uphill battle to get a decent education and any of the benefits that flow with that. If you're a female child, you have a Himalayan snowball's chance in hell.'

'Can you make a difference in three months, Liz?' I ask.

'I want to believe I can help a few of these children, especially some of the girls. Perhaps I can motivate some of them, you know, light a spark. And maybe after I've gone that little fire will keep burning in one or two. Huh – listen to me! Suddenly I've become all poetic.'

'Liz,' I say, 'I'm not sure if you have any idea how similar your frustrations are to ours. Every day in our medical world here we struggle with gender issues and the results of discrimination. But up here you must be tearing your hair out with no one to talk to about this.'

'Oh, I must have written at least a hundred emails to my friends back home.'

'You get internet access up here?' Jayne asks.

'It's a bit hit and miss, but most days I can, yes. And I was smart enough to bring along a solar charger for my laptop.'

'Is that what we saw on top of the toilet shed?' Jayne asks.

'Yeah, they're solar cells, too, but apparently they haven't been working for a long time now. Someone or some group donated the system to the school years ago. Very kind of them, whoever they were, but they hadn't considered maintenance; no one in this region has a clue how to fix things like these. It's such a waste.'

'And the smell – isn't it disgusting?'

'The student toilet used to be on the other side of the main school building, and a lot further away. But they were pretty well destroyed with one of the mudslides – we get a few of those around here, especially around monsoon time. So some genius decided to rebuild the latrine right at our entrance here. It's a beautiful way to welcome you to work each morning.'

'All the children share the same toilet?' I ask. 'No separate toilet for the girls?'

'No there's not. And a lot of the children – boys and girls – relieve themselves outside, behind the trees. It's a real problem. Some of the older girls won't drink water the whole day, just so they don't have to pee. It's crazy, and it can't be healthy.'

'There is running water?' asks Jayne.

'Praise the Lord!' Liz exclaims. 'I'm not actually religious – sometimes those little words of worship just shoot out like that. But yes, we should be thankful for the clean water at least. Apparently they've had running water here for a couple of years now. I hate to think how tough it must have been before that.'

'Liz,' I say, 'I know you'll need to get back to your teaching soon, but I want to ask you about one particular child, a girl from our village.'

Liz cuts me off. 'Let me guess – her name is Ganuradha Shresthra, the one who likes to be called "Poppy".'

My smile in response tells Liz her guess is correct.

'Ah, yes,' she says. 'So gifted. Poppy is in Year 6, and she is head and shoulders above the others in her class, including the boys. She's a delight to teach, a breath of fresh air.'

'Do you know why?' I ask. 'Is she simply naturally talented, or is there some other reason?'

'Like extra tuition after school?' Liz laughs. 'Yeah, as if that's ever gonna happen around here.'

'Poppy has an air of self-confidence,' I say. 'It's not cockiness or arrogance, it's a sort of poise. We haven't seen that in other girls her age.'

'Yeah,' Liz replies, 'I know exactly what you mean. Can't explain that. I'm not sure where she gets that from. I just wish other girls had it, too. In the meantime, I'm doing my best to nurture that. Poppy is one of the ones I'd simply love to see flourish somehow.' Liz stands now and walks towards the entrance of the classroom. 'Let me just check on my children.'

She looks beyond the corridor and the stinking toilet shed to the area where the children continue to play. 'No broken bones that I can see – so far it's been a good day.'

'We should let you get back to doing what you're not paid to do,' I say, 'but we could talk to you for hours about this. I'm sure you know that education and health are intimately connected, especially among women. Can we talk again sometime?'

'Ray, Jayne – I'd be absolutely delighted. I love getting this stuff off my chest. When will you come back?'

Jayne chips in. 'I'm not sure I'd survive another trek out here. I'm not even sure if I'll make it home alive today.'

'Jayne found the journey here today a little challenging,' I explain. 'Liz, perhaps you'd like to visit our little hospital on one of your free days?'

Liz beams. 'How do you Aussie guys say it? That would be bonza, mate.'

Young Endeavours

Day #11. 7:10am, Dining Hall.

As I look around the breakfast table, it's encouraging to see the team looking refreshed after the day's break. The conversation is loud and lively. Jayne talks incessantly about yesterday's trek and its challenges, and she embellishes the adventure and the hazards along the way.

'Honestly, the cliff face must have been, like over a hundred metres, straight down. I had to crawl along this ridiculously skinny path on the edge of the mountain. It was *so* skinny. And slippery, too. I was on my hands and knees trying desperately not to fall. And there was nothing to hold on to, nothing. If I hadn't been so calm, if I'd just slipped a few millimetres to my right – I would be gone, dead meat, all smashed up at the bottom of that God-awful mountain.'

The rest of the team laugh and tease Jayne's account. They respond with mock horror.

'But you're so brave, Jayne!' says Louise.

'Thank goodness you were there to help all those children to safety across all those dangerous paths,' Paul says.

'Impressive stuff,' Norman adds. 'I read about when Hillary and Tenzing conquered Everest – they've got nothing on you, Miss Piggy,'

We look up to see Poppy walk through the kitchen doors. This morning she holds a small infant to her hip. Poppy looks quite comfortable with the child as she serves us with her one free hand. As we watch her, it's easy to imagine Poppy as a very young mother, experienced with this parental balancing act. The child appears no more than 18 months old. He or she looks equally comfortable, secure on Poppy's hip as she continues her morning work. The young child wears a very tattered woolen beanie. Wide, inquiring eyes explore the new faces of our team.

'Yet another task to add to your daily chores?' I ask Poppy.

Poppy doesn't appear to understand my question. She tilts her head to the side and says nothing.

I rephrase. 'You have so much to do here each day, Poppy. And now you have more work to do with a baby to look after.'

'Dr Ray,' she says, 'I follow your words, but caring for this baby – this is not work. This baby is joy.'

I smile broadly, along with the rest of my team who watch our interaction. Poppy introduces the baby to us as Hari, a little boy. We learn that his mother is working today as a labourer in a nearby town. Apparently she often asks Poppy to help out with his care.

Louise chips in, 'I wish I could say it was always a joy to look after my baby. He's all grown up now, and I love him to death. But there were so many times when he was a baby when he was anything but joy.'

Is it simply the novelty of this baby that makes the experience of caring for it a 'joy'? Is it the part-time nature of the experience? Or is this another part of the absorbing collectivist culture in this country?

After we've finished our breakfast Poppy sets Hari down in the corner of the Dining Hall to free both hands as she begins clearing our table.

'Do you go to school today, Poppy?' I ask.

'Not today, Dr Ray,' she replies. 'My father ask me to do many things today. No time for school.'

I look for a suggestion of disappointment in Poppy's face with this response, but none is apparent.

'Would you rather be at school than working here?' I ask.

Poppy stares at me with incredulous eyes. 'Of course I want more to be at school, learning. But this is not possible today.'

I do my best to disguise my own disappointment at this latest restraint on Poppy's education. Our volunteers all stand up and we're about to make our way to the hospital, when Hari begins to cry. His cries are high-pitched, much like a severely wounded animal. Within seconds his screams have become earsplitting. His face is now bright red and drenched with tears.

'Good time for us all to leave,' says Paul.

'*Joy*, is it?' Louise says. 'Huh. Now let's see how much *joy* there is.'

I'm interested to see Poppy's reaction to this screaming onslaught. At this stage she doesn't appear perturbed. All of the team watch as she simply walks over to the baby, picks him up and begins to rock him back and forth. She strokes his shoulders and his tiny, covered head. We hear gentle humming at first, and then, the soothing sounds of a lullaby. It's the first time I've heard Poppy sing, and her voice is warm and gentle. I have not heard these lyrics before either, and they are at once tranquil, calming, hypnotic.

'Naru naru nani
Nani hamro gani
Buli ko sar jana say
Pani peko ramo ray.'

I think to myself, even though these words are entirely foreign to us, the comforting language of lullabies is universal. I guess this settling scene we're watching is being played out a million times right now, in every country throughout the world.

Poppy repeats the lullaby over and over, and no one is surprised to see the baby boy quickly succumb to the song's relaxing charm; within minutes he has drifted away into a deep slumber.

As we all begin our walk to the hospital, Jayne says, 'What is it about lullabies? How is it that they settle toddlers?'

'I can answer that,' says Steph. 'I actually read about this. It was part of my psychology study before medical school.'

'They do psychology on babies now?' Jayne asks. 'Freaky. I can just picture a little baby lying back on the therapist's couch.'

'Actually, it's really interesting,' Steph continues. 'The infants' first awareness of the world is really confusing. As small babies, they exist in their own simple, sheltered world. When they begin to confront the real world, it's disordered and threatening to them. A lullaby brings a soothing sense of order to their consciousness. Apparently it's the swaying rhythm and the simple, repeating melody of a lullaby that settle their fear of this new, crazy world out there.'

Steph's explanation is indeed interesting, but I can't help wondering if this is another case of knowledge spoiling the charm of the unknown.

*

We follow our hospital path around the foothills and reach the open farming area where several small homes surround the broad grassland. A young girl squats in front of one of the homes washing clothes in a small metal tub. She spots our group and waves.

'That's Laxmi,' says Louise, 'The girl we saw with her friends in the field a few days ago.'

Louise and I walk over to the child to greet her.

'*Namaste*, Laxmi,' I say.

'*Namaste*,' she answers, joining her palms together.

'Is this your home?' I ask.

Laxmi stands uncertainly, her shoulders hunched. 'Yes, this is my home. Also home for my father, my brothers and my mother.' Her voice is barely louder than the whisper when we first met.

'Laxmi,' says Louise, 'It's lovely to see you again. Please tell your mother and her friends that if they have any sickness we might be able to help them at our clinic in the hospital. There is no cost.'

'Thank you. I am sorry, I forget your name.'

Louise smiles. 'That's okay. I usually forget names, too. I am Louise, and …' Louise points at me. 'This is … this is … oh, I forget.'

I grin and say, 'I am Dr Ray.'

Laxmi's mouth curls to a soft grin, but she doesn't seem quite relaxed enough to give a genuine smile. She catches our eyes for a short second before she quickly resumes her washing.

'We'll see you again, Laxmi,' Louise says as we walk back to rejoin our group.

'I do believe we're starting to win her confidence, Lu Lu.'

'It's only slight, isn't it? But it's really rewarding,' Louise replies. 'Okay, here's a challenge. By the time we leave this camp in about two and a half weeks, I want us to have a conversation with Laxmi where she doesn't look down to the ground even once. You reckon we can do that?'

'I'm not sure. I'd like to think so. Maybe we should get Poppy to give her some coaching.'

We rejoin the team to continue our walk and approach the small grove of poplar trees near the hospital. We all stop to admire the colourful rain as thousands of riotous leaves tumble and pirouette silently to the ground below. Gusts of chill wind stir the fiery display to forge a fickle dance.

As we open the door to the operating theatre, several of the multicoloured leaves are blown inside and drift across the theatre floor. Jayne gives a lighthearted frown and finds a broom. With a flourish, she sweeps the intruding leaves back outside from where they came.

'Okay, guys,' Jayne says to the leaves. 'You don't belong here. Go out and play with your frisky mates.'

A wind gust catches the leaves once again and they take to the air. One more whimsical dance – perhaps their last chance to frolic before their looming decay.

*

As with every operating day, the team grab the antiseptic wash to cleanse all of the theatre surfaces before we begin our surgery. While Jayne and Paul prepare the surgical instruments for the first two cases of the morning, Steph and I head off towards the ward to begin our postoperative rounds. Bright leaves continue to drift downward, and as we're about to cross through the rice paddies, two young boys approach us from the opposite path.

'There's that boy again,' Steph says.

'Which one?'

'The really thin one. Haven't you seen him? He's outside the Dining Hall nearly every morning.'

'That boy is Milu, Steph. He came with us on the trek to the school a few days back. I haven't really noticed him since then.'

As the boys reach us, Steph puts out a hand to stop them.

'*Namaste*, boys,' she says. 'Hello. You are Milu? And who is your little friend?'

'My name is Sampa,' the other replies.

'*Namaste*, Sampa,' Steph looks from Sampa to Milu. 'Where are you heading now? Shouldn't you be getting ready for school?'

Milu's chin dips as he looks up sheepishly at Steph. 'Yes, miss,' he says. His voice is so much softer than it was a few days ago.

'School is back in this direction.' She points to where they've both come from. 'Why do you walk this way instead?' Steph's tone is gentle and inquisitive, rather than accusing.

'Um … it is ….' A burning crimson flush creeps across Milu's cheeks. Two more flaming casts to join the cascading colours that surround us.

'Miss,' Sampa says, 'Milu wants to walk to school with Ganuradha.'

'*Cupa lagnu* – shut up!' Milu shouts as he thumps Sampa solidly on his shoulder.

'Poppy!' I say, 'Milu – you want to walk to school with Poppy?'

'Oh,' Steph says, 'that's why you wait near the Dining Hall each day! That's so sweet. Is Poppy your girlfriend?'

Milu does not answer Steph's question. He jams his hands into his armpits and glances from side to side as if trying to find an exit from the painful place he finds himself.

'Miss?' It's Sampa again. 'Ganuradha – Poppy – she is not Milu's girlfriend. But Milu – he *want* this.'

Milu lets out a loud groan and punches Sampa's shoulder once more.

'Oh Milu,' says Steph, 'I am so sorry we've embarrassed you. Do not fear – your secret is safe with us.'

The boys turn and resume their walk. They squabble and jostle each other as they continue towards the Dining Hall. Steph and I remain stationary for a few more moments as we watch them on their way.

'Young romance.' Steph says. 'So adorable. Now that brings back some fond memories.'

'More like a one-sided crush than a romance,' I reply. 'I wonder what Poppy's thoughts are on all of this.'

Louise's Plea

Day #11. 1:30pm, Theatre Assessment Room

The team have worked really hard again this morning. So far today we've managed to carry out three operations. All three women had been suffering with quite severe genital prolapse, so we're all feeling very satisfied with ourselves. We've reached the time for our half-hour break, and as with most days on our camp, the Dining Hall staff have been kind enough to deliver our lunch from their kitchen. The volunteers all sit with looks of hungry anticipation as mouthwatering aromas announce the arrival of our vegetable *momo*s.

'Ray, can I talk to you for a few minutes?' Louise's asks. Her face is troubled – a look I rarely see with her. She takes the vacant seat next to me.

'Sure, Lu Lu. Something to get off your chest?'

'Yeah. Something I've been thinking about for a few days now.'

'Okay. Hit me with it.'

'Three nights ago, with the caesarean section. You know that was a pretty amazing thing to happen here in the middle of nowhere.'

'Yep. It really was touch and go for a while there. Obstetrics gets pretty exciting sometimes, doesn't it?'

'I know obstetrics is not the sort of thing we do on these camps.'

'That was a first for us,' I reply. As hungry as I am right now, I don't yet touch the *momos* on my plate. Instead I look into Louise's face to try to work out where this conversation is heading.

'Ray, I know how stretched our resources are. I know how we struggle with our basic manpower, and the ridiculously scanty supplies and equipment.'

'Kind of makes it exhilarating though, don't you think?' I say in a lame attempt to make light of the daily challenges we face in the camps. 'Believe me, Lu Lu, if there was any way we could overcome those shortages, we'd be onto it.'

'No, I know that, Ray,' Louise says, 'and I'm more determined than ever to push ahead with some major fundraising when we get home. I promise you that.'

I give Louise a soft smile. 'Lu Lu, a big part of me wants to say that when you get home next week, just put your feet up and have a well-earned break. You do so much here during the camp, and you grind your guts out every working day. I want to tell you to forget about the struggles of fundraising. But to be honest, I would love every one of us here, including you, to pull out all stops to get more support for these camps once we get back home. This fundraising thing is such a cut-throat business. There are so many charities competing for donations.'

'I understand that,' Louise says, 'and I understand that when resources are limited, it makes sense to cut back, not to expand. If we can't do a lot of things properly, then we should do less things really well.'

Louise's words dumbfound me. I was so not expecting this. 'You, of all people, feel we should *cut back* on our work here? You know we've only really just scratched the surface of this women's health debacle. There is so much more we can do.'

'Ray. Hear me out – that's the exact *opposite* of what I'm thinking. I think we need to *expand*.'

'Expand?' I repeat. 'Go, girl. Tell me what you think we should do.'

'We saved that little baby's life the other night. And the mum's. They both would have died if we hadn't been there. You know that, Ray, you know it. A week or so ago in your Sixty-Second Summary you talked about those "precious moments" in bed each night before we fall off to sleep. Well, for the last few nights I've been lying in bed, tossing and turning. Those precious moments you talked about – well for me they've turned into more like precious *hours*. And I've been thinking about childbirth. How many other mums and babies die in this country in situations like the one we had the other night? I know this sounds really dramatic, but how many others die that could have been saved?

'You also asked "how can we make a major difference?" Well, you know I'm not just a nurse – I'm also a trained midwife. And you're not just a gynaecologist – you're an obstetrician, too. *How* can we make a difference? How can we make a *major* difference? Well, let's not just fix prolapse – let's stop more mums and babies dying, too. Ray – we need to expand into maternal health. There. I've said it.'

I watch Louise's look of desperate hope, and I feel terrible that my response will demoralise her.

'Lu Lu,' I say, 'the caesarean made me think long and hard, too. Just like you, I wondered if there was something else we could do to help, you know, long term. You're right – there are so many thousands of mums and babies who die each year in this country, and it'd be wonderful to make a big difference to this problem.'

'*But*,' Louise interrupts, 'You're going to say *but* now, aren't you?'

'Oh, Lu Lu. Yes, I have to say *but*. We have to be realistic. It's all very well to have great vision and resolve, but the cold hard fact is that we are way too stretched right now. At the moment, you know our supplies are threadbare, and these are only just enough to allow us to do our prolapse surgery. We really are right on the edge of not having enough. If our supplies and our staffing were any less than they are right now, we simply couldn't treat these women properly. And the costs of running a labour ward are enormous. If we had to share our meagre resources with the running of some sort of safe obstetric service, we could end up doing more harm than good.'

Louise looks crushed, and says nothing. I feel mean-spirited for having burst her bubble of enthusiasm, but I know it would be irresponsible to try to expand our work when we're already struggling to get by. Our *momos* sit on the plates in front of us, untouched, forsaken, and getting colder by the minute. But now neither of us has an appetite for lunch.

*

The afternoon surgery lacks the positive energy that usually feeds our theatre sessions. Louise has taken her usual role as theatre scout, assisting Jayne in her role as scrub nurse. The others in our team have picked up on the flat mood Louise and I exude. While our operations continue over the next few hours, I wrack my brain to try to work out some way of overcoming this problem of maternal health. Maybe in a few years from now we could have attracted enough donors to expand into maternal care. Maybe then we could provide safety for mothers and babies in rural Nepal and drive down the appalling numbers of maternal and neonatal deaths.

But even if we could somehow acquire more funds – how would we tackle the problem? Management of pregnancies is not at all like treating prolapse. As distressing as severe genital prolapse is, it's rare that we need to perform corrective surgery as some sort of emergency. Women can at least wait until we turn up on our camps to fix them. Prolapse treatment is suited to regular camps, with concentrated spells of treatment over some weeks at a time. But with childbirth it's a different ballgame. If a mum needs an urgent delivery, or management of a massive haemorrhage or severe preeclampsia, she can't exactly wait a few months for her treatment. Obstetric care requires a year-round, 24/7 effort. Emergencies can occur at any time.

The problem is that it would be almost impossible to find enough qualified volunteers to provide advanced obstetric care continuously throughout the year. We could train local doctors to manage obstetric emergencies and perform caesarean sections, but it would take years for them to reach the necessary standards. In any case, Nepalese doctors don't seem to want to work in these remote regions. And underlying all of this, the ongoing costs of such a demanding project would be overwhelming. I can see no way out.

Cultural Blockade

Day #11. 7:10pm.

'You have shared this home with your brother and his wife for a long time?' I ask.

'Since loss of my wife,' Uttam replies. 'Before then, live in next village.' Nabin explains to me that the next village is a further twenty minutes' walk from here.

I have returned to Uttam's home with Nabin. As a courtesy, and in an effort to develop our friendship further, I've brought along a gift for Uttam – a live chicken that Paul purchased for me earlier in the day. But there is another reason for my apparent generosity. I figure that if Uttam slaughters this chicken tonight, there is a good chance that the meat component of our meal will be something substantially more edible than the repulsive gristle of my first visit.

I'm keen to explore the thoughts and beliefs of Uttam. I want to know what drives him and his patriarchal ways. Uttam seems to represent the views of the other men in this remote corner of Nepal. The three of us men: Uttam, Nabin and I, sit around the fire sipping masala tea while Gorham stirs another threatening pot of mysterious liquid. Suntil has taken Nerum to the village cultural dance production and won't be home until after dinner.

The fire in the open stove is low. Tentative flames lick at the sides of the logs that have recently been added.

'Uttam,' I begin, 'I do not wish to be disrespectful, but may I ask how your wife lost her life?'

Uttam's response through Nabin's translation is a series of rapid bursts of speech. 'Baby came. Girl baby. Crying. Happy crying. Then blood came. Very much blood. More than when slaughter goat. Blood not stop. Wife not breathe. Die.'

There is no emotion in Uttam's voice and I am taken aback at his dispassionate description of the death of his wife. Is this simply bravado? Is he trying to disguise his grief – perhaps a cultural response? Or is he truly now no longer affected by the loss that occurred more than 12 years ago?

Poppy's mother experienced a fatal postpartum haemorrhage – very heavy vaginal bleeding following childbirth. This is the most common cause of maternal death in this country, and it's so very preventable. In the West we treat these haemorrhages frequently – and almost always successfully.

I decide to continue my questioning. 'Your daughter was born at home?'

'Yes. Both children born at home.' Uttam stares at me now with a penetrating look. I wonder if he tries to read my thoughts. If he could read them he would see that his wife would have almost certainly survived if she'd delivered Poppy in a hospital that was reasonably well supplied with medications and trained medical staff. The Health Post 15 or 20 minutes from here – the building where the local midwife, Jyoti and her colleague deliver some babies – would this have been adequate 12 years ago when Poppy was born? Quite possibly. But I do not share these thoughts; they are of no use to Uttam. However I do wonder whether or not they battle for attention in Uttam's mind.

While I'm conscious of the risk of opening old wounds, perhaps it's because of Uttam's impervious description of his wife's death that I push on with my questions.

'Why do you think your wife was taken from you?' I ask. 'Why did she bleed so heavily that she died?'

Another piercing look from Uttam. 'Spirits upset. Shaman not make peace with spirit.'

Whoa. Here we go. This is what we're up against? The animistic beliefs that still pervade remote areas like this in Nepal? Do these sets of religious convictions and practices compete with the conventional medical care that we attempt to introduce? Do some people here choose the chants of a primitive Shaman – essentially a witchdoctor – over the proven benefits of Western medicine? If so, then we have a bigger battle on our hands than I first thought.

But I'm a little confused. Uttam appears grateful that we provide surgical care to the women who suffer with severe prolapse. Does he just have a problem with conventional medical treatment of pregnancy and childbirth?

'The Shaman – when did your wife see him?'

Nabin and Uttam begin a protracted conversation now, longer than I would expect for my short question.

'Wife see Shaman when small bleeding in beginning part pregnancy. See Shaman for son and for daughter. Pregnancy for son – no problem with spirits. Pregnancy with daughter – very bad with spirits.'

'And Uttam, after the Shaman told you the spirits were unhappy with your wife's second pregnancy, did you think it would be worthwhile taking her to a hospital for the birth of your daughter?'

'When spirit unhappy, we make many sacrifice of two goats. This is way to fix spirit – not hospital.'

'Do you still feel this way now, Uttam?' I ask. 'Do you still feel that the hospital and the doctors and midwives cannot help when the spirits are upset?'

Before Nabin can translate the reply I watch Uttam's face for a hint of an answer, but I can't read his expression.

'Maybe sometime they can help,' he says. 'I am not certain.'

Some progress at least.

'And your friends, Uttam, the other people of the village – do they have the same thoughts about the Shaman as you? When other pregnant women in this village become sick, do they see the Shaman or do they see the staff in the hospital?'

'Most people in village, if sick, try Shaman first. If no help, then maybe hospital.'

'Uttam, if the mother does not see the Shaman, if she is not sick, is there any need for her to go to the hospital for her care? Or do you feel she can safely have her baby at home?'

'If woman not much work, hospital maybe. If too busy, if already babies in home, have next baby in home.'

Uttam's opinions are not surprising, particularly in view of his thoughts about girls and education, but they are really discouraging.

And this is here in a village where the Health Post is only 15 or 20 minutes away. What about families who live at long distances from the medical care? What slim hope do we have of getting pregnant women to a Health Post or hospital when they live hours or even days away?

Complications like the massive haemorrhage Poppy's mother suffered usually develop suddenly and severely. In emergencies like these there is nowhere near enough time to carry the ailing mother to a hospital because the transport route from home is usually a series of grueling walking tracks.

Gorham begins to ladle our meals from her large cooking pot, and I'm really disappointed to see that my chicken is not on our menu. It still scratches and pecks – very much alive – in the corner of Uttam's dim, smoke-filled home. I watch uneasily as the food is slowly transferred to my plate. But I'm very relieved to see that no meat appears at all. Tonight's fare is vegetarian. So good.

'Uttam,' I say, 'may I discuss your daughter again?'

As Nabin translates my next question, there is a perceptible flinch in the rigid exterior of Uttam's weathered face.

'The girl who make trouble,' he answers.

'Uttam, do you understand that your daughter is very intelligent? She has a rare gift and enormous potential to be quite successful.'

I know Uttam will be irritated with my comments, and once these have been translated I watch the lines in his furrowed brow deepen further. I look across to the open fire once again. The logs are now fully alight and the brazen flames leap with abandon. As Uttam begins to reply, I cut him off.

'Please let me finish my comments. I am sorry to interrupt you – I am a guest in your home, and I do not wish to be impolite. But what I want to say is very important to me. You and I have conflicting opinions about some things, but I strongly believe we should both be able to express our differences.'

Uttam is quiet now. His steely look is now mixed with one of suspicion.

'I know your feelings, Uttam. I know it is your belief that the role of the woman is to have children and to look after the family home. I know that this is your culture and that you believe it must remain this way. I understand this. The Western culture in my country was this way for many years, too. But Uttam, these constraints, these restrictions on women – they have changed in my country. They have changed in most other countries of the world. And they are gradually changing here in Nepal.'

Uttam continues to stare. He remains intensely focused, but silent, so I continue my homily.

'In Australia, when things changed for women, when it became acceptable for them to advance their education, to take on careers, to do more than just have children and look after the home – the country improved. We became wealthier – not just the women, but the men, too. To be honest, we are still not all the way there yet; there are still lots of areas where the opportunities for women have not yet reached those for men. But in the process of changing that part of our culture, of removing those restrictions on girls and women, we became a more successful country, and I believe we became country where more people were fulfilled.

'I understand that your culture and your heritage are really important to you. Our Western culture is much younger than yours, but our traditions and our heritage are really important to us, too. But that didn't mean we had to continue to put up barriers for women. Since pulling down most of those barriers, we have become a much better country.'

Another drawn-out conversation ensues between Uttam and Nabin. As I watch them both talking back and forth to each other, I have no idea yet of Uttam's reaction to my arguments in favour of gender equality. I remind myself that Uttam's prejudiced beliefs are entrenched; he is not going to simply change his attitude after a single discussion with a foreigner he hardly knows. Why waste my time then, in what is surely a futile attempt to enlighten this man and his archaic ideas?

Perhaps the answer is that in expressing my opinion I may plant a small seed of doubt in Uttam's mind. Perhaps I can get him to ever-so-slightly consider that there could be a better way to treat women in this country. And really, honestly, underlying all of this – I want to do the best for Poppy. I can't stand the thought of her forgoing what is unquestionably massive potential and promise. Obstruction to her educational future would be a deplorable waste of such an aspiring life.

After several minutes, Uttam and Nabin finish their conversation and I look to Uttam for his response. But he says nothing, and instead consumes another three or four mouthfuls of his vegetable dish. Eventually he speaks again through Nabin.

'My father, my grandfather, my mother, my grandmother – they all live this way. Woman is made for babies and for family. You tell me this not right. Why this suddenly change? Why, when this is way forever? This is all we know.'

Uttam does not have the anger in his manner tonight. Instead there is a sadness in his voice and his expression as he presents his counter-argument.

'You good man, Dr Ray,' he continues in his forlorn tone. 'I know this. I know you want do good. I must be trusting you say right things. Maybe in some places better for woman to do work of man. But here is different place. This is my village. We not wealthy like your country, but we happy. No need to change.'

Even though Uttam's response does not surprise me, I feel numb as he utters his cheerless words. Deep inside I know that this attitude is the crux of the problem of gender inequity and women's welfare in general in Nepal. Building a school in a community that forbids adolescent girls to attend will be fruitless in improving their education. Building a hospital in a community that does not believe in conventional medical care for women will not improve their health. Uttam is correct in one area – the people in his country do seem happy. And yet, despite this outward appearance, there are so many thousands of women who are essentially crippled with pelvic floor disfigurement.

I'm determined to stay on good terms with Uttam. I know that a passionate argument between us would be counter-productive. So instead I give him a wry smile. I stand, take his right hand in mine and give him a very firm – and very Western – handshake. I want my look and my actions to convey to him that although I strongly disagree with his views, I respect him, and I respect that he has the right to his disparate opinion. But if I'm honest with myself, I remain disgusted with this bigoted, oppressive mentality. The evidence is so clearly in favour of fostering everything we humanly can do to promote gender equity.

My mind flashes to faces of so many women we've seen suffering with their harrowing genital prolapse. And then it lingers on the innocent face of Poppy and her very vulnerable plight. I think about Poppy's mother, and the thousands of other mothers who have lost their lives from conditions that are so often easily preventable. This battle against these negative cultural influences is far from over. I have no idea how to tackle them, but right now I feel an overwhelming urge to fight them and to win. My team and I are foreigners from a land with different customs and different traditions and a different culture. This makes any intervention in social institutions particularly difficult. We must be shrewd with our campaign and choose our strategies cautiously. If our tactics are misguided, we risk the accusations of arrogance and 'cultural imperialism', and this would clearly stymie our endeavour.

A Welcome Visit

Day #12. 5:10pm, Operating Theatre.

We've paused for a well-earned coffee break between cases. The coffee is one of our luxuries on this camp. Louise was clever enough to bring along a Nespresso machine from her home in Australia. The coffee maker sits on a shelf in the operating theatre and gets a heavy workout throughout the surgery days. Those of us who have milk with our coffee need to contend with the powdered version, but we quickly adjust to the artificial taste. The espresso coffee has been so popular among our volunteers throughout the camp that our supplies of the coffee pods for the machine are now running low.

'Hey, Paullie,' I say. 'You've been pretty impressive at chasing down torch batteries and swabs. Any chance you could get us some more coffee pods?'

'I'm ahead of you, Ray,' Paul replies, 'and the news is not good. I made a few calls two days back. The closest supplier to us is in Calcutta. They said they could probably get a carton to us within a month or two.'

'Express post then, is it?'

'I guess that's express for this part of the world.'

'We'll only be here for another couple of weeks before we go home. If I had to wait for a month or two for coffee, I think I would die a painful death.'

'I'm with you, Ray. I think a lot of our team would die along with you.'

'And there's no other coffee here? Not even instant coffee?'

'Nothing. Didn't know how to break it to you. Sorry.'

'Hate to do this, Paullie, but with the limited coffee pods left, you know we'll need to start a ration system.'

Paul goes to work with the coffee pod inventory. With six coffee drinkers among the volunteers, he calculates that for the remaining days each of us can consume 0.7 pods per day. This could be ugly, because there will clearly be days now when, for some of us, there will be no coffee available.

'Dr Ray, Sister Jayne Piggy – there is woman here to see you.' The voice belongs to our nurse, Guna. It's the first time I have seen Guna since the caesarean section several nights back.

I walk outside the theatre building, where it's no surprise to see that our visitor is Liz.

'Liz! It's so great to see you. I was really hoping you would come. Welcome to our little hospital.'

'Dr. Ray. Delighted to be here,' Liz replies. She casts her eyes around the outside of our operating theatre building. 'Wow. I thought our school building was decrepit. But next to your theatre, our school looks thoroughly 21st century.'

'So you like our rustic charm here,' I say playfully. 'That's such a beautiful compliment. Thank you, Liz.'

'No. I don't mean to be insulting. Quite the opposite. I think it's amazing that you guys do all your work in such primitive surroundings.'

'Well, we could say exactly the same thing to you with your teaching. Liz, we've got one more operation to go here today. We'll be starting that shortly. Can I get someone to show you around the hospital while we do that? You're staying for some time, aren't you?'

'Love to have a look around, thank you. Please take your time with your surgery – I've got all evening.'

Norman kindly offers to give Liz a tour of our hospital. I ask Gamika to accompany them to the wards to provide translation.

7:30pm, Dining Hall

After we complete our final operation for the day, Jayne and I catch up with Liz in the Dining Hall. She and Norman are sipping their drinks in front of the labouring potbelly stove.

'You seem to have a head start on us,' I say, pointing to their drinks.

'If you're like most Aussies,' Liz retorts, 'it shouldn't take you long to catch up to me.'

Jayne and I grab an *Everest* beer each, and join Liz and Norman by the stove.

'How was that trek from your school?' asks Jayne. Her tone suggests she's expecting Liz to have found the journey as arduous as Jayne had.

'Loved it,' replies Liz. 'Totally. And what about those views of the mountains? I was gobsmacked.'

'It's kind of surreal,' I say. I look at Jayne, who seems disheartened. 'And I think even Jayne might admit it was worth the long walk, just to see and feel those mountains.'

Jayne looks from Liz to me. She nods her head as she raises her shoulders, a look to almost suggest she's confessing a crime.

'Liz,' I continue, 'the sun will be down soon. It will be far too dangerous for you to try to walk home in the dark. Can we find a room for you here in our lodge?'

'Yes, I was thinking the same thing. That would be very nice, thank you. But I insist on paying for the room.'

'Let me see,' I say. 'One night, single room. Let's include breakfast with that. The total will come to, in American dollars … approximately 75 cents. And we don't take credit.'

'Wow. You drive a hard bargain here. Especially considering I'm a damsel with no other safe place to go. Okay, sold.'

'Right. That's out of the way now.' I settle into my seat, eager for another conversation with Liz. 'Norman, I'm glad you're still here. Liz, as you know there are massive problems with women's health in this country, especially in rural and remote Nepal. We've been trying to tackle the issue by chipping away at the edges.'

A few other volunteers enter the Dining Hall and join our small group around the fire.

'Hey,' I continue, 'you got poetic when Jayne and I first met you, Liz. You know, when you talked about lighting a spark or something, and keeping the fire going. Can I try one now?'

'Knock yourself out,' Liz says.

'Do you know Uluru? It's also called Ayer's Rock – this enormous rock in central Australia. Well, we've been chipping away at the women's health problems in Nepal just like we were using a tiny chisel to break down Uluru.'

'Oh, Ray,' Jayne groans, 'that is so lame.'

'Best I could come up with,' I reply, contrite. 'I'll workshop that one. Anyway, Liz, it was Norman who opened my eyes to our need to learn as much as we can about *why* women's health is so poor in Nepal. Norman made me realise that in tackling a major problem you need to get to its source.'

I look across to Norman, and I'm not sure if it's pride or his third shandy that gives him a look of dreamy content.

'We need to stretch our wings and explore all the possible causes for the dreadful statistics,' I continue. 'Not just this prolapse thing, but maternal health, too. We want to ask why so many women get this horrible genital prolapse, but also why so many mothers and babies die in this country.'

Liz has my full attention now. She's stopped drinking and stares at me with an uneasy frown.

'Liz, I'm sure you're aware that education – especially female education – plays a really big part in this. You seem to have a pretty good understanding of some of the education troubles. I'd love you to expand on them.'

'You bet,' Liz replies. 'As you saw the other day, I'm so disillusioned with the whole education system in these remote parts of Nepal. But we can't simply blame this on the poverty here. The basic setup of the education system is hopeless.'

The whole team are here now. Liz is introduced to those she's not previously met, and after welcoming her, the volunteers sit in a close circle around the potbelly, most of them watching our conversation in silence.

'I touched on some of those things when we first met,' Liz continues. 'Let me give you an example. For several years now, primary school education in this country has been officially "free" in government schools. That's great in theory, but in practice families still have to find money for admission fees, exam fees, books, and so forth.'

'Out of date books,' Jayne adds.

'Yes, many books are out of date, but that's not all. The storybooks – fictional and non-fictional – all the heroes are male. All the breadwinners are male. The women are relegated to be good little housewives for their brave husbands.'

Liz is wearing the same bright pink headscarf she wore when Jayne and I first met her. And just like this first day, the more animated she becomes, the more wild tufts of bright red hair escape from their vibrant constraints. And as she elaborates on the widespread gender bias in education, I look around at the faces of the volunteers whose eyes all focus on Liz. They seem captivated with her lively account of the multifaceted educational struggles in this country. And as I listen to Liz myself, I become increasingly convinced that we will not make major inroads into the plight of women's health in Nepal until there are substantial improvements in school education.

'As they get older, so many can't afford to keep up their schooling,' Liz continues, 'and for the few girls who do, the teaching is next to useless for them.'

'But what about scholarships?' It's Norman who pipes up now, suddenly released from his tranquil slumber. 'I've heard there are millions of dollars given for scholarships for girls in Nepal, every year. Surely these have helped with this economic problem?'

'I so wish,' Liz replies. 'These education scholarships have been hopelessly inadequate. Each school in this country gets a few scholarships from the Nepal government, and most of these are for less than four American dollars a year. That sort of money doesn't even scratch the surface. On top of that, so many headmasters don't even seem to know what to do with the money. The scholarships you mention, Norman – they haven't led to any more girls attending school, and they haven't reduced the appalling numbers who drop out.'

'And the toilets?' Jayne asks.

'Oh dear God, those awful toilets. They would put me off going to school, I'm sure. Jayne and Ray can tell you about the delightful sewer we have at the front door of our own school. Do you know only one-third of schools in Nepal have separate toilets for boys and girls? It's outrageous.'

'Liz,' I say. 'I have another question for you right now.'

'Okay,' she replies. 'You know, I've got to tell you – I'm really enjoying this discussion. What have you got, Ray?'

A few of us refill our glasses and sit back down. It's clear that Liz is genuine when she says she's enjoying the talk – she hasn't touched her drink for twenty minutes.

'Everything you say about the education problems makes sense,' I continue, 'the financial barriers, the gender bias, the books, the toilets. It seems so obvious that if we want to improve education in this country we need to fix these things. But here is my question – and I think this is crucial – where is there evidence? Do we *know* that if we somehow eliminate these problems with the system, better educational standards for girls will automatically follow?'

Liz recoils with a look of mild surprise.

'Let's say we build separate toilets,' I continue, 'or provide more balanced, up to date books, or more female teachers – do we know for sure that more girls will turn up for school? Do we know that they definitely get a better education? Is there any evidence-base to this?'

Liz considers her response. 'Well, I guess most of these things haven't been proven,' she says. 'I understand what you're suggesting. Updated textbooks aren't likely to improve things if we don't have properly trained teachers. Building a new school won't help if it's still too expensive for the children to come.'

'This is my concern,' I say. 'There are kind-hearted people in the West who want to help these people. When we return home to Australia, and when you get back to the States, they'll ask us what they can do. I guess what I'm asking is – how can we be sure these donors are doing things that are useful? Or, maybe this is a better question – what is the most effective way for people to help?'

Every volunteer still appears absorbed in our conversation. Liz is about to reply when the doors from the kitchen burst open to announce the arrival of our dinner. We smell the unmistakable aroma of the local version of *dal baht* as the kitchen staff bound through the doors carrying plates of their most popular dish. We all move our seats to the dining table in preparation for our meal. Poppy is among the helpers again tonight, and once she spots Liz among the diners she looks puzzled.

'Hello, Ganuradha,' Liz says as Poppy approaches our end of the table.

'Good evening, Ms Beeyan,' Poppy replies. 'Do you help in hospital also now?'

'Good heavens, no,' Liz says. 'Dr Ray invited me down tonight as a guest.'

There is still some confusion on Poppy's face as she continues to deliver tonight's meal.

'Liz,' I say once Poppy leaves, 'Poppy works such long hours each day – like so many other girls here. I struggle to see when she and the others get the time to study or do any homework.'

'I feel the same,' Liz replies. 'I'm mindful of that when I do set them homework, so I try to keep this to a minimum. But as you know, in the later years of school, students need to study even more. In a few years' time, if girls like Poppy are lucky enough to still attend school, the home study will become an even bigger predicament.'

Unlike our meal in Uttam's home, tonight we're given forks and spoons to eat our *dal baht*. Despite the challenges of the meal at Uttam's, I'm surprised how much more I miss the primal feeling of eating with my hand rather than with utensils.

As we begin our dinner, I return to an earlier point. 'So, Liz, do you have an answer to my question? If people back home want to improve the education among girls in Nepal, what is the most effective way?'

'That is such a difficult question, Ray,' Liz replies. 'I don't think we can know the answer to that. Charities are very good at their marketing for donations and tugging at heartstrings. They're good at providing statistics on how many schools have been built or how many computers they've provided and so forth, but most of the charities are useless at providing figures on the things that really count – like improvements to literacy and increases in the standard of living.'

'We have the same problem in our medical world. Just take a disease like tetanus, for example. In pregnancy this infection can be life-threatening to a baby. And we know that we can easily prevent tetanus with a vaccination to the mother. But even when this vaccine is available, so many women in developing countries won't take it up. What's the point in spending loads of money on a container load of tetanus vaccine if most of it is going to sit unused in the cupboards of Health Posts, until one day it's out of date? We should be spending money on researching ways to increase the uptake of vaccines.'

'But what are you saying, Ray? Hold off providing vaccines, or toilets, or books until the research has been done? Wait 'til we can prove these things will actually help? Years might pass before we can prove a project actually works. By then we may have missed the boat.'

'It's my belief that we should do our best to steer donors to only support charities whose work has been proven to be effective, or at least to charities that are doing the research to confirm they're effective. Right now, most charities are flying blind.'

Liz looks across in earnest at each of the volunteers, and then back to me. 'You want us to ignore all those thousands of other charities that haven't got proof that they're making a difference? Are you crazy? Whether it's health or education, there must be so many charities that are doing enormous good, even though they haven't got studies to back it up. If these charities suddenly stopped receiving donations, surely there would be masses of people who would suffer. This would be madness.'

'Hear me out, Liz. We know the female scholarships were a miserable failure. I recall the solar panels at your school are simply sitting there gathering dust. Whoever donated those panels has wasted their money. So many thousands of other donations have frittered away without helping anyone. It's far more sensible to only support projects that can show they work – projects that have an evidence-base, or ones that are at least working towards this.'

Liz simply frowns.

'I can assure you,' I continue, 'no matter how hard you or I or others push donors in this direction, we're not going to stop the many thousands of people donating to other causes that appeal to them. As you said yourself, charities are so very clever at marketing. They know how to touch people's soft spots, and generally they're really successful getting them to contribute to their cause. These charities are not going to suddenly crash and burn.'

There is a long silence as Liz looks to consider this argument. Eventually she nods slowly and begins to speak again.

'I could have been a little rash with my comments … I have to admit that this does make some sense, but I'm not sure it's practical. When the average soul is approached by someone representing a charity, how in the world would this soul have any idea that the charity was a valid one? I'm sure you agree that most people have no idea of the meaning of "evidence-based research", let alone how to weigh up these things.'

'You don't have to have a PhD to work out which charities are effective. There are lots of very credible organisations that do this for you. These organisations are not-for-profit groups that analyse the work of charities.[31] They list the ones that provide sound research, and the foundations where you can be confident your donation will genuinely help those whose lives you're trying to improve. With two or three clicks on your computer you can learn these things about the charities that chase your money.'

Most of us have finished our meals and the kitchen staff have returned to collect our plates.

'Okay, Liz,' I say, changing the subject. 'We've reached a really important time of the evening. We're about to start what we call our Sixty-Second Summaries. You're going to hear each of our volunteers stand up and talk for one minute about a significant event during the day. You're very welcome to join in, but please don't feel any obligation.'

'What an interesting idea,' Liz says. 'Well I'd love to give it a try. But I think I would struggle to keep my talk to only sixty seconds. Are there penalties if you go over?'

'I don't think that's ever happened. I suspect the penalty would be pretty minor though. You'd probably be cast outside for the night into the Himalayan sub-zero chill. Nothing serious.'

'Such a forgiving lot, your crew. I'm impressed.'

*

8:35pm, Dining Hall

'Dr Ray warned me that if I go over my sixty-second time limit I'll be thrown outside to spend the night sleeping with the yaks on the side of this scary, freezing mountain. Let me start by saying how impressed I am with the work you're all doing here. You seem to exist on a shoestring, but I don't hear complaints from anyone.'

Paul interjects, 'You will when the coffee runs out!'

'Oh. I hope I'm not here when that happens then,' Liz replies.

'And the women you fix,' she continues '– I managed to speak to several of them today. I hope you all realise you're not just rebuilding their pelvic organs – you're rebuilding their lives. You all know that I'm a teacher, and like you guys, I struggle with the system in this country and try to work out how on earth I can help to improve it. What I hadn't realised until today was how similar the problems are in your world – the medical world – to mine in education. And if we can improve education we will improve health, and if we can improve health we will improve education. This applies to everyone in this country, but it especially applies to women and girls.

'Every one of you has donated your precious time and skills to revolutionise these women's lives. What I know, and what I've come to understand a lot more tonight, is that in education and in health, not all projects are worthwhile. When we all return home we need to encourage as many people as possible to donate time, and energy, and money – but to do this in the most effective way possible. What I'm saying is – and I'm paraphrasing Dr Ray here – harness that virtuousness, but use it wisely. It's all too easy to relieve our consciences by donating to something that seems worthwhile, but what a terrible waste if that project or that organisation doesn't improve the lives of the people we're trying to help. Be discretionary, and encourage your friends to be discretionary, as well.

'Some of us donate money, or books, or blankets. Others, like you guys, donate your time and skills. And while this volunteer organisation you work for is clearly doing wonderful things, I must warn you that there are others that do not. In fact, there are some volunteer organisations that are out and out scams. Just as we need to be cautious and discretionary about which organisations we donate money to, tell your friends that if they're planning to volunteer overseas, just as much vigilance needs to be given to these aid organisations as well.

'Keep up your life-changing work. I've only been here with you for an afternoon and evening, and I'm totally inspired. When you return home and people learn about what you've done and what you're doing, they will be inspired, too. No doubt you will stir them, you'll motivate them to improve people's lives as well. Your good is not only in the women you heal here, it's the flow-on effect you'll create by stimulating others into helping the hundreds and thousands of other underprivileged people in the years to come.

'Thank you.'

As one, every volunteer gets to his or her feet in a standing ovation for Liz's eloquent delivery. She seems surprised at the enthusiastic response.

'That was so totally impressive, Liz,' I whisper in her ear. 'You speak so well, and off the cuff, too. Sixty seconds – tonight I think I would have been happy to relax the time limit to 60 minutes.'

Why Is Prolapse
So Prevalent Here?

Okay, Norman is so right; we need to find the source of this genital prolapse curse. Why is prolapse so terribly prevalent in this part of the world? And why does it happen to women and girls at such a young age? Once we determine the reasons for this debilitating prolapse problem, once we find out why it's so rampant, we can then set in motion processes to prevent the disorder.

We understand the causes of genital prolapse in Australia and in other Western countries. In developed countries like ours, the leading cause of prolapse is damage to the pelvic floor tissues during childbirth. The greater the number of vaginal births, the greater the risk of the condition. We know there are other factors that increase pressure on the pelvic floor and add to the risk of prolapse.

These are things like obesity, chronic coughing or constipation, and heavy lifting. During the ageing process and with the natural loss of oestrogen following the menopause, pelvic floor tissues become more susceptible to wearing and tearing, and less able to compensate for the damage from injury that occurred years before. While the initial damage to pelvic floor supports often occurs during pregnancy and childbirth, in the West symptoms of prolapse usually don't begin to emerge until years, or even decades later.

In developing countries, including Nepal, the risk factors for genital prolapse take on a different hue. Childbirth remains the common, fundamental cause for the condition, but a large proportion of pregnancies occur in young adolescents, and pregnancies at a young age are particularly common in rural areas. In most developing countries, including Nepal, it's common for women to have multiple children with little spacing between pregnancies. On top of that, many girls and women suffer damaging abdominal pressures from heavy lifting and straining, or from the improper management of childbirth. Adding to these risk factors is so little information is available for girls and women to protect themselves against the development of genital prolapse.

But we need to explore these risk factors in more detail. If we're going to have any hope of slowing down the numbers of women suffering from severe prolapse, we need to understand these conditions in the context of rural Nepal.

Adolescent marriage and pregnancy

There is a strong association between childbirth in adolescence and genital prolapse.[23,32,33] If the pelvic floor supports have not fully developed there is a greater risk of permanent damage to these tissues during birth. Exacerbating the problem in Nepal, puberty and organ development are delayed in girls experiencing poor nutrition or poverty[34,35] – conditions highly prevalent, particularly in rural areas. In 2013 the average marriage age for women suffering from severe prolapse was 14 years, and the average age at first pregnancy was 18 years.[36] Many Nepalese girls have a short timespan between pregnancies and this greatly adds to their risk of prolapse.[37]

But on top of the physical stresses of childbirth at a young age, teenage pregnancy has a number of damaging social impacts. Once married, it's rare that girls continue with, or recommence schooling. Of the very small numbers of girls who do return to school, academic performance is very poor.[38] The interrupted education leads to less job opportunities and economic deprivation.[39] And with the next generation the depressing cycle continues.

Day #14. 8:10am, Postoperative Ward

One of our postoperative patients, Ronita, had experienced severe genital prolapse for several years. She underwent corrective surgery with *Australians for Women's Health* nine days ago and she is about to leave our hospital to begin her long journey home. She lives with her husband and children on a small farm on a hillside, three days' walk from here.

Ronita is not sure of her age, but she thinks it is around 25 years. Her parents and her brother arranged her marriage when she was about 14. She had her first child the following year. She now has four healthy children between the ages of five and 10; all of these were born at home. She was aware of an uncomfortable vaginal bulge shortly after the birth of her first child, and this bulge became progressively larger and more painful with each successive pregnancy. Somehow, despite her obvious discomfort and the hindrance to her movement, she managed to walk the three days to reach our camp for treatment.

I approach Ronita for what should be the final time for this camp. She's packed her few belongings into a small sack in preparation for her departure. Gamika joins me to translate our conversation.

'*Namaste*, Ronita,' I say. 'Do you feel well enough to walk to your home now?'

'*Namaste*, doctor,' Ronita replies through Gamika. 'I feel best for many, many years. I feel happy to walk home even four, five days ago.'

'That's good news. As you know, we felt it was best to keep you here for these extra days to recover a little more.'

Ronita acknowledges this comment by pressing of her palms together and bowing her head.

'Ronita,' I continue, 'before you leave, may I ask some questions about your home life?'

'I am very happy for your questions.'

'Some of these questions might be a little uncomfortable for you. Please do not feel obliged to answer any question if it makes you feel this way.'

Ronita responds with a curious expression that is simultaneously a smile and a frown.

'You were married at a very young age,' I say. 'Was this what you wanted?'

Ronita pauses briefly in thought. 'At the time I marry it is something I think not much,' she says eventually. 'For many years my father and mother tell me I marry when breasts come. Breasts came; I marry.'

'Yes, but were you *happy* that you married so young?'

Ronita smiles sadly. 'At marriage, everybody in village singing, dancing. There is much food. Make me feel good person.'

'Now that it's 10 or 11 years on since then, how do you feel looking back at that time of your marriage? Do you think this was fair? Do you feel any regret?'

It is a long time before Ronita responds to these next questions. As I study the look of deep concentration on her face, I begin to wonder – are my *questions* fair? Am I probing too deeply? Is it possible I could be stirring up suppressed emotions? Could the very nature of my questions lead to a resentment that at the moment is tolerably subdued?

Finally, Ronita says simply, 'My husband a good man.'

As she utters these words there is no eye contact, and the comment does appear evasive. I have a strong sense there are deeper, negative feelings she shelters, and I feel frustrated that I don't have the skills to reach them.

I decide to try a different angle. 'Ronita,' I say, 'you have two daughters. Do you wish them also to be married at the age of 14 or 15?'

Ronita's response could not have been more disheartening. 'If this is wish of my husband.'

I do my best to hide my crushing disappointment. 'You did not know your husband before you married him; your marriage was arranged. Was this the same for other people in your village?'

'Yes, same. My husband meet me one week before marriage. My father and brother fix marriage for me. My friends the same. Not know their husbands, too.'

Ronita pauses again, and then raises her face once more to look at me. 'Except for one friend. She does know husband before. Parents not happy. My friend run away for love marriage.'

The number of children marrying spouses of their own choosing is increasing.[40] Many of these children elope because they are aware they are about to be forced into an alternative, arranged marriage. Others elope because of the social pressures and stigma of being in a relationship. Some feel it was safer to elope because they might get pregnant.[41]

'You became pregnant very soon after your marriage. Is this what you wanted? Did you choose to have a baby?'

'When I marry, husband want baby. Father and mother of husband want baby.'

'And after you had your baby, you were pregnant again very soon. And then again. You had a baby almost every year for the next five years. I guess your family expected this from you, but did you want this? Did you want so many babies so soon?'

'I am not knowing anything when I marry. Now I know tablets to stop baby. First two babies – girls. My husband not happy. He want son. Third baby son, but husband want two sons.'

'Yes, Ronita,' I say, with some exasperation now, 'I understand that your husband wanted you to keep having babies until you had sons. But what about *you*? What did *you* want?'

This conversation feels more like an interrogation than a dialogue. I so wish that I had better interviewing skills. I have lost hope of a genuine, heartfelt answer to my latest questions, but after a short, whispered conversation between her and Gamika, Gamika says to me, 'Dr Ray, Ronita wishes to speak in other room.'

I look around the ward and realise my foolishness. There are a number of patients who are in earshot of our conversation. We're so used to the ward so crowded with staff and patients and their relatives, I hadn't even considered the confidentiality of our current conversation. I apologise for my stupid oversight, and the three of us move to the ward assessment room where we can continue our conversation in private.

Once we're all seated and the assessment room door is closed, Ronita speaks again through Gamika.

'Dr Ray. You and everybody here at hospital fix my life. I want to give good answer for your questions. I don't want other people hear.'

Ronita's expression has changed. Her eyes are focused now with a look of sincerity. I'm surprised her demeanor has changed so quickly.

'You ask me what I want?' she says. 'You ask me if things fair? Many things not fair. No – not fair that girls marry so young age. Not fair that girls have babies. Boys have no babies. Boys have no monthlies. Not fair. But why complain? No help to complain.'

As I gradually process Ronita's open outburst, it becomes clear to me that she considers the culture and the norms of her community to be as natural as her own physiology. She feels that we have no more hope in overcoming the injustice and the inequities of child marriage and child pregnancy than we do of transforming men into creatures who have menstrual periods and pregnancies.

*

Nepal has one of the highest child marriage rates in the world.[42] Currently 37% of girls are married in Nepal before the age of 18, and 82% of these use no form of contraception.[43,44] The large majority who marry in their teens conceive within the first 12 months of marriage.[45]

In Nepal the legal minimum age of marriage is 20 years for both men and women, however, despite this legislation there are large numbers of marriages that take place before this age, particularly in rural areas. Few child marriages are registered with the police, and prosecution is rare. Many parents complain that they cannot afford to continue to feed and educate their daughters.[46] Others freely admit, 'the younger the bride is, the cheaper the dowry'.[47]

Although the minimum marriage age law exists in Nepal, the mechanisms to enforce this legislation are lacking. There is little or no government accountability, and virtually no political will to prioritise the issue at the national level.[48]

In 2006 the Supreme Court of Nepal stated that the government must pay 'urgent attention' to the prevention of child marriage because the law was not being implemented effectively.[49] Unfortunately, the court did not specify which Ministry was to oversee this 'urgent attention' and as a result, inevitable buck passing has further delayed enforcement of the marriage law.[8]

The standard, government issue Grade 9 textbook we found in Poppy's school, *Health, Population and Environment*, explains Nepali law regarding the minimum age of marriage and the right to choice of spouse.[8] However, many girls from rural Nepal have dropped out of school by Year 9, or have not attended school at all.[50] In any case, it's usually parents or other family members who decide on the marriage of an adolescent girl.[51] While the textbook mentions some risks of teenage pregnancy, it does not mention genital prolapse as a possible consequence.[8]

Every day, 20,000 girls younger than 18 years give birth in developing countries. The overwhelming majority of adolescent girls who become pregnant in Nepal are married and pressured to have a child.[52] In 2006, 74% of Nepalese girls had given birth to their first child by age 19 years.[53] The majority of these adolescent pregnancies are in rural areas of the country. This adolescent pregnancy rate is falling, but only at a slow pace.[54] Furthermore, the true pregnancy rate is bound to be significantly higher than this official rate as pregnancy outside marriage is taboo, and usually not reported.[53]

Ronita represents the plight of many thousands of Nepalese girls and women. Her genital prolapse has almost certainly resulted from her young age at the time of childbirth and the very short spacing between the births of her four babies. There may have been additional factors that contributed to her prolapse.

Despite her suffering, in a number of other ways Ronita may have been quite fortunate. Teenage mothers in Nepal are significantly more likely to suffer with a number of pregnancy complications including severe growth restriction of their babies and preterm labour.[55] As a result, the stillbirth rate is 50% greater than in adult mothers.[56,57] Among the babies of adolescent mothers in Nepal, 10% do not survive beyond the age of 12 months.[58]

The other hazard confronting Ronita was the potential loss of her own life. At the age of approximately 15 years when she delivered her first baby, Ronita was five times more likely die during pregnancy compared to a woman experiencing pregnancy as an adult.[56,57] Pregnancy is the leading cause of death in 15 to 19 year old girls in Nepal, and a number of other countries.[59]

In Nepal, as in many other developing countries, women are often compelled to have at least one son.[60] Families are aware that, unlike daughters, sons can care and provide for the parents, and eventually inherit the property. In contrast, daughters are often perceived as a financial burden on the family.[46]

The most recent Nepal National Health Survey found that although the proportion of married women using some form of contraception was increasing, almost 47% of adolescents have 'unmet needs' for contraception.[43] In other words, almost half of all married women who did not wish to conceive were not using any form of contraception. This alarming figure was even higher in rural areas of Nepal.

The World Health Organisation defines reproductive rights as '... the basic right of all couples and individuals to decide freely and responsibly the number, spacing and timing of their children and the means to do so ...'[60]

Women and girls have a fundamental right to make informed decisions on all matters relating to sexual and reproductive health, free from coercion. They have the right to accurate, comprehensive health information and right to choose contraception. Ronita, and very large numbers of girls in other qualitative studies, have been denied that inherent human right. While it is the girls who suffer the devastating effects of unprotected intercourse, it is their husbands or in-laws who are the decision makers.[8,45]

Nepalese teachers report that they are reluctant to discuss sexual health matters. They believe it is not their role to discuss these 'private issues' and leave it to the students to educate themselves.[45,61,62]

The local teachers at Poppy's school symbolise the failure of the Nepalese school curriculum to address sex education. Several days earlier, Liz and I discussed this aspect of the teaching at the school. As she expressed her fury at the incompetence of the system, it was probably the most animated I have seen her.

'Get this, Dr Ray,' Liz said. 'None of the teachers at my school feels it is his role to cover this topic. They tell me they feel too uncomfortable or inexperienced to teach sex education. *Inexperienced*, for fuck's sake! These are middle-aged men with their own kids. Totally pathetic. One of the students told me that his teacher simply wrote on the blackboard a page number of their health textbook. The teacher then said, "For tonight's homework – read this section". And that was it – that was the sum total of their school sex education. I was totally disgusted when I heard that. I'm not a violent person, Dr. Ray, please don't get the wrong idea – but right then I could have ripped out someone's liver.' Somewhat graphic, but I guess it gets the point across.

The standard issue school health textbooks in Nepal for Years 8, 9, and 10 contain minimal information regarding sex education and contraception. The books comment that 'women need to be provided information on family planning', but there is no mention of where adolescents can obtain that information.[63,64,65]

More recently the government has commenced an out-of-school adolescent health program in 49 of the 75 districts of Nepal. This program was designed to provide a number of reproductive health services to adolescents, including contraception. Regrettably, the government has failed to monitor any aspects of the program.[66,67]

Adolescents in Nepal enter into marriage with little or no knowledge about family planning, contraception, and pregnancy. Their knowledge regarding sexuality comes from their individual experiences after having conceived, rather than from teachers, textbooks, and health workers. Sexual and reproductive health issues are not discussed in the public domain or with elders.[45,68]

Marriage and pregnancy are occasions of celebration in the community. At these times girls receive greater attention, care, and food.[45] The young bride is expected to prove her fertility within the first year of her marriage, but the consequences of early marriage and pregnancy are often disastrous to the health of both the young mother and her child, and lead to major social and educational disadvantages.

Ronita's experience reflects the sense of powerlessness that vast numbers of girls experience from the strong social expectations for early marriage and childbearing. Many studies in South Asia and Africa have confirmed that the primary role for girls and women is that of wife and mother[69]; their social role is firmly rooted in their capacity for reproduction.[70] Male dominance and preference for male offspring has led to low status for girls and women, and a female child is often neglected in the family.

Unwanted teenage pregnancy is associated with increased levels of physical and sexual abuse.[71] Adolescent girls in Nepal who suffer domestic violence are unlikely to seek care and support.

Following adolescent pregnancy and childbirth, the volume of work rises and the freedom to move and study falls. Most studies have found that once the woman realises these full impacts of her early marriage and pregnancy she experiences a profound sense of regret[45] and a blow to her self-confidence.[38]

It was no surprise to learn that Ronita never returned to school.

Drama in Theatre: Part II

It's pitch black. At first I hear the murmurs of indistinct voices, and then silence. Unsettling silence. Suddenly, deep bass bursts of a drumbeat. Slow, rich, booming pulses echo like a low-pitched bell. The effect of the deafening display in darkness is entrancing.

Several minutes of spine-tingling thunder. The shadowy figure of a single man. He sits cross-legged, a madal drum horizontal in his lap. Both palms pound each head of the instrument that responds staunchly to each strike. The drummer's profile slowly sharpens. His face – a picture of stormy concentration. He plays as if possessed. Without discernible rhythm, the sounds rise and fall, rise and fall. Loud and intense; softly subdued. The beat bursts forward in a potent charge of authority. The music heaves ahead to a full melodic rhythm before abruptly, the drummer ends his powerful display. The final few overpowering notes remain suspended in the stupefied air.

It's pitch black and hushed once again. I have a compelling urge to applaud, but something stops me. As if in a daunting dream, my hands are anchored, immovable. Disconcerted, and yet transfixed, I remain still and silent.

The drummer's outline returns to view. He restarts his spellbinding rhythm. And while the pulsation of the drumbeat proceeds, the sounds of a second instrument emerge. Slowly, softly, as if drifting down from the heavens above, the soothing voice of a lone murali flute. The air gradually fills with its warm and gentle song. The faint figure of the flautist appears. His mellow tones meander on their journey to a joyful chorus.

The drummer responds with a challenging backdrop. Back and forth the two instruments dance to form a moving, upbeat melody of earth and flight.

And now, from nowhere – the sounds of strings. The distinctive tone and timbre of the classical Asian sitar. I can't see the instrument or its player. The new sounds are haunting, foreboding, dream-like; the melody slow and sinister. The ancient strings now battle the flute for response from the booming drum. The gentle notes of the flute seem defeated as they dwindle to a muted slumber ... But now the flute fights back with a lively, decisive assault. The strings retort with contempt. A frantic battle begins between the two primal instruments before finally they appear to settle with some form of uneasy musical compromise. The result is an astonishing interplay of melodies of flute and sitar with the madal drum keeping steady, reliable rhythm.

I have just been transported by a mesmerising overture of happy and sad, good against evil; a musical prelude that declares the pleasure and pain of the performance to come. I am spellbound, and as the trance gradually fades I slowly become aware of the audience around me. Their silence and stillness tell me that they, too, are already captivated in anticipation.

The room lights appear and I look around to the faces of our team, and the other members of the audience. There are around 30 people here, and they appear as engrossed as I do with this enthralling musical introduction.

We sit in a large room within an old stone building I've walked past a number of times without realising that this is the Village Hall. Tonight I've learned that this is where a number of religious and cultural ceremonies are held throughout the year. Sadly, the building is in the same dilapidated state of most of the structures in this region of Nepal. The crumbling walls and floorboards remind me of the ramshackle state of our little hospital ten minutes' walk from here. The stage here has a noticeable slant. The exposed supports of the dais appear precariously feeble, and I begin to fear for the safety of the performers to follow.

The room lights are dimmed, and the remainder of the overhead lights flood the stage. There are now five young women illuminated, all dressed in traditional red saris. Each performer has a number of red ribbons tied to her fingers. I recognise two of the girls from our village. Each time I've met these girls they've been distinctly shy, and I wonder how they'll cope with the stress of stage performance to come.

The five girls are frozen and expressionless as the music restarts. The refrain is a cheerful melody of flute and drum again, and I wonder why there is still no movement among the girls; they simply stand there – lifeless statues.

But then, as one, as if some hidden switch has been flicked, the five commence their dance. Their slender arms move at first while the remainder of their bodies remain still. Their arms and hands glide with fluid, graceful arcs, in perfect time with the contented chords of the flute. The red ribbons on their fingers trace flowing loops. Their faces are blissful and relaxed as they launch their intriguing display.

The dancers arch their spines, heads tilted back, their arms reaching high with fingers spread wide. Their hips begin to sway as they slowly shift their weight from one leg to the next. And now, with unflinching focus, the girls begin to glide across the small stage. Their gestures are slow and elegant; the genuine joy and the freedom in their faces now have physical form. They are poised and balanced, and although their movements are intricate, all five remain in seamless harmony. As they advance and retreat to the cyclical rhythms of the entrancing musical score, the young dancers appear almost weightless. It is as if they are made of the very same fabric of the ribbons they gracefully twirl.

The drumbeat increases tempo now. The girls respond with faster movements as they pivot and twist and weave, but their precision and poise do not fade. Their garments and ribbons a blur of red now with their limbs and their bodies in constant, rapturous motion. And as I watch their enthralling performance, I slowly realise that these five young women are not simply talented dancers acting out a blissful state; the captivating music flows through them, every one an eager victim to its compelling power.

Inevitably, the slow, sinister sounds of the sitar strings return to the musical score. The five dancers continue their carefree movements to the cheerful melody of flute; all seem oblivious to new threatening tones. The strings and flute return to their brawling blend of the overture: slow and menacing; swift and bright.

I hear a gasp from the audience. A strange creature has appeared from the back corner of the stage; the ogre – a beast of distorted human form. He wears a large, crimson, terrifying mask with vulgar, bulging eyes. His dark red hair is long and wild. Large protruding fangs and serrated teeth heighten his savage cast. He dances slowly with threatening pulse to the menacing melody of sitar strains.

I know this creature. He is Lakhe, the flesh-eating demon of Nepalese lore. But despite his hideous and intimidating form, the girls dance on in playful innocence, as if completely unaware of the presence of this monster. Lakhe struts and cavorts in and around the lines and circles formed by the five girls, but still they dance on. After several minutes the girls slowly return to their fixed stance of the start of their show. Their limbs and bodies and faces – all frozen once again.

The sunny song of the flute has softened, and now dissolves. With the retreat of the flute, the haunting sounds of sitar strings surge. The dance of the demon redoubles.

A new noise now: for the first time, the shrill sounds of cymbals join the drum and strings. In time to the loud clash of cymbals the demon begins to thrash his limbs with fury; each of his crazed movements highlighted now by the heavy, frenzied tempo.

After several more minutes of frenetic dancing, Lakhe abruptly ceases all movement as the music suddenly stops. Within seconds the lights fade again, and once more we are in darkness. After a short time, the lights return to reveal an empty stage. This time the audience does begin to clap, and unrestrained, I join them with gusto. As I look around the audience, I'm buoyed to see that my team, too, are passionate with applause. Some are standing in ovation.

This evening has been so totally unexpected; far from the being dull and tedious affair we'd anticipated, the performance has been intoxicating. From the opening moments of the hypnotic solo drumbeat, I have been in silent awe. And I'm fiercely hoping that this is not the end of the show, but merely a tantalising break.

Jyoti's Health Post

'It's actually considered healthy,' said Narang. 'For centuries, the Nepalese believe that the harder a woman works while pregnant, the easier the delivery will be.'[72]

We're aware that pelvic floor supports are vulnerable to severe damage during childbirth, particularly in girls who are not fully mature, and in women who have multiple children. And yet we see a number of women with severe prolapse who have had only one child, and in some cases no children at all. And why is it that some girls suffer this pelvic floor damage leading to prolapse, while others with the same obstetric experiences do not? Clearly there are other factors at play.

Within Nepal, women contribute 60-80% of all agricultural production[73]. They are the ones responsible for transforming agricultural products into food for their families.[74] It is women who perform the daily tasks of fetching water and firewood, grinding grain, tending livestock, tending young, cleaning the home and the animal sheds, with little or no assistance from men. This takes its toll on their general health and most particularly, their reproductive health.[75] By contrast men are more likely to be involved in more 'attractive' activities, such as the eventual selling of the produce.[76]

In the mountainous areas of Nepal where the majority of the *Australians for Women's Health* camps are based, the steep terrain and the primitive working conditions add to the daily burden these women face. Most domestic and farm work is managed with traditional, simple tools, and relies on human and animal power.[74] Communities in these areas are dependent on firewood as their major energy source. Due to climate variability and unsustainable overuse, firewood and other natural resources required for daily life, such as water and animal fodder are becoming increasingly scarce.[77] As a result, the collection of a bundle of firewood can take up to six hours.[78] Water used for cooking, cleaning, and irrigation must be collected several times each day – almost unfailingly by women and girls.

The majority of Nepalese women continue their heavy workload during pregnancy.[79] Almost 80% resume heavy physical work within two to three weeks of childbirth.[80] A number of our own surgical camp patients admitted to working during their pregnancies as labourers in construction jobs. The majority of women understand that it is unhealthy to carry out heavy physical work during pregnancy and the early postpartum period, and yet they continue to toil during these hazardous times.[8]

The heavy, time-consuming burden that women endure almost every day of their lives has a damaging impact on their pelvic floor supports.[81] A number of studies have identified heavy physical work during pregnancy and shortly following delivery as a major risk factor in the development of genital prolapse.[4,32,33,82]

Day #15. 4:20pm

I want to understand why women continue to work so hard during their pregnancies. Is this simply another cultural effect? Are there other forces at work here? I need to speak to someone who is more likely to understand the psyche and the dynamics of pregnant women in the area, and the obvious choice is Jyoti, the trained midwife who normally works in the village near our camp. Jyoti has been keen to discuss maternal care in this region of Nepal, and when our final surgery case for the day is cancelled, I take the opportunity to contact her again. I'm surprised and encouraged that, despite the remoteness and the primitive state of this part of the country, there is a functioning mobile phone service. Well, functional some of the time.

Jyoti is delighted when I ask to meet up with her again, and I arrange to visit her this afternoon at the village Health Post where she is based.

The Health Post is on the lower side of the mountain – an area I've yet to explore. I walk along a narrow track cut into the side of the mountain and descend down a slippery, pebble-strewn path through tiered terraces of rice and maize paddies. After only several minutes I'm struck by the sparseness of the vegetation in this area. The emerald forest that surrounds the expanse of our camp is gone. There are very few established trees, and many of the terraces that have replaced them are void of crops. Sections of many terrace walls have collapsed. Much of their stone structure has crumbled down the slopes along with the dull, grey, infertile soil that was once retained. Landslips and small landslides cut through the steep terrain. Scattered donkeys graze on the flimsy vegetation that remains, oblivious to the perils of severe soil erosion and land degradation.

Several mud huts dot the arid landscape. Further down the mountain both the dwellings and the vegetation become slightly more abundant. As the winding path takes me towards the side of one particular hut, I hear the rhythmic beating sounds, *thwack, thwack, thwack*. The sounds appear to be coming from inside the hut. As I get nearer to the hut, I can hear a high-pitched grunt that coincides with each of the thwacks. I'm taken back to another tennis match – a women's Grand Slam game. Synchronised shrieking and thwacking – a statement of furious effort with each slice and volley.

The path eventually takes me around to the front of the hut, where I see that the unusual noises are coming from a young woman, alone on the porch. She sits cross-legged, beating a pile of rice on the ground in front of her. Her small face is flushed with effort. Using both hands, she wields a long, wide, wooden pole to strike the grains vigorously, gradually separating the rice from the husks. Although she wears a traditional sari, most of her midriff is bare. Her exposed abdomen displays the unmistakable bulge of an advanced pregnancy.

Although I'm now quite close to this intense, threshing woman, she does not appear to notice me; she's focused on her vigorous task. As I stand there, watching her fervently shatter the rough brown grains, I picture the supports of her pelvic floor and the very fibres of her defenseless pelvic ligaments. With each of her violent blows, do these delicate tissues suffer a similar destructive fate?

Another five minutes and I reach the small village where Jyoti said her Health Post is based. At least the rice thresher woman won't have far to travel when her labour begins, but what sort of labour is she likely to have? How will her care here compare to the care of women in labour in Australia? Indeed, will she even turn up to the Health Post when the labour begins?

Along the road through the village, local men spill from unpretentious teashops and supply stores, and gape at me as I pass; it seems that this is another region where few other Westerners venture. When I reach a small, weatherworn pagoda temple, an elderly, hunched man approaches me and begins to speak Nepali. He seems friendly enough, but I don't understand any of his words.

In English, I ask him for directions for the Health Post, and I'm pleasantly surprised when he appears to understand my query. He directs me along another narrow path, until I finally arrive at the Health Post. It's a humble single-storey structure formed with stone and timber. Numerous posters and drawings on the front of the building promote family planning. Several men and women are milling around the outside of the building. They ignore me as I step past them towards the clinic's entrance.

I walk through the open front doors to a dark room with low ceilings. The ageing timber floorboards shift and groan in protest with each of my hesitant footsteps. The only light inside is the narrow strip that spills through the doorway, and I wonder why there are no windows or lights to brighten the room's sombre mood. There are no other people inside, but as my eyes adjust to the darkness in the corners of the room, I make out a few pieces of timber furniture: a small desk and chair, and a very old cupboard sporting a lock that is so sturdy it looks bombproof. In the back corner I see a carved wooden door. As I approach it, I hear soft voices coming from the other side.

When I tap on the door, the voices stop and a few seconds later the door opens slowly. It is Jyoti, and her gentle face beams as she sees me.

'Dr Ray!' she says. 'It is so good you come to see us.'

'I am very happy to be here, Jyoti,' I reply. 'I have been very keen to see where you work.'

I look past Jyoti to see her examination room. It's fairly large, but also quite dim – not much brighter than the dark corners of the room I've been inspecting. The only light in her room comes from a small, grimy window in the far wall. There is an unpleasant odour of dampness, and perhaps bodily secretions. A young, heavily pregnant woman lies on the examination table.

'Jyoti, I see you are busy. I will come back later.'

'No, Dr Ray, I am nearly finished. Please wait in clinic for a few moments.'

I leave Jyoti to attend her patient, and explore the first room. I use the light on my phone to study some of the paperwork on the desk. Almost all of the writing is in Nepalese scripts, and there are a number of wordless laminated cartoon drawings of women showing various danger signs in pregnancy: fevers, severe headaches, bleeding, swollen hands and feet. *Birth Preparedness* – this is essential antenatal education, particularly when help can be a long way away. As Louise pointed out, there are large numbers of mothers and babies who don't survive in this part of the world, and almost all of these deaths occur when women deliver at home, or when they delay their journey to a health facility until it's far too late. Every effort needs to be made to encourage women to attend Health Posts like this for antenatal care and delivery.

Jyoti and her patient emerge. The patient gives me a silent *Namaste* as she leaves.

'Dr Ray,' Jyoti says, 'let's talk. Would you like some tea?'

There is an open wood stove in the corner of the examination room, and within minutes Jyoti has an impressive fire burning. I'm pleased to see that this stove has a chimney attached. Jyoti places a very old cast iron kettle on the stove, and as the water starts to heat we begin our conversation.

'Jyoti,' I say, 'why is it so dark in here?'

'We do have electric light,' she replies, 'but right now we have no power. Maybe in one more hour.'

Only 8% of rural Nepal has access to electricity[83] – strikingly low levels compared to many other developing countries.[84] Despite enormous hydropower potential, all parts of Nepal suffer from severe shortages of electrical power, particularly during the dry winter months.

The *Nepal Electricity Authority* manages this shortfall of power supply with a load sharing system, where power is cut to each region of the country for variable times on most days. In winter, power can be cut for up to 18 hours a day.[83]

'No generator?' I ask.

'Yes, once we had generator. But usually there is no fuel. And somebody has taken generator away anyway. If necessary in nighttime we have candle to help.'

I'm impressed that Jyoti is so laid back about the light issue. I think back to our drama of the haemorrhage during Dilli's surgery, and try to imagine the challenges of managing an obstetric emergency by candlelight.

'I understand that many women continue to do heavy physical work during pregnancy and soon after birth. Why don't they take things easy during these times?'

'Oh, Dr. Ray – it is so much their culture. We tell every woman, "Do not carry heavy loads when you are pregnant. After you have baby, wait six more weeks before heavy work." But women just shake their head. Some even laugh at us. "Who will get water, then? Who will get wood for stove? Who will make food for family?"'

'Their husbands? Why can't their husbands do these things for at least this one time in their lives?' But sadly, I know the answer to this question. I may as well be asking Uttam to allow his daughter to continue at school and go on to university.

'You do not understand how strong culture is here in Nepal. Many husbands leave home to earn money in India, or other places. But even when husband is here in home, it is not husband's role to do carrying and cleaning and making food. His friends and family will think he is weak man if he does these things.'

I try to grasp the power of this cultural influence. In rural Nepal a man would clearly be humiliated if he were seen doing women's work. As I absorb the significance of Jyoti's words, I consider the gender roles in Australia and in other Western countries. Over the last 50 or 60 years in the West, the traditional, patriarchal gender roles within marriage have evolved to a social structure that approaches gender equality. While nearly all would argue that there is still a long way to go before the West reaches gender egalitarianism, the last several decades do show that culture and gender stereotypes can, and do change. And if they can change in my country, surely they can change here, too. It's just that we can't afford to wait another 50 or 60 years.

'There are so many wonderful things about the culture in your country, Jyoti,' I say, 'but there are some parts of the culture that are so cruel and prejudiced against women. Have you got any ideas how we can overcome this discrimination?'

'I think that trying to change one woman or one man at a time is not possible. I think best chance is to get women together. Together they have better chance to make change. And children, girls and boys, they need to learn from young age what is fair for woman.'

Jyoti's wise words buoy me with seeds of hope. It makes a lot of sense to take a communal approach. The culture of Nepal is collectivistic rather than individual; the woman sees herself as part of an extended family and caste, rather than as a unique entity.[85] This is probably why public health strategies that involve family and community mobilisation have been shown to improve the maternal and neonatal health.[86,87]

Gender roles are predominantly constructed socially rather than biologically. While the very nature of gender discrimination in this country is biased towards boys and limits the education of girls, if we can break this cycle and educate both sexes in equitable gender attitudes, surely we have a decent chance at speeding up this critical cultural change.

I'm keen to learn a little more about the Health Post and its role in maternal care. 'How many babies do you deliver here each week?'

'Most weeks we have one or two babies.'

'And there is you and one other midwife?'

'Yes. When baby comes we are both present – one for mother, one for baby.'

'And you are always on call, both of you, 24 hours every day?'

'Yes, but we are not so often called. Most nights we can sleep.'

'And what do you do when you are not delivering babies?'

'There are many things, Dr Ray. We give antenatal checkups like the woman who is here just before, we give vaccination for children, we give family planning. Some people need first aid, also.'

'Is there a fee for these services you provide?' I ask.

'No, Dr Ray. All free. Government pays for all these things.'

The water is boiling now, and Jyoti uses a soiled towel to lift the ancient kettle and pour its steaming contents into a thoroughly modern ceramic teapot.

'And the pregnant women, if they come to a Health Post like this for their delivery, they are paid by the government?'

'Yes, every woman who delivers at Health Post or hospital in Nepal mountains is paid 1,500 rupees for travelling expenses. Plus, if they come for four antenatal visits they are paid also 400 rupees more.'

Fifteen hundred rupees is approximately $US14 – a moderately high amount by rural Nepalese standards. At first thought this would usually be considerably more than the 'travelling expenses' would entail. Transport in these regions of Nepal is essentially walking, or being carried. But the journey would usually require at least one or two other adults to assist the labouring mother, and if the walk was for a day or two, this would mean they'd be away from their farms for at least a few days. The 1,500 rupees may not cover the lost earnings for that period, particularly during harvest time.

Financial incentives to pregnant women in Nepal (now called the Aama Program) began in in 2009.[88] Cash payments to pregnant mothers who deliver in health centres appear to have increased the numbers women delivering in health facilities and with Skilled Birth Attendants[89], however, the health budget depends heavily on external donor agencies for this assistance. As a result, there are concerns that this program may not be sustainable.[90]

'Jyoti, do you know the numbers of women who still deliver their babies at home?'

'Yes. District Hospital keeps these records. In this district still more than three quarters of women have their babies in home. It is same in most remote districts. We try hard to make them come to Health Post or hospital where it is safe.' There is a burden now in Jyoti's deep cinnamon eyes. 'So many still do not come. This is so sad, because we know when delivery happens in home, many, many mothers and babies die.'

We watch the hungry flames in Jyoti's stove now leap in excitement as the fire devours each defenseless log within its greedy reach. The crescendo sounds of frenzied crackling from the blaze – maniacal laughter at its merciless destruction.

Jyoti pours our tea and we continue our solemn conversation.

'What sort of things are you doing to encourage the women to deliver in a health facility?' I ask.

'When women come for antenatal care, we tell them to get their friends from same village to come, too. We give women government handouts for information, like danger signs in pregnancy. Also, we sometime have women's meetings in villages to explain importance of delivery in Health Post. Since we do these things, compared to before, some more come here for antenatal care and for childbirth, but still not many.'

'So, most people in Nepal live within several kilometres of a Health Post like this,' I say, 'You and your colleague are trained midwives, and the mothers are given a reasonable cash payment if they come here. You also provide education about the dangers of home birth and the benefits of delivering in the Health Post. And to get the message across you hold meetings to involve the community. But in spite all of this most do not come. Can you explain why? Why do they not come here where it is far safer for the mother and her baby?'

'I know many times woman is not allowed to come. Husband will not let her come. Sometimes it is mother-in-law who stop woman coming. Young woman in Nepal has not much power.'

The patriarchal and cultural practices of remote Nepal raise their ugly heads once again. These social norms and structures leave the woman undervalued and disempowered. We know it's the fundamental cause of genital prolapse in this country, but it also seems to be the reason why so many shun professional maternal services that are potentially life-saving.[90,91]

'But Dr Ray, there is something else. I do not like to say this, but I know it is important, too.' Jyoti shifts in her seat uneasily. 'I hear that many women do not trust us. They think the care here is not good. No matter what we say, many think it is safer to have baby at home.'

I had heard this was an issue with a number of Health Posts[85], but this is the first time I have heard criticism or mistrust of Jyoti's. I know she's well-trained and I have seen her very competent skills in action, but I do have concerns about the small number of deliveries that take place here. This Health Post manages about 75 deliveries each year. Some Health Posts only manage one delivery each month. Thankfully, life-threatening emergencies only occur in a minority of deliveries, but this means that in these settings many midwives would rarely encounter some obstetric emergencies – perhaps only once every few years.

No matter how good the training, if skills are not continually practised, they will surely fade. There is no doubt that in the event of a severe complication during labour it is far safer the woman to be cared for by a trained midwife – experienced or not – than at home with no professional care. But this lack of exposure to obstetric emergencies must lessen the value of these remote midwife placements. And I wonder if this waning of skills reflects in the falling confidence of the midwives. If so, this may contribute to the mistrust that is expressed by some mothers.

'Jyoti, what is the morale like among the midwives at these Health Posts? Are you and your colleague happy to work here? Do you know if midwives at other Health Posts are happy?'

'I have been here for nearly one year now, and I am happy, yes. But I wish more mothers would come. We could deliver many more babies here. My colleague, Bussi, she has been here only nine months. She does not seem so happy. She says she trained to look after pregnancy and deliveries, but there are so few mothers who come here. I hear that many midwives from other Health Posts are not very happy and often do not turn up to clinics.'

'Do you see an answer to this, Jyoti?'

'I think this is very difficult problem. As midwives we cannot go to woman's home for delivery of baby. It is not possible for midwives to travel to so many places. We must do more things to bring mothers here. We must give more education to women and make them stronger. We have women's groups in village – these seem to help. But we must educate men, too. Perhaps on radio. Perhaps in street theatre.'

I'm really impressed that Jyoti has not given up hope. The problems in maternal health are so entrenched here, and the barriers so high, it would be understandable to simply throw up your hands and concede defeat. Culture will eventually change, but the pace of change is painfully slow, and unless we can speed up these changes and overcome the multitude of problems, many more thousands of mothers and babies will perish.

*

In the dying light of the early Himalayan evening, I make my way back to our camp. A dew has already begun to settle on the still landscape, and every so often my feet slip on the narrow mountain path as it curls its way back towards our camp. I realise now that I'm tracing the route of the woman who underwent the caesarean section several nights back. In near darkness she was carried along this very same track.

I think more about the culture of Nepal, and its painfully patriarchal frame. How is it that our own cultural values in the West have changed so much, while here in Nepal the levels of patriarchalism have remained the same? Women in Australia and most Western countries suffered similar gender inequity and oppression until we encountered the waves of feminist activism. And it's clear that the activism has led to major advances in gender equality. While discrimination and violence against women remain significant issues, most would agree these problems are far less pervasive than they were decades ago. Do we need feminist activism here in rural Nepal? Absolutely. But how? As a foreigner, and as a man, it's ludicrous to think I could have any sort of impact.

I'm aware of smatterings of feminist activity emerging in Kathmandu. Over the past several years Nepal has passed several major laws and made a number of international commitments to address gender discrimination. But the application of these edicts and pledges has been shamefully inadequate. In practice, the decision-making power among women is woeful. Access to education and health services remains poor. Child marriage and violence against women continue at horrifying levels. All of these injustices plague the struggle for gender equality across the country, and most particularly in rural areas – where the large majority of the population exists. For these millions of women living in poverty, life is a litany of discrimination and oppression that continues the cycle of poor health, inadequate education, unsafe childbirth and exploitation.

I think back to my conversations with Uttam. Uttam epitomises the patriarchal values and beliefs of men in rural Nepal. He is not a malevolent person. In fact, I believe he's a kindhearted man who wants the best for his remaining family. But like so many men here, he is swept up in the powerful, ancient culture and traditions of this land. In many ways I understand why he refuses to consider giving his daughter the same opportunities he gives his son. But how on earth do we change this?

I told Uttam that in my country, we largely managed to dismantle these patriarchal aspects of our culture, and as a result we are a better country. But the Western culture in Australia has only existed for 200 years. Changing the nature of a culture that has existed for thousands of years will require a great deal more drive and momentum.

Gorham's Distress

Day #16. 7:10am, Dining Hall

'I stayed up late last night because I was keen to speak to you,' Louise says. 'I wanted to tell you about Laxmi. You remember how horribly shy she and her two friends were when we met them in our first week here?'

Louise and I warm our hands on our cups of tea as we wait for the rest of the volunteers to come down from upstairs and join us.

'Yeah,' I reply. 'How are you going with your challenge? Have you managed to get her to hold your gaze?'

'Almost. Since we saw her that second time on her own, Paul and I have been seeing her at her home now and then. She's really coming along, Ray. She's not like Poppy, of course, but over the last couple of weeks she's got so much more self-confidence when she talks. When she sees us coming now, she even runs up to us with a big smile.'

'Good on you, Lu Lu. That's gotta be really satisfying.'

'And she's developed so quickly. Yeah, it's totally satisfying. I think the young girls here just need a little nudge to come out of their shell.'

'Let's go see her together when things settle down a bit here.'

8:00am, Preliminary Assessment Clinic

We're past the halfway point of this camp, and still the women flock to our clinic each day. It's busy again today as we continue to assess the crush of women who queue restlessly for their turn to be seen.

'Dr Ray!' From behind me, it's the voice of the local nurse, Mani. 'There is woman you must see, please.'

'Is she very sick, Mani?' I ask.

'No, Dr Ray, but she must please see you very soon.'

With a trace of unease, I follow Mani outside and through the crowd of patients who jostle for our attention. Mani continues away from the clinic and toward the grove of poplar trees. Many of the fallen leaves have already begun to fade. A woman squats at the base of one of the trees, her head and eyes downcast.

'*Didi*,' Mani says to the woman, 'I brought Dr Ray.'

I don't recognise the woman at first, but then she slowly lifts her head to face me. It is Poppy's auntie, Gorham – the woman who shares Poppy's home and cooks the mysterious dinners. Gorham's eyes flash at me briefly before she quickly returns her gaze to the ground beneath her.

I squat down myself so that my head is near Gorham's and I study her features. How different she looks in the bright light of day. Her skin is weathered and grey with weariness. Above her left cheek, a small ginger stain hints at a healing wound.

'Gorham,' I say, 'are you unwell?'

I wait for Mani to translate my question.

'Gorham understand your words, Dr Ray,' Mani says.

I stare at Mani in confusion. Poppy's uncle, Suntil, and her father, Uttam understand virtually no English. How could it be that Gorham – who surely has had little or no education – is able to comprehend my words?

After a few moments I turn back to Gorham. "Are you sick?'

Gorham responds to my question with a lopsided shake of her head. This gesture is so common in these parts of South Asia, but I'm still unsure whether this means, 'Yes, I am unwell,' or, 'No, I'm okay.'

'Do you want me to help you?' I ask as gently as I can.

There is no further response from Gorham. I turn to Mani in the hope that she'll be able to enlighten me.

'Dr Ray,' Mani says, 'Gorham has sickness in private parts. She does not want to tell, but I say to her this is most important to fix.'

'I understand,' I say, and turn back to Gorham. '*Didi*, I can only help you if you want me to do so. If you prefer I can ask one of the other doctors to help you.'

After a time Gorham looks up at me again, and I see now her eyes are quite puffy. Her neck is tarnished with faded blotches of yellow and brown. She whispers, almost inaudibly. 'Please help.'

'Of course we will help,' I reply, bewildered now to hear Gorham speak with English. 'Are things falling down between your legs?'

'No, doctor,' Gorham says, slightly louder now, 'no falling down. There is pain, and bad smell. Please help.'

We will need to examine Gorham. I look across to the assessment clinic, and the disordered gridlock of women who continue to scramble in an effort to be seen. It would feel so unfair to take Gorham to the clinic where others may learn of her condition. I decide instead to take her for assessment in the operating theatre recovery room, where it will be considerably more private. Gorham does appear relieved when I explain we will avoid the very public assessment clinic. We head off in the direction towards the theatre and Mani joins us as chaperone.

Gorham's examination shows that she almost certainly has a Sexually Transmitted Infection (STI) – probably chlamydia or gonorrhoea. The infection appears to have spread to her pelvis, a condition we call pelvic inflammatory disease. We can't test for these infections on this camp – we simply don't have the equipment. As with most women with likely STIs, we treat empirically with three antibiotics.

'Do you have any allergies to drugs?' I ask – the standard question before prescribing medications. And the standard answer for this part of the world follows.

'I never before have drugs.'

Gorham's signs do not appear severe enough to suggest major sepsis or a pelvic abscess, so we should be able to correct her infection. But as the disease has probably spread to her fallopian tubes, she may experience further infections down the track. My more immediate concern is how she contracted the infection, and the possibility of her harbouring additional more serious infections.

'Gorham,' I say, 'I am going to ask you a number of questions now. These are routine questions we must ask everyone in your situation. I do not wish to embarrass you. They are very important.'

Gorham's jaw tightens, and then she gives her lopsided nod once more.

'Have you had any discharge like this before?'

Gorham looks to the floor again and gives a soft, 'No.'

'In the past few months have you had sexual intercourse with anyone other than your husband, Suntil?'

'I only ever be with my husband.'

'Is it possible your husband has had sexual intercourse with someone other than you?'

Gorham blinks back tears and swallows with obvious discomfort. After a long, awkward silence, she says, 'My husband go away sometimes.' Her tone is flat, desolate.

'Gorham, it is most important that Suntil also receives treatment. And it is vital that we perform a blood test on both of you to make sure you do not have any other infections.'

I learn from Mani that Suntil often travels to northern India for work. My heart sinks when I hear this news. Seasonal migrant workers from Nepal are at high risk of infections; the prevalence of STIs in these men is alarmingly high.[92] And, chillingly, many migrant workers returning from India are infected with HIV.

I think back to the first encounter I had with Suntil and Gorham in their family home. There was a tangible tension between Suntil and his brother, Uttam, and between Suntil and Gorham. I wonder if this was connected with Gorham's current plight.

We must test Gorham immediately for the presence of HIV and hepatitis. On our prolapse camps we use field test kits that allow us to screen for these infections on every patient who is planned to undergo surgery. We will run this test on both Gorham and, assuming he allows us, Suntil. The discussion with Suntil will be very challenging.

Gorham hangs her head once again. I try to imagine the shame she must be facing right now, and I want to reassure her. But if I'm being honest, I can't tell her that everything will be okay. I can't tell her that we'll cure her – I'm simply not sure that she *will* be OK.

'*Didi*,' I say to Gorham. 'Please can you look at me?'

Although her head remains bowed, her swollen eyes move up from the floor to fix on mine. She has the body language of a guilty child who's been caught misbehaving and is about to be punished.

'I want you to believe that I will be completely honest with you,' I say. 'I will not say words simply to make you feel better. I will not say words that are not true. Do you understand?'

Gorham bobbles her head in that crazy diagonal way once more. My eyes remain fixed on hers while I address Mani. 'Is that a "yes", Mani?'

'Yes, Dr Ray. This means "yes".'

'Gorham, I cannot promise that we can fix you. But I do promise that we will do everything we possibly can to make you better.'

Gorham continues to hold my gaze as she slowly lifts her head. She gives me a silent *Namaste*, and although her mouth forms a weak smile, her eyes do not.

Mani and Gorham now speak to each other in Nepali. Eventually Mani translates their brief conversation, 'Dr Ray, we have more problem. We must not tell Gorham's husband that she comes here.'

'What?' I exclaim. 'That is ridiculous. Suntil almost certainly has an STI. We must tell him about this. It would crazy not to test and treat him.'

I look at Gorham, who cowers in obvious fear, but I know it's essential to treat Suntil, not simply for his sake, but to protect any other person he may be engaging with sexually. And on top of that, if Suntil is not treated, he will eventually re-infect Gorham.

'No, Dr Ray,' Mani continues, 'if Gorham's husband finds out she is coming here, this will be very bad for her. Very, very bad.'

I ponder this hopeless situation. Ethically, without his wife's permission we can't tell Suntil that Gorham has been here or that she has an infection. But morally it seems so wrong *not* to test and treat him. When we confront this predicament in Australia, when a woman contracts an STI but does not want to tell her sexual partner of the infection, it's only ever ethical and legal to go against her wishes and tell her partner of the STI if the infection is blood-borne (i.e., if the infection is HIV or hepatitis). Only then does patient welfare trump patient confidentiality. But here in Nepal I have no idea on the rules regarding this dilemma.

'Gorham, if there is no disease in your blood, I will not tell your husband that you have been here or that you have developed an infection.'

Despite my attempts to reassure her, the look of fear lingers on Gorham's pitiful face.

'In the meantime, Gorham,' I continue, 'and this is very important – you must not have sexual intercourse without a condom. Not until we have the results of some tests.'

Gorham looks to Mani, presumably for translation. But as Mani clarifies my advice in Nepali, Gorham hangs her head once more with a look of hopeless despair.

'Dr Ray,' Mani says, 'this will be not possible for Gorham.'

Engaging Suntil

Day #16. 9:35am

'Tricky situation, Ray. Your hands are tied. How are you going to get around this one?'

It's Mack who speaks. I've told him about the dilemma we face with Gorham's pelvic infection. Mack and I are on our morning walk from the assessment clinic to the operating theatre.

'I'll wait for Gorham's blood results,' I say. 'I've organised her screening for HIV and Hepatitis B. If she's got a viral infection this situation will go from a real challenge to a real disaster – a public health disaster.'

'So,' Mack says, 'let me get this right. Somehow, you need to collect a blood sample from Suntil, work out whether or not he's got HIV, and treat him with antibiotics for an STI – but you've got to do all this without telling him why.'

'If we let on that Gorham has come to see us, and that we're aware he has given her an infection, it sounds like she'll either be physically beaten, or driven from the home, or both. It's outrageous.'

Mack ponders for a while, 'You could always try the bin Laden technique.'

'The "bin Laden technique"? As in, Osama bin Laden? Please don't tell me this has anything to do with planes.'

'Good heavens, no – nothing like that. Remember when they were trying to find the whereabouts of bin Laden to capture him or kill him? The CIA were suspicious of a particular villa in Pakistan. They

146

felt that there was a good chance that bin Laden and his family were living there, but they wanted to be more certain; they wanted more evidence. So the CIA arranged a false vaccination campaign in the neighbourhood. They got a Pakistani doctor and nurse to go door to door to give hepatitis B vaccinations to all the children in the area. Once the children who lived at this villa were vaccinated, the plan was to analyse the DNA from the syringes to determine whether or not they were related to Osama bin Laden. I don't think the plan actually worked, but this is what some people call the *bin Laden technique*.'

'What?' I say, dumbfounded. 'Are you seriously suggesting that we run a mock treatment campaign in this village in order to test and treat one person?'

'It's worth considering. And if you do this you might even find more than one person is infected.'

I turn to Mack and put my hands on his shoulders to bring us to a halt.

'Mack – you cannot be serious. I *do* know that story, and I think this was one of the worst decisions the CIA has ever made. After that debacle, people lost trust in the *genuine* vaccination workers in Pakistan. Every vaccination worker in Pakistan fell under suspicion. Quite a few were even murdered by the Taliban. And now polio – the disease that had almost been eradicated in Pakistan – it's on the rise again. I know we don't have the Taliban in this country, Mack, but it's crucial that we earn the trust of the people here. If it gets out that we've set up a testing and treating program under false pretenses – well, we'll totally blow that trust.'

Mack studies my face, and then he breaks out one of his huge, uneven grins. 'Well played, sir. I hear you, and I accept your argument. Clearly I had not thought this through.'

I return Mack's smile, and he continues, 'So then, what will you do?'

'I really don't know, Mack. Maybe I'll just try talking to him, you know, man to man.'

*

1:45pm

'Nabin,' I say. 'Where is the best *Rakshi* in this town?'

Nabin gives me a puzzled look. 'That will be Riken's, sir. Riken make best *Rakshi* in whole area.'

'That's a teahouse in the village here?'

'Yes, Dr Ray. You very much like *Rakshi* now?'

'Oh, it's very good, yes, but I want you to do something for me, Nabin. Do you think you could arrange to have Suntil meet me at this teahouse soon? With you, too, of course – to translate. Just Suntil and you and me, nobody else. It's important that Uttam does not come.'

'I can arrange meeting, yes, sir.'

'We should set this up at a time that Uttam is working, so that it won't seem strange that he's not invited. Tell Suntil that I want to learn more about *Rakshi* and more about him. My shout.'

Another puzzled look from Nabin.

'What is it, Nabin? What is troubling you?'

'You will shout at Suntil?'

'Ha! No, I will not shout *at* him. "My shout" means I will pay. I will pay for our drinks when we meet.'

Nabin looks at me vacantly and agrees to arrange our meeting.

5:55pm

Riken's Teahouse is a charming mud brick building nestled under a thicket of graceful white birch trees. Inside, a large yak-dung stove sits at the centre of the cosy, timber–clad room. Although the stove has a central chimney, smoke escapes from the side of the burner, creating a hazy, dream-like scene. Unlike the smoke in Uttam's home, these fumes have almost no odour. It's as if a gentle fog has simply rolled into the room.

Nabin and I are sitting on timber benches that are covered with brightly coloured carpet. While we wait for Suntil to join us, I look around at the features that add so much character to the homely room. The honeyed timber walls throw off a rich, welcoming warmth. Books and prints and foreign flags spill over from time-worn shelves. At back of the room, several ageing Nepalese men sit, murmuring in a mysterious corner.

A large, middle-aged man approaches our bench and strikes up a conversation with Nabin. His voice is deep, almost thunderous. Nabin introduces the man to me as Riken.

'*Namaste*, Riken,' I say. 'Your teahouse is very comfortable. I have heard about your *Rakshi*. What makes it so good?'

After Nabin translates my question, Riken gives a hearty laugh. 'Yes, many people come for my *Rakshi*. Is recipe from many generation in my family. Everybody like Riken *Rakshi* because is good, strong – not weak like other *Rakshi*.'

Oh great, I think. *The Rakshi here is stronger than the one that almost blew out my brains at Uttam's home. I can hardly wait.*

The door to the teahouse opens and Suntil walks inside. Riken greets Suntil with an expansive welcome. Ignoring us, the two walk to the opposite corner of the room and greet the murmuring men, who also appear very pleased to see Suntil. After several minutes of cheerful, animated discussion, Suntil leaves the group and joins Nabin and me. He begins speaking in Nepali, and once again Nabin translates.

'I am not wishing rudeness for you,' Suntil says. 'I not see my friends since I come from India, more than one week before now.'

'I do not feel you are rude, Suntil,' I say, 'it was good that you saw your friends. Now, are you ready for some of this famous *Rakshi*?'

We don't have to order our drinks before three cups of the clear liquor arrive at our table. I'm even more apprehensive than I was at my first encounter with the spirit several days ago. I remind myself how important this meeting is and tell myself to be brave as I begin to sip the threatening fluid before me. But immediately my tongue screams from the scorching heat. My lips are already numb before I manage to force myself to swallow the potent brew. And as the *Rakshi* ravages the back of my throat, it's as if all the tissues in my neck erupt in a savage firestorm. I try to talk, but no words come out.

Suntil studies me and speaks. Nabin translates. 'You are sad, Dr Ray?'

My eyes water profusely from the effect of this powerful liquor. It must appear that I'm crying. And as I begin to wonder if my larynx will ever recover from this searing onslaught, the pain is slowly replaced by the rich, creamy velvet sensation I experienced with the milder form of *Rakshi*.

'Not at all,' I whisper hoarsely. 'This is how I react to such a beautiful drink.'

I'm amazed once again at how quickly Suntil can throw back the cups of the brutal spirit. Within minutes he's onto his third cup.

Finding more strength in my voice now, I begin my questions to Suntil through Nabin. 'Tell me about yourself, Suntil. I know very little about you.'

'I am normal, hard-working man,' he says.

'You and Gorham have no children?'

'No children. Something wrong with that woman. Not give children. None.' Suntil is quite intense now as he continues to speak, but Nabin does not translate the remarks that follow. I suspect there are some expletives in Suntil's description of his childless marriage. When he eventually settles down, I continue my questions.

'And you are a farmer, Suntil?'

'Yes, for crops. But not much work here. Wage is low. Go to Uttarakhand for more work. Make roads in mountains. Better pay.'

Uttarakhand is a Northern Indian state where many men from Nepal and Bangladesh migrate for work. The number of Nepalese who travel to this region and other areas of India to work is not recorded due to the open border between the two countries, however officials believe the figure is in the millions.[91] Working conditions in these regions are often atrocious.[92]

'Are there many men in this village who travel to India for work?' I ask.

'Only Badal and me go from this village. From other village, many men go.'

I have not met Badal yet, but I learn from Suntil that he and Badal travel to northern India for three to four months each year. They have been taking part in this seasonal migration for the past five years.

'Tell me about Uttarakhand,' I say. 'What is it like there?'

'Not much clean. Many people. Very busy.' Suntil swallows another cup of *Rakshi* with no perceptible flinch in his face.

'And do you work long days, Suntil?'

'Of course, long days. Why travel long distance if not work hard? Start with sun coming up; finish with sun gone.'

'And you must need to relax after the long days. What do you do to relax? What do you do for fun when you're in India?'

When Nabin translates this question, Suntil looks at me with a penetrating stare. He pauses for a moment before answering.

'Play cards, drink *Rakshi*.'

'That's it? Don't you do anything more exciting than that after a hard day?'

'Play cards, drink *Rakshi*.' Suntil repeats.

We stare at each other in silence for a few moments. This is going nowhere. I will have to be more direct. I don't want to put Gorham at risk of abuse (or further abuse), but I know I must press on.

'Suntil, there is something that I must say to you now. This may make you angry, but that is not my intention.'

I pause now for the full effect of Nabin's translated words to sink in. Suntil's eyes remain intense, but his mouth now moves peculiarly to one side.

'I am a doctor, and I am not doing my duty unless I tell you this. Many men who work in India and return to Nepal have infections. If you or your friend, Badal, have an infection you can become very sick.'

I watch Suntil as he begins to shake his head. His face takes on a look of defiance. 'I am strong. No sickness.'

'Suntil,' I say, 'you must try to believe me when I say this. At least half of men who carry this sickness have no symptoms. If you or Badal have an infection, by the time you become sick it may be too late for us to cure you. We have medicines to treat many infections. Please let us test you, and please persuade Badal to also come to us for a testing.'

Discouragingly, Suntil shakes his head once again, but his expression suggests he is thinking, considering his options. Is the door ajar, ever so slightly? I have another card or two to play, but for the moment I hold these to my chest.

But as Suntil looks back towards me once more, I hear the demoralising words.

'No test.'

Riken returns to fill Suntil's cup once again and I decide to plunge ahead with my strongest cards.

'Suntil, do you believe we do good work in the hospital here?' I ask.

'Yes, of course good work. But this different.'

'Do you believe me when I say that when any patient has an illness, we keep this illness a secret?'

'Cannot keep secret,' Suntil replies assuredly. 'Everybody in hospital knows a person's illness.'

'Yes, when patients are in hospital, the staff of the hospital are aware of the illness. But when patients are treated outside the hospital, their illness is a secret.'

Suntil does not look convinced. I search for a fitting analogy. 'Suntil,' I say, 'would you ever kill a cow?'

In Nepal, as in most states of India, the cow is sacred, and the slaughter of cows is forbidden.

He scoffs. 'Stupid question. Of course no kill cow. Fully against rules to kill cow.'

'Suntil, it is the same with a doctor telling other people about a patient's illness; it is completely against the rules.'

I can tell this has had an effect on Suntil as he turns away again and gives his pensive look. It's time to play my strongest card.

'Suntil,' I continue, 'there is one more thing you must know.' I wait until he looks back into my eyes. 'If you have a disease and we do not treat this, you may die.'

My words are harsh, and possibly too extreme, but in my mind I justify this severe approach. Generalised sepsis and death from bacterial infections like gonorrhoea are rare, but the mortality of untreated HIV is well established.

Suntil does not respond to my final comment, but simply finishes his latest *Rakshi* and stands up. 'I go now,' he says.

There is no *Namaste* as he turns to leave. Instead he gives Nabin and me a single firm nod of his head, and walks away.

I turn to Nabin. 'That didn't go so well, did it?'

'I think this is like with Uttam, sir,' Nabin replies. 'Very hard to change tradition.'

I understand Nabin's point. Infidelity has probably been taking place since the dawn of time. But in this day and age, when the mobility of populations and individuals is so much greater, the risk of severe STIs may be even higher. If bacterial and blood-born sexual infections were to take hold in a remote region like this, the fallout could be devastating. So far, none of our surgical patients has tested positive for HIV or hepatitis. But could this all suddenly change? For Gorham, I feel a sense of exasperation. Due to her husband's probable sexual exploits, and his barefaced pigheadedness, she is at very high risk of further infections. But for this whole community, I feel a sense of appalling despair.

Crisis in the Camp

Day #17. 6:00am, Bedroom

Early morning in the freezing Himalayan foothills. It's time to get up. Like the rest of the volunteers, I dread these first moments of the day as I contemplate the bitter onslaught of the biting sub-zero air to come. Blankets cover all but the base of my nose, and yet I can feel that today is even colder than usual. And as I slowly will myself to get up, I sense that something is wrong.

It's not simply the extra cold. Perhaps it's the noise – or rather the lack of noise. Usually by this time of the day we hear an assortment of sounds outside: bird calls; cattle bells; local people talking and singing and going about their early morning tasks. But today it's strangely quiet, and for some reason I don't comprehend, the effect is unsettling, forbidding.

By now the courtyard below my first floor bedroom is usually bustling with activity. But today, as I turn my head and peer down through the small window above my bed, there is not a single person or animal in sight. The bright green grass that covers most of the yard has changed overnight to a cheerless frosted white.

Eventually I throw off the bedcovers, and the ice-cold room rapidly leaches the heat from my body. My fingers and toes are already numb. With each breath I expel I watch the heat swirl in flurries of dense, white vapour. Making my way along the hallway towards the shower, I feel like I'm in some sort of disturbing dream. Even the other rooms in the lodge are silent; it seems that the other volunteers still sleep, or at least remain snug in their beds. Perhaps they're conjuring courage to brave the hostile chill. I'm tempted to knock on the doors of the volunteers to rouse them, to see what they make of this strange morning, but decide instead to let them rest a little longer.

The taps in the shower are marked both 'hot' and 'cold'. Our team are convinced that this is some form of heartless joke, because on no occasion on this camp has the shower delivered any hot water. Nevertheless, this morning again I turn on both taps and stare up at the showerhead with a look of imploring hope. I test the water with my cupped, outstretched hand, as if to beg the taps for a reprieve. Perhaps today, perhaps for the first time, warm water will flow.

I wait, and I wait … but no. Once again there is no heat. And like most mornings, the water doesn't exactly flow, but instead spits and sputters in untidy spurts.

With a sense of defeat, I look into the stammering frigid stream, step forward, and brace myself for the ice-cold pain to come. Today the wash is even colder than usual, and I feel embarrassed when impulsively, I cry out as the freezing water strikes my skin. I lack the strength to brave the chill for more than a few moments before quickly retreating to the mercy of a dry towel. But even after drying I'm left shaking, with my fingers and toes now a dejected shade of blue. My body heat has retreated to my core, to hide and hoard the meagre warmth that remains.

'Another day in paradise,' I say to myself in a flash of self-pity. During the course of our medical camps there are many times we all miss our family and friends, but right at this moment I yearn more for the simple warmth of a soothing hot shower. Then I shake my head and remind myself that most people in these parts of the world have never experienced this sort of luxury.

Back in my room, in a fight against the oppressive cold I dress as quickly as I can. I check my watch again – perhaps the reason it's so quiet and lifeless this morning is that it's earlier in the day than I'd thought. But no – it's after 6:30 am now. Still no noises outside, and still no signs of life from the rest of the team. *What is going on?*

Suddenly, the brittle silence is broken by a violent scream. It comes from outside, and frantic shouting soon follows. I look through my bedroom window again, and see that the courtyard, which a short time ago was devoid of life, is now throbbing with the mania of 10 or 12 very agitated people. I throw on my coat and race downstairs, confused and concerned.

Outside now, still several metres from the frenzied crowd, I see the splattering trail of blood before I see its hapless source. My first thought is that somebody has been stabbed. Surely damage to a major vessel for such a great loss of blood. Brutal violence – but in a land of such tranquility?

I look over to the chaotic crowd who continue to yell and wave wildly. They all appear to be Nepalese. I can feel my heart pound as, tentatively now, I walk towards them. They spot me, and immediately direct their despairing shouts and gestures at me. Their words are incomprehensible, and I have no idea what is going on.

Two men in the crowd grab at my clothes and push me towards the centre of the fuming horde. And it is here that I see the focus of their distress. A woman lies there in a large pool of bright blood. Her face is a ghostly white, her sunken eyes wide with desperate fear. The outraged mob continue to shout and jostle me. One of them lifts the blood-stained blanket that loosely covers the woman's lower body. And right then I understand the crux of this terrifying, baffling confrontation.

This massive blood loss is not from any stab wound or other obvious external trauma. This fated woman is heavily pregnant, and the blood flows from between her pallid, lifeless legs.

She has a pulse – thready and weakening. She is conscious, but drowsy. My mind spins with multiple, haphazard thoughts. First aid. Stop the bleeding. Resuscitate. Intravenous access. Fluids, IV fluids. The mother. The baby. I need help.

'English?' I yell. 'Does anyone here speak English?'

There is no response from the startled crowd.

I try to focus. We can't do this here. There is no equipment. All of our vital medical supplies sit in our hospital – 10 or 15 minutes from here. And where are my team? Surely they've heard this commotion and they're coming to investigate as I have done.

I try to block out the panicking noise of those around me. There are no obvious contractions. The baby's head is high above the mother's pelvis.

Think. Think. First aid. Basic first aid. Stop the bleeding. I need to apply pressure to the source of the bleeding. But the uterus? A very large, pregnant uterus? I have no idea of the exact site of the bleeding – effective pressure is simply impossible. Okay then, the artery that supplies the uterus. The aorta. I can compress this large vessel through her abdominal wall.

I make a fist, and with all my might I push down firmly above the uterus to compress the tissues against her spine. I can feel the feeble pulse as the artery fights a pathetic battle against the urgent force of my fist.

Blood has been pooling in the uterus and vagina, so the immediate effect of my pressure on the abdomen is to expel this collection; there is a sudden extra gush of bright blood from between the woman's legs.

A violent jolt to my shoulder pushes me sideways and backwards, and I lose balance and fall to the ground. Stunned, I look up from the frosty, blood-stained path and shake my head in further confusion. It is one of the men in the frantic group who has fiercely thrust me aside. I have not seen this man before. Did he think I was trying to harm the bleeding woman? The sight of my fist deep within her abdomen and the heightened blood loss that promptly followed must have given the impression that I was causing harm.

Another man helps me to my feet. I recognise this one from our village. I'm too stunned to even thank him, and as I try to regain my composure, a heated argument begins between this villager and the other who pushed me to the ground. While the two men argue I repeat my maneuver to compress the woman's aorta.

We need to get this dying woman to an area where we can have some sort of chance of resuscitating her. Right now it is too far to our hospital. In the time it would take to carry her there she is likely to die from the excessive blood loss. I find my voice again, and I shout, 'Dining Hall! Dining Hall!' I wave my free hand in the direction of the ground floor room.

Several of the crowd lift the bleeding woman who is lying on a makeshift stretcher. I reluctantly release my fist from her abdomen. The men seem to understand my furious instructions as they carry the woman towards the Dining Hall. I look down at the path. There must be at least two litres of blood that have accumulated here on the frosted gravel. Heavily, I realise that our chances of saving this woman are very slim.

We are almost at the Dining Hall when Mack and Louise finally appear. They are both in dressing gowns.

'Thank God you're here!' I shout to them desperately. 'We've got a major crisis. Massive blood loss. Full term or near full term pregnancy. Probable placenta praevia. At least three litres of blood loss and continuing. I seem to be able to slow the bleeding with aortic compression, but we need urgent IV fluids.'

'Jesus, Ray,' Mack exclaims.

The moribund woman is placed down roughly on the Dining Hall floor. Several of the men in the anxious crowd follow us inside. I resume my desperate aortic compression. 'I think we've got a better chance of a resuss here, Mack. Best if we bring the gear to her. She won't survive the trip to the hospital. Lu Lu – can you elevate her legs?'

Louise steps in front of some of the men and grasps the woman's feet. She lifts the legs to about 45 degrees to assist the crucial blood flow to the brain. She then passes on the task to one of the men standing nearby. The crowd have quietened now and look on with faces of fierce concern.

Steph and Jayne arrive, and I bark instructions to them, 'Steph, run to the hospital, fast. Grab IV fluids – four or five bags, large bore cannulas, blood pressure sphygmo, gloves.' Steph races to the door. 'And pathology tubes,' I yell.

'Got it,' she yells back as she sprints away.

The woman is becoming drowsier now. Mack steadies her head and then reaches down to take her pulse. 'Not much here, Ray. Very feeble. I don't like our chances with this one.'

Jayne's eyes balloon in a look of horror. In a tremulous voice she says, 'What can I do?'

'There is a chance we'll need to go to theatre urgently, Jayne,' I say. 'Grab Paul and set up for another possible emergency caesarean section. And the local team. Nurses, doctors, pathology technician – all hands on deck.'

'Absolutely,' Jayne says, 'I'll find Paul first.' She charges up the stairs.

'Mack,' I say, 'can you help me with this aortic compression? I'm losing my strength here.'

As Mack exchanges his fist for mine, he looks into my eyes. 'Ray. I don't think we're going to win here.'

'I know, Mack. But we need to at least try, right?'

Mack nods slowly, without resolve.

'Lu Lu. Can you find some more blankets? The cold isn't helping this lady.'

'Onto it, Ray.'

Norman appears, looking almost as pale as the haemorrhaging woman. 'Oh my God,' he exclaims.

'Norman,' I say. 'Not our normal breakfast this morning, I'm afraid. We need an interpreter. Urgently. And Fazi and Laya. Can you do your best to find them?'

'Ah, sure,' Norman replies, uneasily. He looks lost and shaken as he wanders away.

Steph returns, out of breath. She quickly hands over the equipment she's grabbed from the hospital. I take over the aortic compression again as Mack somehow finds a vein in the woman's arm. Steph rapidly connects the IV tubing and squeezes the fluid bag vigorously to infuse the saline solution as quickly as possible. Mack inserts a second cannula into the jugular vein in the woman's neck and collects a blood sample into one of the pathology tubes before surging more IV fluids through this port.

'Lu Lu,' I say, 'we need a blood pressure.'

As I look up, Louise seems to be in a daze. It takes a second or two for her to respond to my request. Her head jerks back and she kneels down to take the woman's blood pressure from the arm without the cannula.

'50 on 10,' Louise yells.

This is terrible, but in view of the massive blood loss, not at all surprising. The woman has probably lost two thirds of her blood volume.

'Mack,' I say, 'we've got no idea of this woman's blood group. Do you think we should transfuse O negative blood?'

Mack contorts his face as he considers this. 'Can't hurt, I guess. We probably need at least four units though. Do we have anyone with O negative blood?'

'None of our team' I say gravely. It occurs to me that none of the local Nepalese here is likely to know his or her blood type, and I grasp the galling futility of our plight.

'Mack,' I continue, 'you know that the only way we can stop this bleeding is to operate and deliver this baby and placenta. We may even need to do a hysterectomy.'

'There's no way this lass will survive surgery in this state,' Mack says. 'You know that, Ray.'

'This is Catch-22,' I say, 'she'll die if we don't operate; she'll die if we do.'

'Let's see how she responds to these fluids.'

Mack and I continue to tag team with aortic compression. As Mack takes over again I re-examine the woman's abdomen. The baby's head remains high, and now that we have a stethoscope I listen for its heartbeat. But it is no surprise to find there is none. This little baby must have died some time ago.

I look up to Mack and then across to Louise, who both stare at me with expressions of grim hope. Slowly and solemnly I shake my head.

'Dr Ray, can I help?' The sweet sounds of Poppy's voice.

Unfolding Calamity

I'm surprised to see Poppy here, but I shouldn't be. This is her workplace, and breakfast would normally be served at this time.

'Oh, Poppy,' I say. 'Thank you, but this really is not a good place for you now. It will be best if you can leave us.'

Poppy does not move. Softly she says, 'Norman says you need interpreter. I can be interpreter.'

'Yes, we do, Poppy. But this is no place for a child. I'm sorry.'

'Dr Ray thinks Poppy not strong,' she says defiantly. 'Poppy is strong. You will see.'

'I think you're very strong, Poppy, but it is wrong for you to be here right now. Please leave us.'

'You need help for translation. I can do this, Dr Ray.'

I'm torn. We desperately do need an interpreter – for the woman, who appears to be coming in and out of consciousness now, but also for the local Nepalese people who surround her. To have even a remote chance of saving this woman we need their help. And I assume one of the men here is the woman's husband. It's only fair that we explain this dire situation to him as soon as possible. But a child – a 12-year old – it's clearly unfair on her. We risk traumatising her, and causing deep, indelible scars.

I know I must make a decision quickly. My head spins again with uncertainty, and I look to Mack and Louise and Steph for guidance. All three shrug their shoulders, but Louise raises her eyebrows and gives me a gentle nod. Her subtle affirmation is enough to sway my decision.

'Okay, Poppy,' I say with a sigh, 'you may stay. This is a very sad situation. This baby inside this mother has died. It is likely the mother will also die. I know this will hurt you a lot to know this, but you must also know we are trying our best. Sometimes we do not win these battles.'

Poppy simply nods her head. She does not appear troubled at hearing this grave news. She walks to the woman's head and leans down close to her face. She strokes the woman's dark hair as she speaks to her softly in Nepalese. It's not clear whether or not the woman registers Poppy's words. The woman slowly twists her head from side to side and makes occasional low-pitched grunts.

Poppy then stands and addresses the five Nepalese men who continue to observe the perilous scene. One of the men answers, and a conversation begins between him and Poppy.

I interrupt their exchange and say, 'Poppy, this is the husband?'

'Yes, Dr Ray.'

'Please tell him that we are doing everything we can to stop the bleeding and save his wife.'

I watch the husband as Poppy translates this message. He has a look of steely resolve, and it does not change throughout their discussion.

'Does the husband want the other men to leave this room?' I ask.

After another brief exchange, Poppy says, 'No, Dr Ray. This man say these people are friends from his village. He want them to stay.'

We learn from the husband through Poppy that this is his wife's first pregnancy. Apart from some light bleeding on and off he does not think there have been any problems during the pregnancy. His wife has had no formal antenatal care, but she has seen a woman from her village on two or three occasions. This local woman has performed a number of home births over the years and is not attached to a hospital. The husband has described the precise features of a Traditional Birth Attendant. His wife was planning to deliver their baby at home until early this morning when the heavy bleeding commenced.

Norman returns, out of breath. 'I'm sorry, Ray,' he says, 'no luck. I've looked everywhere, but I can't find you an interpreter. Fazi and Laya won't be here for another hour yet.'

'Thanks Norman,' I reply. 'Can you try the hospital? There must be a nurse who can help with translation. Or even Suman, the pathology guy.'

'Roger,' Norman says. He walks quickly in the direction of the door. But I know it's most unlikely he will find anybody there who can suitably translate.

The mother's bleeding has slowed; the loss from the uterus is not much more than an ooze now. But as I inspect the recent blood that has collected between her legs, I note with alarm that there are no blood clots present. There is also a steady trickle now from the cannula site in her neck.

'Mack,' I say, 'the blood you collected in the path tube – it's still here?'

'It is, Ray. We've got no one to test it yet.'

'I think we can test this ourselves, Mack. It's been in that tube for at least 15 minutes, right? Please tell me it's clotted.'

Mack reaches to his side and picks up the glass tube. He turns it sideways and then vertically. I can't see the tube's contents clearly, but the expression on Mack's face tells me there is no clot.

Coagulation of our blood – the ability to form clots – it's essential for the regulation and control of bleeding. In times of massive blood loss, our coagulation system can be overwhelmed. In a cruel twist of physiological fate, very heavy bleeding can lead to exhaustion or destruction of our bleeding defences, which in turn leads to even heavier bleeding. A disastrous downward spiral that ultimately leads to our demise.

Mack looks back at me and says quietly, 'It's over, Ray. There's no way back from here.'

And this time I know he's right. Even with treatment in a modern hospital setting, this condition is notoriously tough to treat and overcome. But here, right now, without the ability to transfuse blood or blood products and no high-tech equipment, we have no hope of saving this woman's life.

Louise and Steph wait with looks of anxious anticipation. Gravely, I say to them, 'We've lost this, guys,' and in unison their expressions change to a scowl.

'But we can't give up,' Steph says, hurriedly. 'We still have a blood pressure. Her bleeding has slowed. Surely we can do something.'

'Steph,' I reply, 'we've been doing our best to get on top of this. If we could have stabilised this woman, there was a remote chance we could get her to theatre to stop the bleeding with a caesarean or a hysterectomy. But she's run out of coagulation factors. She may even have DIC.†* Everything we touch now will bleed. I'm sorry, but there's no way out of this.'

Louise is silent, her stare intense and frozen as she absorbs the horrible, distressing truth.

'Dr Ray?' Poppy says. She looks worried and confused.

'Poppy,' I reply. 'This is very, very hard. I am so sorry that you have to be involved in this.'

'This lady will die now?' she asks gently. Her innocence is overpowering.

'Yes, Poppy. There is nothing more we can do.'

I look around the room in the hope of seeing another interpreter, but still there is none. The husband and four other Nepali men look on with expressions I cannot read. I realise we need to talk to the husband again to explain that his wife's death is imminent. But how damaging would this be for Poppy if she is the one to translate this news? I close my eyes and try to work my way through the ethics of this most difficult situation. When I open my eyes I look up to see that Poppy has already approached the husband and begun talking.

'Poppy!' I exclaim. 'What are you saying?'

'I tell husband that you all do best for his wife, you try very, very hard, but no good – spirits are too strong.'

'Poppy, I cannot ask you to do this. It is very unfair on you.'

'I tell husband that his wife will soon be with spirits.' Poppy appears solemn and composed.

The husband's gaunt face is drained and expressionless. His fists clench firmly, and in the heavy silence that follows I notice for the first time that his hands are stained with dried blood. The pigment has concentrated in the folds of his knuckles. Creases in the skin – normally so ivory white – have now become morbidly dark.

The four Nepalese men now surround the husband, but no words are exchanged. The woman's legs are lowered back down to the floor, and in silence, all of the men slowly walk to the Dining Hall door and exit the building.

---

† * Disseminated Intravascular Coagulation (DIC) is a condition where multiple clots form in small blood vessels throughout the body. The clots use up the body's limited numbers of coagulation proteins and platelets. As a result, uncontrolled bleeding occurs in other areas of the body.

The dying woman is now left with five of us from our team, plus Poppy. The blood loss from the cannula site in her jugular vein is more noticeable now, and bleeding has begun from her mouth. Mack releases his fist from the woman's abdomen and looks up at me soberly. I meet his gaze and shake my head; there is no longer any sense in persisting with this pressure. I look up at the two bags of IV fluids and think there is no real point in continuing those either.

The woman continues to fade in and out of consciousness, and again begins to toss her head from side to side. She now mumbles soft, incoherent words. I put my ear closer to her bleeding mouth and slowly begin to comprehend her plea.

'*Mero baccha,*' she whispers, '*mero baccha.*'

Despite my very limited Nepali vocabulary I do understand these two words. *My baby. My baby.*

I look across to Louise and Mack. It's clear that they heard and understand these words as well because, like me, their eyes begin to well with tears. This wretched woman has no idea that her baby inside her has died, and she has no idea that within the next few minutes she will lose her own life.

I turn to Poppy once more. 'I am going to ask you to translate something else,' I say. 'This is very important. I want you to be very clear and very accurate with this next translation.'

She looks at me intensely. Her luminous brown eyes are now brimmed with tears of her own. 'Yes, Dr Ray.'

'I want you to tell this woman that I promise that she will be with her baby very soon.'

Poppy kneels down and begins her translation.

As doctors and nurses and midwives, we are trained for tragedy and loss of life. We are trained to divorce ourselves from unnecessary emotions and to remain professionally distant. Emotional detachment allows us to remain composed in the face of medical crises. And yet, it's equally fundamental to provide empathy and compassion for patients under our care. This balance – to be at once both dispassionate and compassionate – is one of the greatest challenges of a medical worker during any emotional encounter. But when the encounter is the loss of a mother or a child – let alone a mother *and* her child – this task is profound.

I hear a sharp, broken sob, and look up to see Jayne's face crumpled in pain. Unfettered tears flow down her cheeks. Her shoulders heave with despair. Steph puts her arm around Jayne's shoulder and together, unsteadily, they walk upstairs.

Louise rests her head on Mack's shoulder as they comfort each other. As much as I try to keep my own emotions in check, my own tears stream.

And then, without warning, we hear the beautiful tones of Poppy's singing voice. We all look down to see her stroking the bloodied face and hair of the dying woman.

'*Naru naru nani,*
Nani hamro gani,
Buli ko sar jana say,
Pani peko ramo ray.'

Close your eyes. Close your eyes, and you can picture Poppy singing to baby Hari several days earlier. And just as the soothing sounds of the lullaby settle the baby as he confronts the strange, looming adult world, I think how fitting it is that this dying woman receives the same calming solace as she approaches the daunting unknown of the spirit world.

As I open my eyes and watch the harrowing, heart-rending scene before us, I grasp the woman's hand. It's my own feeble effort to help ease her journey. My hands are still numb from the bitter cold, but the hand I hold feels as icy as the frosted ground outside. Poppy continues her soothing lullaby and I wonder – does she see this mother before her as her own? Poppy will make this woman's last moments peaceful and draped in her love. Is this the love she was unable to give her own mother?

The woman's body is limp now. The tone has left her freezing hand. All colour and life has drained from her face, and her eyes have become hauntingly dim. A guttural growl snares each of her laboured breaths. As Poppy's calming melody continues, the rattling gasps slow, and slow, and finally cease.

As moving and painfully poignant as it is right now while these final mortal moments unfurl, I think – when *my* time comes, when *my* life is ending, I would wish for nothing more than the same soothing sounds from the mouth of my own daughter.

Immediate Aftermath

8:45am, Dining Hall

Desolation. Gut-wrenching desolation.

It's over, we lost, and now there is a massive, piercing hole. And we plummet to its depths with a crushing sense of failure.

We have failed this poor woman, and her baby. I know there must have been something else we could have done to save them. But as I rack my brain and replay each harrowing moment of the frantic last two hours, I remind myself that now is not the time for critical review. Right now there are more important things to be taken care of.

Poppy has stopped her captivating lullaby, but she continues to stroke the woman's head. The woman's eyes have closed softly and her face is finally calm, as if in a peaceful sleep.

There is so much to consider. The husband – I must see the husband. How will he react? Why did he choose to leave the room when it was clear his wife was about to lose her life? My team – they will be tormented by this. I need to sit down and talk to them, to reassure them somehow. And Poppy – I fear for her. I fear this whole debacle will scar her. And yet, watching her right now as she silently caresses this lifeless mother, the scene conjures a striking, forlorn beauty. Somehow, some sweetness within this bitter melancholy.

Jayne and Steph have returned from the upstairs bedrooms. They approach us slowly and quietly, their eyes mournful and knowing.

'Is there anything we can do?' asks Steph in a whisper.

'Thanks, Steph,' I reply softly. 'We need to cancel this morning's operating. I don't think any of us would be up to our best standards right now. We'll need some time to absorb all of this, to regroup. Can you and Jayne go to the hospital and explain what's happened?'

'Ray,' says Mack, 'perhaps we should cancel the whole day's surgery. It might take some people more than a morning to get through this.'

'You might be right, Mack,' I say, 'but let's not cancel the afternoon right yet. Let's keep it on hold and see how people are feeling in a few hours' time. Some might feel better with things to do.'

As Steph and Jayne open the Dining Hall door to make their way to the hospital, Norman storms through and joins us. He's out of breath again, but the colour has returned to his face.

'Nabin!' Norman says. 'Finally, I found Nabin!'

Nabin follows a few steps behind. They both look down at the pitiful scene before us.

'Oh dear,' says Norman, his face shocked now, and rapidly losing its colour once again.

'We lost this fight, Norman,' says Mack. 'We did everything we could here, but she was too far gone before she got to us.'

'And the baby?' Norman asks, his tone weighty and dispirited.

Mack shakes his head. 'The little one lost its life some time before its mother did.'

'Norman,' I say, 'thank you for finding Nabin. I suggest you sit down. You're really not looking great right now.'

Norman wanders slowly to the other side of the Dining Hall and sets down his large frame at one of the side tables, alone.

'Lu Lu,' I murmur, 'would you mind ...?' but before I finish my sentence she has anticipated my request.

'Of course,' she says as she walks over to Norman to provide him some support.

'Nabin,' I say, 'I appreciate you coming in early today. As you can see, we've had a horror morning. Before you arrived we needed someone urgently to translate to the mother and her husband. Poppy was here and she's been wonderful helping us out.'

Nabin simply nods. He does not appear surprised that we've engaged a child in a task that could be brutally distressing to someone so young.

'I need to speak to the husband, now,' I continue.' Can you come with me to translate?'

'Most certainly, Dr Ray,' Nabin replies, as he solemnly nods his head once again.

Nabin and I walk outside where the original crowd of concerned Nepalese has grown to about 20 people. As soon as they spot us, they surround us. Two of the men fire questions at Nabin who responds grimly. Immediately there is frenzied shouting from the group. The effect is threatening. Uneasily, I look across to Nabin who also seems apprehensive. He utters a few more words to them, which only causes them to shout more intensely.

'Nabin, they seem angry at us.'

'Not angry at me, Dr Ray. Just you.'

'Oh great. This morning just gets better and better.'

'You want me to translate that, Dr Ray?'

'I think that will not translate well. No, Nabin.'

Nabin continues. 'People say that they brought woman here from home because you can fix her. They told you save life of mothers and life of babies. They angry you no save these lives.'

'What do you suggest I say to them, Nabin?' I ask.

'It best to say that spirit who want this woman – too great. Best to say you fight very hard, but this spirit very strong.' Familiar words – so remarkably similar to Poppy's.

I look into the faces of the outraged crowd. There are several women amongst them now, and they join the furious clamour. I catch the eyes of the husband who simply stares at me, silently, wretchedly.

'I wish to speak to the husband alone, Nabin.'

I walk up to the dejected man and look into his sorrowful eyes. I join my palms together, fingers pointing upward, and give him the most earnest *Namaste* I can muster.

There is no response from the husband. He simply stares back at me. His face does not move, but his shoulders rise and fall with deep, forceful breaths. I remain still in my *Namaste* pose, hoping for … hoping for what? An acceptance? A, 'Thanks – I know you guys did your best in there. Really appreciate your efforts'?

I'm not sure what I want from this distraught man, who cannot have any idea of all we did to try to save his family.

Our standoff continues for what seems like minutes, my uncertain gaze fighting his dogged eyes. And throughout this impasse, the rowdy crowd continues its uproar. The noise is slowly blocked from my senses as I continue to stare at the husband, my numb hands now frozen in the sacred pose. Silently, I implore him for a positive response.

Slowly, as if through a haze now, and after what seems to be an eternity, I watch the husband painfully bring his own palms together to finally respond with his own *Namaste*.

The crowd is hushed. Nabin joins us and mutters a few words to the husband. The three of us then break from the crowd and walk together towards the Dining Hall. Nabin continues to talk to the husband, and outside the Dining Hall entrance I stop and break their conversation.

'What is the husband's name, Nabin?'

'Puru,' Nabin replies. 'Husband name is Puru.'

I look at Puru in the eye and say, 'Namaste, Puru,' and pointing my hand at my chest. 'Dr Ray.'

I study Puru's features again. The deep sorrow has returned to his eyes, but his face remains stubbornly dry.

'What is the name of Puru's wife?' I ask Nabin.

Nabin and Puru exchange a few words. 'Puru's wife name is Arpan.'

'Does Puru want to see the body of Arpan?' I ask.

'Yes, Dr Ray, but husband is sad because his wife will go to low spirit world.'

What? Low spirit world? How does this work? What strange rules declare that when a woman dies in pregnancy her soul goes down instead of up?

'Can you explain this, Nabin?'

'Yes, Dr Ray. When person die angry or die with fear, they go to low world. Always so.'

'But that seems so unfair, Nabin. No one has a choice if they die with fear. And what about karma? I thought it was all about karma.'

'That is next life, sir. Not spirit life.'

Mental note: try to learn more about these baffling religious beliefs. Right now, I'm so very confused.

We enter the Dining Hall again. Mack and Poppy remain crouched down next to Arpan. The blanket has been pulled up to cover her head.

'Would you like to be alone with your wife?' I say to Puru.

'No,' Nabin replies, 'Puru say he want you people to stay.'

As Puru bends down to the head of his wife Mack slowly pulls down the blanket to reveal her peaceful face. This feels like a tragic mortuary identification scene.

I'm not expecting much emotion from Puru. When Poppy told him of his wife's imminent death his reaction was stoic, glacial. I study his features once again as he observes the face of his wife in death. His face shows no contortion or pain. There is not even so much as a frown. What I do see surprises me; Puru's expression has become something that resembles a soft, wistful smile.

The room is silent while Puru holds his enigmatic expression. His eyes remain fixed on the face of his deceased wife when he eventually mumbles a few faint words.

'Puru not understand why his wife not have fear, says Nabin. 'He expect fear in wife's face, but instead wife is calm. Puru pleased that wife is calm.'

'Oh, that is entirely Poppy's doing,' I explain gently. 'Poppy was singing a beautiful, peaceful song to Arpan as she left us.'

When Nabin translates this information, Puru looks across to Poppy, his head tilted to one side. He and Poppy raise their hands and exchange a heart-warming *Namaste*. A simple fragment of raw joy within this space of overwhelming despair. And it brings tears to the eyes of Mack and Poppy once again, and now, at last, to the eyes of Puru.

We kneel in silence for some time before I turn to Nabin. 'So, this means Arpan's spirit will no longer go to the low world?'

'Perhaps,' replies Nabin. 'We speak to Lhapa. Lhapa will know this.'

I have no idea who Lhapa is, and Nabin picks up on my confused expression.

'Lhapa is Shaman in this region.'

After several more minutes Puru and Nabin begin another conversation. Nabin translates again. 'Puru must take his wife home for death rites.'

'Yes, of course,' I reply. I understand that the religious traditions here, and in most parts of Nepal involve cremation of the deceased. This will usually take place within 24 hours of death. This is in keeping with the Hindu belief that burning the body helps the departed soul release any residual attachment it may have developed for the deceased person.

'But there is more, Dr Ray,' continues Nabin. 'Puru also wishes to have baby.'

'Of course the baby will go with its mother.'

'But, Dr Ray,' Nabin continues, 'baby must go differently to mother.'

'I'm not following you, Nabin. The baby is inside the mother. They will obviously go together.'

'No, Dr Ray. Mother and baby cannot go together. Mother must be burned. Baby must be buried.'

Suddenly, with horror, I comprehend Nabin's words.

'You want us to take the baby out of the mother for separate funeral rites?' I cannot hide my astonishment, and I look to Mack who appears equally bewildered.

'Yes, Dr Ray.'

With alarm I turn to Poppy, hoping that somehow she will refute Nabin's outrageous comments.

Poppy looks at me and nods her head slowly. 'Is most important, Dr Ray,' she says earnestly, 'Mother must be burned; baby must be buried. If death rites not go properly, soul can be disturbed. When soul disturbed it not find its way to spirit world. Then soul comes back to haunt relatives.'

'But ... but,' I stammer and turn back to Nabin, 'what happens when there is no doctor, no hospital? What happens when a mother and baby die together at home, when there is no medical help?'

'This happen many time, Dr Ray,' Nabin says slowly. 'Then husband or brother will take baby from mother.'

Until this moment I've had no idea that the Hindu custom of cremation does not apply to babies and children and saints. These beings are believed to be pure and unattached to their bodies. My mind flashes to horror scenes of a grieving close relative desperately cutting open the abdomen of a recently lost wife or sister to extract a dead baby. The anguish would be unfathomable.

'I need some time to think this over,' I say to no one in particular.

We crouch in silence for a few more minutes while I consider our options. We can carry out Puru's wishes and perform a post-mortem caesarean section to deliver his stillborn baby, or we can refuse his request and have him or someone close to him perform the gruesome task. It's been such a confronting morning, my head still spins with untamed thoughts. But I already know what I must do.

Through Nabin I ask Puru if some of his friends could carry his wife's body from the Dining Hall here to the recovery room of the hospital. Without our usual surgery this morning the recovery room will be empty. This will be a more appropriate place for people to pay respects.

Puru looks me in the eye and bows his head solemnly before leaving the Dining Hall with Nabin. Mack and I remove the cannulas from Arpan's arm and neck, and clean the face and body as best we can. Shortly after Nabin returns with four men from the crowd outside. We cover Arpan's face with the blanket once more before the men lift the body and carry the small frame out of the Dining Hall door and towards the hospital.

'Poppy,' I say, 'you have been magnificent this morning. Thank you so very much. Are you okay?' I search for signs of pain in her eyes.

'Dr Ray,' she replies, 'I am happy to help. I told you I am strong. Now you know I am strong.' If there is pain, she hides it well.

'We need to talk a lot more about what happened this morning, Poppy, but right now our team should try to have some food. I doubt they feel like eating, but it's important they keep up their strength. Would you be kind enough to organise breakfast for us?'

'Of course, Dr Ray.'

'And could you get someone to light the fire? I suspect we will be here for most of the morning.'

Poppy smiles softly and slips away to the kitchen.

'Tell me your thoughts, Mack,' I say.

'It's a crazy world, Ray,' he says. 'You'll do the caesarean?'

'The idea is repulsive,' I reply, 'but I can't stand the thought of the alternative.'

'Ray, I know we've had some tough calls today. And this is another big one. I know you were tortured with your decision to get Poppy to translate and all. It was impossible to be sure of the correct thing to do there. But for the record – I think you were spot on involving her with this.'

'I so hope you're right, Mack.'

'You know she would have only been in the next room anyway. It's not as if she wouldn't have known what was happening. It's possible that by being deeply involved as she was, she could have even gained some strength from this.'

For the first time today, I smile. 'Mack, you're a tonic.'

Team Meeting

9:55am, Dining Hall

The whole team have assembled for the toughest breakfast of our camp. The room is unusually quiet; no one speaks as we all sit in shared sadness. The fire in the potbelly is modest, and the only noise right now is the quiet crackling of the dry wood as it submits to the small, hesitant flames. It seems to whisper in respect for our downcast mood.

It's no surprise that very little of the food on our table has been touched, and I wonder if I've made the right decision to call everyone to meet here – merely metres from where the terrible loss occurred only an hour ago.

Louise leans forward and says to me softly, 'I tried to eat, Ray. I know it's important, but the food just gets stuck.'

'It's OK, Lu Lu,' I reply quietly. 'I'm the same. My insides feel raw. It's like they don't want to be bothered right now with something as frivolous as food.'

Steph and Jayne are across from me, their faces distant as they simply push at the food on their plates. I look past them to the Dining Hall window where a crust of frost has appeared around its edges. Outside, feeble rays struggle to shine through a broken layer of cloud.

I turn back to Louise. 'We need a debrief. I'm going to talk to the whole group now.'

I stand up from my chair.

'Okay, guys,' I begin in a louder voice. 'There are a few things I need to say. Every one of us has come here on this camp because we want to help these people whose health is so poor. And every one of us will be devastated right now because we had a double tragedy this morning. The fact that this happened in this very room makes our distress even more acute. We're not prepared for this. We're not prepared for this happening *anywhere* on the camp. This is not what we're about. We treat women with severe genital prolapse, and we make them better. We're not set up for emergency obstetrics, and even if we were, I doubt we could have saved the life of this woman and her baby. Mack and I have gone over everything we've done this morning, and I can tell you – there is nothing else we could have done to prevent these deaths. I am proud of every one of you who helped out this morning.'

Every volunteer is silent. Every expression, forlorn.

'Most of us here are doctors or nurses or midwives. We're pretty good at caring for others and supporting them, but most of us are not so good at caring for ourselves. We know there are some out there in the medical establishment who would see an emotional response to death as a sign of weakness and even incompetence. They would say we medical people should somehow be above all of that sentimentality, that we should stifle those emotions; suck it up and move on. Well, I say to the people who make these statements – you have no idea; you are totally out of touch. The person I want on my team is the one who can express himself or herself, the person who's not afraid to show his heart or her heart. Of course we need to be steady in a crisis, but that does not mean we can't shed a tear when we're challenged.'

'Here, here,' says Mack.

'For the two of you here who are not medical – thank you for your support, too. What happened this morning has probably hit you even harder then it hit us, the medical crew; we're in pain, too, but we're probably a little more used to these heartbreaking dramas. But understand this – all we can do is our best. And this morning we did our best. It wasn't meant to be.

'And I speak to everyone here now. Some of you – most of you, I guess – will benefit from the company and the support of the others in our team. Talk about this; share your feelings with each other, share them with me. But some of you will prefer solitude. That's okay. No way is right or wrong. But I will say this – if you're a solitude person, if you prefer to work through this on your own and keep your feelings to yourself, I urge you, write them down. Write down your feelings, label them. Don't try to pretend they're not there. Stifle them, and you will slow the healing process. If you don't want to share your pain with a person, share it with a piece of paper or your laptop. I can say this with absolute certainty – describing your feelings will help you get through this.'

I look around the room again to each of the team members. Every face is focused. All of these volunteers are a long way from their families and friends, the people who would normally support them in tough times like these. But here in remote Nepal they must turn to their colleagues. I look over to Mack, and our eyes lock in a shared understanding. He gives me the subtlest of reassuring grins.

'There is one more thing,' I continue. 'As you all know, we have cancelled this morning's operating so we can catch our breath and work our way through this. Now we all need to decide when we restart the surgery. Should we wait until tomorrow? Or should we get back on the horse this afternoon?'

Some of the team begin to look around at each other, searchingly.

'This needs to be an individual decision from each of us,' I continue. 'If any one of you wants to wait until tomorrow, you should not feel you are letting the team down. Yes, there are lots of women piled up, waiting for their surgery. But if you don't think you'll be at your best, we don't want you there. We need to know that when we do operate on these women with their prolapses, we can give them the best treatment possible. Is this today or is it tomorrow?'

Several of the team now begin to mumble amongst themselves.

'This needs to be a secret ballot,' I say. 'In order to get your honest answers to this I am going to pass around a piece of paper to each of you. You need to mark an X next to either *today* or *tomorrow*.'

Louise distributes the ballot papers to each of the volunteers who mark their choice before collecting them up.

'Lu Lu,' I say, 'could you do the honours?'

It doesn't take her long to tally the results. 'Okay, team,' she says, 'listen up! I have the results. And I know that despite what Dr Ray just said, he would be really keen to get back to operating this afternoon – we've already lost precious operating time.'

I shake my head, but Louise is spot on with her assessment.

'Well,' Louise continues as she looks down at the ballot papers, 'I'm very sorry to say that despite Dr Ray's secret wishes, the results are ... those in favour of waiting until tomorrow: zero. Those in favour of starting this afternoon: seven. It is unanimous, guys – we restart today.'

Spontaneous applause erupts from our small gathering. I'm as stunned at the clapping as I am at the unanimous result, and for the second time today, I smile. My pride in this team could not be greater.

Louise leans across to me again, her eyes with a mischievous glint. 'Sorry to tease you just then. Just thought I'd add a little drama to the announcement.'

'Thanks Lu Lu,' I reply, 'we needed a little more drama in our day.'

'Ray,' Louise says, 'this is a terrific group of volunteers, and everyone gets on so well with each other. I know you know that. But despite the horrible, horrible business of this morning, I think this might make the bond between all of us even stronger.'

And with that, Louise's generous lips flatten out to a heart-warming grin.

Meltdown

10:35am, Dining Hall

Cheerless conversation has broken out in the room. The tone among the volunteers is grim, but I'm pleased to at least hear them opening up with their reactions to this morning's tragic events.

After an hour or so of mingling with the various groups I announce to the team that I'm going out for a walk to clear my head. When I step outside, the sudden cold snatches the breath from my throat. I hug my coat in close and walk along the frosted pathway towards the surgery recovery ward where Arpan's body lies. Like the courtyard grass, the cypress trees that flank the path have surrendered their lively green. Overnight they've been shocked to an ashen shade of white. Heavy branches hang low, shrouded with ghostly frost. Despite the bitter cold, young Nepalese boys run and laugh on the icy ground. How can they be so happy when the rest of us are so sad?

The frigid air begins to soak my clothes. I bow my head until my chin touches my chest and keep walking ahead, slowly. Despite my attempts to reassure my team, I'm still overwhelmed by the knowledge that I failed Arpan and her baby. But I must not let the team know the thoughts that torment me; I am their leader, and I know if I stumble, the whole team will be at risk.

Beside the narrow path, slow-flowing sections of the stream have turned to ice overnight. I stop in front of a wide, deep frozen pool, and study its convoluted beauty. The liquid water beneath the clear glass formation must be two or three metres deep. It has been trapped in icy form; a labyrinth of glacial tendrils has become its staunch and frozen prison. Leaning in for a closer view, I'm caught off guard to see reflected in the mirror surface, the image of my startled face.

The clear frozen pool above the trapped water appears as solid as concrete as I step forward, placing my foot at the centre of its icy crown. Moving further forward, and balanced on one leg now, I'm impressed at the strength of the crystals as the ice engages my full weight.

But then, a crack. Small at first, but slowly extending. I know I should move from here; the ice structure is more fragile than it first seemed. This frozen framework will surely collapse and I will plunge to the freezing water below. I have no wish for self-harm, but something compels me to stay here; I am bound to this perilous surface, and watch on, fascinated and helpless as the silent cracks slowly spread. Branching, radiating ice fractures expand in every direction until a thousand shards have formed on what was only moments ago a solid, gleaming, crystalline surface. What began as a single breach in the armour of this structure has now penetrated and permeated its entire makeup.

Distant voices now. Young voices. Boys. Louder, more urgent now. My leaden trance is broken as I become aware of two Nepalese boys running towards me. They appear frantic. The bigger of the two charges at me and seizes me at the waist. His momentum carries us both away from the shattered ice, and we slide gracelessly onto the solid path. I lie there, stunned and breathless, while the young boy gets to his feet.

'Not safe, sir,' he says panting, as he helps me to my feet. 'You will fall.'

I look across to the collapsing frozen pool. I feel foolish and confused to have taken such a crazy risk. 'I kind of did fall,' I say. 'Possibly you have saved my life.'

The smaller of the two boys now speaks, 'Dr Ray – you are okay?'

'Yes, thank you. I am fine.' I give the boys a weak smile. In truth, my left shoulder screams in pain from the fall, but I'm too proud to complain. 'Thank you so much, both of you.'

Feeling fazed and dazed and really sore, I hobble in the direction of the recovery ward. Not for the first time today, countless thoughts fight furiously for my attention. Twice in the one morning I have been thrown violently to the ground – maybe this is some sort or record in these parts. And what on earth got into my head that I ignored clear signs of danger? A deep, unstable frozen pond? Idiot! And yet it felt like I had no control over my actions. So weird. So disturbing.

Approaching the operating theatre and recovery room, the fallen leaves on the path ahead have lost their vibrant colours. I look up to the poplar trees that bore them. Nearly all of the branches are naked now. The trees stand forlorn – alienated, estranged. The closest of the trees rises from the edge of the path where I stand. With a gloved hand I reach out and touch the bare trunk. Dark, craggy lines in the bark simulate deep serpentine scars.

I enter the small recovery room of our operating theatre through a low timber door. I'm expecting to see Arpan's body lying on one of the three recovery beds, but all of the beds are empty. I'm confused at first, and wonder if Puru and his friends have instead decided to take Arpan's body home immediately. There are no signs that the body has been here at all; the sheets on all three beds appear untouched. I walk through another door and into the operating theatre. It's eerily silent, and the theatre room seems darker than usual for this time of the day. Here, on the operating table in the very centre of the dark room, lies Arpan's body.

I pause and take in the surreal scene. There is no other person present, and the room has taken on a macabre stillness. The chill is less intense than the bitter cold outside, but the air that surrounds me is heavy. Dim light shines through the two high windows and illuminates the tiny, frail body. At first it feels like I have entered a tomb or mausoleum, but as I look over again at the haunting appearance of Arpan's body, the set reminds me more of a sacrificial altar.

I know what I now have to do, and I know I must do it alone. It's so cruel and unfair, but that is the nature of so much of this land. This task is hard enough for even one person; it would be so wrong to put anyone else through this.

Slowly, I walk towards the theatre table and study Arpan's body more closely. Her feeble arms are folded over her chest. Despite our earlier attempts to clean the blood from her face, brown seepage has dried into her lifeless skin and hair. Her expression remains tranquil, but now her face betrays a hopelessness I hadn't seen before.

I look up from the body to the shadowy edges of the room, and I have to remind myself: this is our workplace; this is where we spend so very many hours of each day. And despite the crumbling walls and broken timber floorboards, when we're here, working away each day, this room is so full of energy and hope. This is where we make people better. We don't do death here – we do life. But right now, the decay of the collapsing structures around me reinforces a sense of gloom and despair.

Detached and adrift now, my eyes wander further to a smaller table in the far corner of the room. Here lie the surgical instruments that Paul has sterilised in preparation for the emergency caesarean section we never managed to perform. I walk over to the table and study each of the carefully laid out instruments. In my mind's eye I picture the surgical steps we would have taken to try to stop Arpan's fatal bleeding.

I wheel the instrument table away from the wall. A small shadow on the floor beneath the table catches my attention. It's an irregular shape, the size of a large glove. I grab one of our torches and bend down to examine the shape more closely. It is simply a pile of leaves. They must have been blown into this corner of the room, and been missed during the daily sweeping.

These confined leaves have also lost their vivid colours to a barren shade of brown. For strange reasons I can't fathom, despite all of the heartbreaking tragedy of the day, despite the calamity that has resulted in two dead bodies in this very room, I feel a sense of pity that these leaves have been trapped here, unable to join their siblings in their final whimsical dance with the wind.

The chilling numbness slowly fades from my fingers and fists. As if in a trance, I grasp the shining scalpel and begin my entry to free the tragic child from its feckless confines. This delivery must be delicate, with all the respect and care of a standard surgical birth. But there is an emptiness, a vacuum in the silence as I slowly work through the thin, stretched layers of the low abdominal wall.

Slowly advancing downward, and now to the visceral depths, I reach the wall of the womb and pause. I can feel my cheeks wet with tears. Hot tears. With heavy hands, I'm about to enter the womb when something erupts inside me.

'Where are you, spirits?' I shout. ' Where are you? Do you watch us with contempt? What price, spirits? What price? Do you lick your sordid lips in vulgar delight? Do you covet the soul of this tiny, defenceless life? Do you suck some sort of depraved pleasure from dividing this mother and child? You couldn't claim these two defenceless souls *together*? What price for your debauched, self-absorbed thrill? What price? You *disgust* me!'

I find it hard to catch my breath, and I'm amazed with the force of the words that have burst from some deep, hidden inner space.

Slowly and painfully I lift the tiny child from Arpan's body. It is a boy, fully-formed, and looking as if he could cry at any moment.

'I'm so sorry, Little One,' I splutter. 'I am so sorry.'

I lay the pitiful soul on his dead mother's abdomen and cut his sallow cord. His slender limbs are soft, his eyes fixed and vacant. I close his lids and study his feeble features. A miniature monk in silent meditation.

'You will never know this world, Little Guy,' I stammer. 'You won't know its beauty and its pain. No one will hold your hand and dote on you. You will never cry and be soothed. You will not suckle. You will not know love. I am so sorry.'

Over the years of training and clinical work, virtually all obstetricians and midwives are involved with the loss of babies, and rarely of mothers. But the anguish of today's double disaster and its ghastly aftermath is crushing. As I begin to close the uterus and each of the abdominal layers, my hands struggle with the arc of each incessant stitch. I pause and force myself to take deep, slow breaths. I'm alarmed that I can't discard this oppressive, brooding state.

And now, voices. Familiar voices. 'Ray? Are you in here, Ray?' It's a distinctive Scottish accent.

I look up to the recovery room door and see both Mack and Louise, who look horrified.

'Had a feeling you were up to something,' Mack says.

'Ray,' Louise says, 'Oh my God – you did this alone?'

'Figured I didn't really need an anaesthetist for this one,' I reply. 'No offence, Mack.'

Mack and Louise walk over to me now, mouths agape as they regard the stillborn baby.

'Ray,' Mack says, 'this would have been soul-destroying to do on your own.'

Louise picks up the little boy. She wipes his face with a surgical swab, and cuddles him like a mother.

'It would be really unfair to expect any of you to go through this.'

'Unfair?' Mack replies. 'Unfair? What about how unfair this might be on you?' He folds his arms and juts his disgruntled jaw. 'We are a team, Ray. I understand your thinking, but this is not teamwork.'

I look across to Louise who continues to embrace the tiny boy. She catches my eye and nods in agreement with Mack's rebuke. And I know they are both right.

I look down at the unfinished operation, and then back up to Mack. Right now I'm lost for words.

'And another thing,' Mack continues. 'Louise and I have been talking. For all your talk about us needing to care for ourselves, and opening up and getting support from the rest of the group – we don't see you doing this yourself, Ray. You've been terrific supporting the team, but who is supporting you?'

Both Mack and Louise stare at me waiting for my response. 'Give me a minute,' I say.

We stand in silence while I recall all that has happened since I left the team in the Dining Hall an hour or so ago. It's quite some time before I speak again.

'Of course, you're right,' I say eventually. 'I'm the leader, and somehow I thought I was above this. I'm not above this. To be honest, Mack, Lu Lu – I'm struggling here. Big time. And what a harsh irony this is to suffer with the very problem I warned others about. I guess this is one whopping lesson.'

I force an embarrassed smile. Louise puts down the baby and gives me one of the biggest hugs I can remember. She steps back and Mack moves in, with a hug almost as strong as Louise's. More tears flow now, from all three of us.

Mack and Louise stay with me while I close the remainder of the abdomen and skin. I step back from Arpan's body to make sure I'm happy with the neatness of the skin closure. Apart from the ghostly white colour, it looks no different to the wound of a live mother.

We clear away the surgical instruments and place a fresh towel on the small table. Louise then places the baby on the towel. She folds his tiny arms over his chest to mimic the pose of his mother. We push the baby's table in beside the operating table to allow Arpan and her baby to lie next to each other. The scene is both touching and deplorable.

I look to Mack, and then to Louise. 'It's still not right,' I say.

I pick up the little boy again, and stare into his innocent face once more. I lift up his mother's crossed arms and place the child over her chest. With no assistance from me, her arms fold back down over her son to form an inexpressibly heartbreaking embrace.

Private Grief

11:50am, Recovery Room

I begin to wonder where Puru and his friends have gone. We haven't seen them since Arpan's body was removed from the Dining Hall a few hours earlier. We had been told that their plan was to carry the two bodies back to their village today to allow funeral rites to take place the following morning.

Louise and Mack and I are about to leave the theatre recovery room when two Nepalese men enter the room. I recognise them from the group that confronted us earlier this morning and I'm thankful that neither is the one who struck me to the ground.

One of the men approaches me and utters some words in Nepali. I shrug my shoulders and open my palms to indicate I have no idea of his meaning. He repeats his phrase over and over, each time louder and more intense than the last. I continue to shrug my shoulders when he eventually looks past me to the two bodies on the operating theatre table. He and the other Nepalese man then bow their heads and walk slowly towards the embracing mother and child. I give them both a silent *Namaste*, before leaving them to mourn together.

As I rejoin Mack and Louise in the theatre recovery area, Puru enters the room. He's followed by another man I recognise. It's the strange, very short man who performed some sort of crazy chant on his timber crate two weeks ago. There is no acknowledgement from him or Puru. They simply walk past us into the operating theatre and join the other two Nepalese men beside the Arpan and her baby.

I'm about to join Puru and the short man when the outside door to the recovery ward opens again. This time Nabin enters the room. He's panting as he says, 'Dr Ray, Dr Mack, Sister Louise, we find Shaman. Now we can take bodies back to village.'

'They will take the bodies shortly, Nabin?' I ask.

'Yes, Dr Ray.'

'And that very short man – he is the village Shaman?'

'Yes. He is Lhapa. He is Shaman for whole area, Dr Ray. This Shaman will perform funeral for both mother and for baby.'

'Nabin,' I say, 'we've taken the baby from his mother. It is a boy. Will you come with me into the theatre to translate for Puru and the Shaman?'

'Of course, Dr Ray.'

'Ray,' Mack says, 'it might be best if Louise and I wait for you here.'

Nabin and I enter the operating theatre and slowly walk towards the grieving party. The four men who surround the bodies are silent with heads bowed. When Puru eventually looks up, I catch his eye and once again join my palms in respect. Puru returns the gesture and nods slowly and gravely. I try to imagine the pain this man must be suffering, but his face is stoic and, as if in some sort of defiance, his nostrils are visibly flared.

The Shaman begins to chant a low-pitched drone. The sound progresses to a continuous monotone howl, and it reverberates in the starkness of the unadorned theatre.

I remain with the five men for several minutes more while the Shaman continues his mournful chant with various subtle changes to its pitch. I'm not sure if I belong here anymore, and I begin to feel very much out of place. As I look around at the men before me, I fear that in some way I may be hindering the progress of their grief. I want to show Puru and his friends my support and respect, but I don't want to intrude.

The lingering mantra appears to be some sort of early funeral ritual, and I was not expecting this. Even though I've been intimately involved with the loss of this man's wife and child, I am a foreigner, and essentially a stranger. How would I feel if I was the one grieving, if this was *my* wife and child? How would I feel if the outsider here was the person who failed in his duty to protect *my* family?

I want to ask Nabin what I should do right now, but it's clear it would be inappropriate to talk during this peculiar sacred ceremony. Instead, slowly and quietly I move away from the group to allow them privacy in their bereavement. I rejoin Mack and Louise in the recovery room, and in a strange giddy silence, the three of us walk back to the Dining Hall to reunite with our team.

Jayne's Struggle

12:25pm, Dining Hall

There's a warmth in the room that's more than a simple break from the harshness of the outside chill. There is more freedom in the volunteers' conversation than there was when I left here a couple of hours ago, but the chatter remains respectfully hushed. Fazi and Laya have joined the group, and they sit in deep conversation with Steph and Paul. As Louise and I approach their table, Steph stands to greet us. Her eyebrows are raised.

'It's done, Steph,' says Louise.

'The baby has been delivered?' Steph asks.

Louise nods her head, slowly and heavily.

Steph looks at me. 'I wondered if that's where you went.'

'It's a crazy world over here sometimes,' I say.

'You're okay?' Steph asks.

'Yeah. Thanks to these two.' I gesture to Louise and Mack.

Fazi stands now and joins us. 'Dr Ray, I am so sorry Laya and I were not there to help you this morning. As you know, we do not arrive at the camp until 8:30 each morning. We would have come earlier if we knew.'

'There is no need to apologise,' I reply. 'I'm sure it would have made no difference. There was nothing we could do to save those lives.'

'Dr Ray, there is something else I need to apologise for.'

'Yes?'

'Laya and I need to leave your camp soon. As you know, when the other doctors did not come for training, we stayed longer than we had planned. But now we are needed back in our hospital in Pokhara.'

Even though I knew this was imminent, my heart sinks. Our assessment of the clinic and the hospital patients is so much more efficient when the Nepalese doctors are here. Their absence will add hours to each day.

'Of course, Fazi,' I say. 'You have been more than kind to stay these extra days. Will you still be able to return for a few days at the end of the camp?'

'Yes, as we planned. We will return in ten days when you leave here. We will stay until all of the patients have left the hospital.'

'Fazi, Laya – both of you – your work here has been exceptional. We really appreciate the help you've given us.'

Steph approaches me again. 'Can I see you alone for a minute?' she asks.

We walk over to a corner of the room. 'Ray,' she says, 'I'm a bit worried about Jayne. She seems to be taking this harder than the rest of us.'

I look around the room and realise that Jayne is not here. 'Where is she?'

'I think she's in her room. I didn't follow her upstairs because I think she might need some time alone.'

'You tried talking to her?'

'A few of us did, but she just kept shaking her head and looking down. I'm not sure what to do.'

'Thanks, Steph. We may need to hold off with surgery today after all.'

I climb the stairs to our bedrooms above the Dining Hall, and softly tap on the door to Jayne's room.

'Yes?' Jayne's voice is firm.

'Jayne, it's Ray. Can we talk?'

When I enter, I find Jayne sitting on her bed, hugging her knees. Her red scarf circles her neck several times. She holds its edges to her flushed cheeks.

'I feel like such a fool,' she says.

'I understand why you're upset,' I say, 'but I don't understand why you feel like a fool.'

'I know you said it was okay to cry and that, but the others downstairs seem to be able to push this aside. I just can't get those images out of my head. And the husband – that poor, poor man. He's lost his wife and his only child.'

I sit down on Jayne's bed and allow her to continue talking.

'I've seen death before, Ray. I've lost patients back home – we all have. But I don't understand why this is so much harder. I didn't even know the woman. Or the husband. But this cuts so deep. My heart feels, like, butchered.'

'Do you believe we could have prevented this?' I ask.

'No. I really don't.'

'Jayne, I've doubted myself a few times this morning, but I can also say I honestly believe there is nothing else we could have done to save those two lives. We can only play the hand we are dealt.'

'That's not why I'm upset though, Ray. It's not because I think we stuffed up or anything, I know that. I know she lost too much blood before she got to us. It's just that I keep getting into that poor husband's head. His pain must be, like, devastating.'

I stare at Jayne and give her a soft smile.

'What?' she asks.

'This is one of the things that makes you such a great nurse. You don't just empathise big time with the patients, you empathise with their loved ones, too.'

'Thanks, but this still hurts like hell. The others downstairs have got empathy, too, but they don't carry on like this.'

'We all express our pain in different ways.'

'Yeah, but look at you and Mack. You were both right in the thick of it this morning. You've got empathy, but this stuff just seems to bounce right off you guys. Whereas me – I feel like a feeble little flower. Pathetic.'

I'm about to reply, but Jayne cuts me off.

'My mum was a nurse,' she continues, 'did you know that? And her mum, too. They were great nurses.' She holds her scarf in front of her face now. Some of the thick, woolen threads have begun to unravel. 'They had so much respect from everyone around them. I wanted to be just like them and carry on the tradition. You know, the nursing tradition. I wanted them to be proud of me. But if they were here right now, I reckon they'd be embarrassed with me. They'd say, "For God's sake, Jayne. Just move on, girl. This is just self-pity rubbish."'

'Enough, Jayne,' I say firmly. She looks up with her bloodshot eyes and they lock onto mine in a doleful stare. 'Firstly, let's be clear – this is not self-pity. This is compassion for others, and far from deserving criticism, it needs to be applauded. Secondly, you need to know that I have been anything but the solid rock you seem to envisage. Let me tell you about the horror last couple of hours I've had. I pretty well lost it this morning after I left you. I walked over to the operating theatre to see Arpan's body again, and on the way a thousand thoughts were screaming at me in my head.'

'*You* lost it?' Jayne repeats. '*You*?'

'Despite me telling you guys how important it was to open up with these awful emotions you're feeling – just as you're doing right now, by the way – I chose to ignore my own advice. I found myself standing on a really precarious ice formation as it was collapsing into some deep, freezing waters. If it hadn't been for some quick-thinking local boys, that might have been the end of me. And then, I found myself screaming at the top of my lungs at some crazy Nepalese spirits.'

'You saw spirits?'

'No, I didn't *see* spirits. I just screamed at them a bit.'

'Oo, ahh. You're sicker than I thought, Dr Ray. I think maybe *you* need some help.' It's satisfying at last to see Jayne flash a fleeting smile.

'The point I'm making, Jayne, is that there are lots of ways people respond to tragedies like this morning. I'm not entirely sure why today's events are so much tougher to accept than tragedies at home, but for whatever reason they *are* tougher. But let's put this in perspective – we're a hell of a long way from our close friends and families. And it's only been a few hours since all of this has happened. I'm no expert here, but I'm certain that your reaction – and my reaction – are perfectly normal, reasonable responses for this sort of thing.'

Jayne smiles again. 'Yeah, but I still think you're a bit crazy, Dr Ray.'

'We're probably both a bit crazy. Maybe that's why we get on so well.'

I return Jayne's grin, and we give each other a long, warmhearted hug.

There is a knock at Jayne's door. 'Hello? Jayne? Ray?' Steph walks in as Jayne and I continue our embrace.

'Oh no – you caught us!' Jayne jokes.

'Scandalous!' Steph laughs, 'but we do need a decent prolapse camp romance.'

'Dr Ray was very clever just now, Steph,' Jayne says as we separate. 'He told me how psycho he is, so now I feel positively normal.'

'I'm happy for you, Jayne,' Steph says. She looks across to me, and the smile quickly leaves her face. 'Ray, Puru is downstairs. He wants to see you. Um … he looks angry.'

Confronting Puru

12:55pm, Dining Hall

Downstairs Puru and Nabin are waiting. They're in conversation with Poppy and Louise. I walk up to the group and study Puru's face once more. Is there anger there? Or is his expression more of the stern defiance he's displayed for most of the brief times we've been together?

I take in a big breath and ask Puru if everything is OK.

Puru's response is gruff, and I wait for Nabin's translation. 'You leave bodies during funeral rites. You not speak to me.'

'No,' I reply, 'I did not speak to you during the funeral rites. And I left as a sign of respect to you and your friends. I am sorry if this offended you.'

Puru shakes his head. 'You have no understanding, sir. Everyone is welcome at funeral rite. I am sad because you leave and I do not thank you.' His surly tone and expression remain, but the words are far from angry or churlish.

'I speak to Nabin and I speak to Shaman,' Puru continues. 'They say you people do best you can. We know you fight spirits, best fight possible. But these spirits very strong. And spirits want baby different place to mother. You take baby from mother. When I look at mother I almost not see cut. You people very excellent.' He gives me one more *Namaste*.

I look around to my team who have wandered over to join us. They beam broad smiles, and yet their eyes are moist. I wish Jayne had come downstairs to witness this as well. I'm sure this would help her healing.

193

'It is an absolute pleasure to help you,' I say. 'I wish we could have helped you so much more.' Puru bows his head a few more times. 'You will take the bodies to your village now?'

'Yes. Bodies outside.' Puru points to the Dining Hall door. 'We go now.'

We follow Puru as he walks towards the door. I turn to Steph and ask her to ask Jayne to come down from her room to say goodbye. But before Steph reaches the stairs, Jayne appears.

'Jayne,' Louise says, 'Puru is just about to return to his village with the bodies of his wife and baby. He's been thanking us for all our help.'

Jayne's blank expression has returned. She does not respond to Louise's comment.

Puru opens the door to the bitter cold air. In the courtyard we see several of the crowd who were here earlier today. Two of them carry a stretcher that bears Arpan's shrouded body. Her face remains exposed to the air. I can't see a separate shroud for her baby, and I hope that he remains embraced in his mother's arms.

As Puru is about to walk through the doorway, Jayne reaches out and tugs at his arm. Puru stops, and confronts Jayne. Silently they stare at each other, as if trying to read each other's thoughts.

Jayne's eyes well with tears once again and she bites down on her lower lip. Without speaking she kneels down at Puru's feet. The two continue to stare at each other before Jayne eventually reaches in to her coat pocket to produce a package in a grey plastic bag. She hands the package to Puru who accepts it hesitantly. He opens the bag and pulls out Jayne's bright red woolen scarf.

Tears are now flooding down Jayne's face. She stands again, takes the scarf from Puru, and places it around his neck. Her face is contorted as she bows her head in one final *Namaste*, before she turns and runs towards the stairs.

'No, Jayne!' Steph protests, but Jayne disappears from sight. The rest of the team look too astonished to speak. Louise pushes her palms to her cheeks.

'Her family heirloom,' Louise finally says. 'She's unbelievable.'

Confounded, we watch Puru and his friends leave the courtyard. And as they begin their long walk back to their village, I try to understand the reason for Jayne's extraordinary act. What did she hope to achieve? Give Puru a little extra protection from the cold? But to Jayne, the sentimental value of the scarf would overwhelmingly outweigh any physical benefits to Puru. After this morning's awful events, Jayne was clearly suffering. Giving away her famous scarf will have caused her even more pain.

Why would any sane person add to her own misery? Can one form of pain somehow relieve another? The misery Jayne experienced this morning was out of her control. Now with this new pain, at least she has ownership, and added to that, the sense of some sort of virtue. Human behaviour is a fascinating science.

Jayne's Return

1:15pm, Dining Hall

The team return inside and surround the potbelly stove once more as it continues its valiant battle to warm the room.

'Strange day,' says Mack.

'Understatement of the century,' says Paul.

'Is Jayne going to be okay to scrub this afternoon?' asks Mack.

'I doubt it now, Mack,' I reply. 'Even though this morning she voted to restart the surgery today, it's obvious that she's pretty emotional right now. I don't think it would be fair to put this on her.'

'Do you think we should see if she's alright?' asks Steph.

'I suspect she wants some solitude right now,' I reply, 'But you're probably right. We should at least let her know that we're here if she needs us.'

'I'll go,' Steph says. She leaves us and climbs the stairs to Jayne's room.

'Can we operate today if Jayne's not there?' ask Mack.

'No,' I reply. 'The local scrub nurses aren't trained up enough yet. It would be too risky if we were to develop complications.'

'This is a tricky situation then,' Mack says. 'If Jayne can't work today, we cancel the surgery. Then she'll feel she's let the team down.'

'Exactly my thoughts. And that will make her feel even more miserable. If we do need to cancel, I'll find some other excuse so Jayne doesn't have to feel she's responsible.'

All of a sudden, spontaneous clapping breaks out among the team. Mack and I look up to see that Jayne has returned to the Dining Hall.

Steph follows closely behind her and joins the applause. A few cheers break out from the group and Jayne's face lights up with a sparkling smile.

'Legendary stuff, Piggy,' Paul shouts as the applause in the room continues. Jayne gives out two loud snort noises in response to Paul's quip. It's clear that she's embraced her unflattering nickname.

The team stand and surround Jayne and praise her for her selfless act. Each of the volunteers spills out surprise and admiration that she would give away her cherished red scarf. And as I watch Jayne connect with the group, gone is the heavy weight in her posture. She looks genuinely untroubled, and I marvel at her rapid transformation. When the rumpus among the group eventually settles I take Jayne aside for a chat.

'That really was impressive, Piggy,' I say as we move to a quiet corner of the room. 'You totally surprised me.'

'Honestly, it was no big deal,' Jayne replies.

'Oh, yeah, well now I know you're lying.'

'Okay, it was a moderately big deal,' she says, 'but I'm totally okay with it.'

'Take me through it,' I say.

'Well, you know I was feeling pretty tragic today. Actually, I was burning up inside. And I did like you told me – I kept repeating to myself that we did our best, it wasn't meant to be; we did our best, it wasn't meant to be. But I still just couldn't throw this rotten painful feeling. I felt awful for the mum and her baby, of course I did – who wouldn't? But I felt even worse for the dad, for Puru. I suppose one day he can remarry and have other children and that, but right now he's got a massive hole there. And like, there's nothing that can fill that.

'It just seemed so wrong, Ray. We've got so much, and he's got so little. I felt guilty. Yep, that's it – I felt guilty. Puru has lost something that's so important to him, and I haven't. That's what I thought. And I looked down at my scarf, and I thought about my mum and my grandma, and I imagined them watching me. I wanted to do something that would make them proud of me. And in my mind, when I pictured myself handing the scarf to Puru, I saw them both smile. Warm smiles. Proud smiles.

'And Ray, when I did give that scarf to Puru, it hurt – of course, it hurt – but at the same time it felt really, really good. Don't get me wrong – I'm not into pain and stuff like that, but this felt like *good* pain. Maybe a bit like the pain you'd get if you donated a kidney to someone. I know Puru doesn't really need a scarf like you might need a kidney, but it still felt right. Does that make any sense?'

'Oh, Jayne,' I reply. 'It makes beautiful sense.'

'You don't think I'm crazy?'

'No, Jayne. I don't think you're crazy. I think you're amazing.' I pause. 'Why did you come here? Why did you volunteer on this camp?'

Jayne looks across to the volunteers on the other side of the room, and then back to me. 'For the same reason that we all did – to help people.'

'Yes, but why did you want to help people?'

'You know the reasons why, Ray. Like you, I wanted to give back. I wanted to help with the imbalance in the world.'

'But what makes you *want* to help? What makes you want to redress this imbalance?'

Jayne pauses for a moment. 'I wanted to feel good inside. I wanted to feel like, virtuous.' She gives out a loud sigh. 'Is that wrong?'

'There is absolutely nothing wrong with that,' I say. 'Do you know, I don't believe there is such a thing as true altruism.'

'I don't understand how you can say that,' Jayne frowns in confusion. 'Surely we're all being altruistic. Aid workers in other organisations are altruistic.'

'I don't believe that. The only way you can do something that is truly altruistic is for you to gain nothing for yourself from your action. Let's say you donate to a charity anonymously, so you're the only person in the world who knows you've donated. You'd still feel an inner pleasure, some sort of gratification from your selfless act. Even though it's intangible, you'd still gain something from your kind-hearted deed. I believe we need to acknowledge this feeling of satisfaction when we do something that's generous or humanitarian. I think if we try to hide these warm, rewarding emotions we're deluding ourselves. Here in the backwaters of remote Nepal we get enormous fulfillment from helping all of these women. I reckon that's a very healthy way to be.'

'Yeah,' Jayne says distractedly, 'well, I hadn't really thought of it like that.'

'But it's not always that way,' I continue. 'There are some volunteers who just want to impress their friends and families back home, or to pump up their CVs, or have a little adventure. We do our best to screen out these people from our camps with our interviewing process at home. But we don't always get it right. Some people are very good actors.'

Jayne looks deep in thought. 'Why are you telling me this?' she asks.

'Jayne, we so got it right with you. Your need to help others is so powerful that you go to extremes to get that reward of some gratification inside. I am proud to have you as part of my team.'

Jayne smiles softly. 'I have one more question, Dr Ray.'

'Hit me with it.'

'What time do we start in theatre this afternoon?'

'You're serious? After all of this, you still want to get back to surgery today?'

'You bet. I've never been more ready.'

Sixty-Second Stimulants

7:45pm, Dining Hall

The surgery this afternoon went smoothly. The volunteers were focused and steadfast with their work. If anything, today their resolve seemed even stronger than usual.

Dinner is about to start and I look around the room. All of the volunteers are here, and I'm pleased to see that the conversation has the same gentle, respectful tone of the early afternoon. But I haven't seen Poppy. Perhaps she's not working tonight. How on earth will she cope with the traumatic events of this morning? In the heat of the moment she seemed to deal with the stresses surprisingly well. But now that she's had time to absorb the horror of the today's tragedies, will she remain calm and composed? As soon as it's possible I want to sit down with her and have a long, open debrief.

We complete our meal and after the plates are collected I clink my glass to announce the beginning of tonight's Sixty-Second Summaries. First up is Steph.

'What a strange day,' she says. 'The horrendous events that ... that besieged our morning ... this morning ... *this* morning – God, it seems like so long ago now.' She lowers her gaze. 'Please don't get me wrong when I say this next bit, but as painful as it was, as *hideous* as it was to see this awful crisis unfold here this morning, and to be part of it, well, I'm actually *glad* that I was here to experience the whole thing.'

She looks almost apologetic. 'I hate this pain, but I know it will gradually fade. During my time here, like the rest of us, I've seen some pretty appalling things that the women in this country go through, you know, with their awful prolapses and so on. At home we take so much for granted. But I think maybe today I needed to be shown another horrible thing that so many women here have to suffer. I needed to be reminded of how difficult it is to be a woman in these parts of Nepal.'

Steph sits down, and the rest of the volunteers are silent. It's clear from their faces that they're heavily moved. After a few moments one or two begin to clap, and soon after, warm applause breaks out from the whole team. And as their noise gradually settles, Louise stands to deliver her Summary.

'I want to also say that I am proud to work with this team. I'm proud of the professional way everyone went about their work today. Not just the clinical work, but the way everyone supported each other.' She pauses for a few moments. 'We can't always win. We can't save the world with one camp. We can't save the world with a *hundred* camps. There is so much I want us to do to stop disasters like this morning's ever happening again. But I understand we can only do our best with the resources we have, and sadly our resources are very limited.'

Louise looks at me as she sits down, and I know she's thinking back to our conversation several days ago. There is no way we could support an obstetric arm to our organisation. The costs and the logistics of running of a maternity service would be impossibly crippling.

The applause from the volunteers is stifled. They seem surprised at Louise's delivery, and I'm not sure if this is because of her comments were so brief or because of her uncharacteristic negative tone.

Jayne stands up. 'Well, I think out of everyone here in this room, I'm the one who has struggled most. And I really want to thank every one of you who helped me today. I know it's early days, I know that, but I really do think that what's happened will make me a stronger person.' She takes a couple of deep breaths and continues. 'A few of us have been trying to understand why this hurts so much. Especially because in our hospitals at home, most of us lose patients from time to time. And we usually cope with that okay. Dr. Ray reminded me today that here in Nepal we're a long way from our friends and family, so it's natural that this hits us harder. But I think it's more than just that. I think I'm like every one of you guys here – I've joined this organisation and I've come along to help out on this camp because I wanted to give a bit back. Like Steph just said, we're so privileged where we live; it's like, we've got *so much*. And people who we see each day here have got so little. But this morning, we saw a man lose his wife and his only child. He had so little to start with, and, well suddenly he's got even less.' Jayne is charged; there is more passion and conviction than in any of her previous Summaries.

'So, I thought to myself – I'm rich, he's poor. And after this morning he's even poorer. Things were like, lopsided before; now they're even more out of whack. It just seemed so stupid and unfair. And maybe some of you guys thought *I* was a bit stupid handing over my old scarf. But for me it was a way I could kind of balance things a bit. Just a bit.'

I look around the other volunteers again, and every one of them is beaming proud smiles.

'I know it was only a little thing, and, of course he's still like, destitute. And my heart was sort of screaming in pain before. And I know this will sound silly, but after I gave him something that was really close to me, well, my heart wasn't screaming anymore. Now it's kind of warm in there.'

Even though she smiles, tears stream down Jayne's face as she sits down. All of the volunteers stand and applaud and cheer. Some of them pound their hands on the table to create a thunderous roar. The clamor continues for several minutes before the room finally settles.

It's my turn.

'This is a day that every one of us will remember for the rest of our lives. I think we all learnt some valuable lessons today. I am no different.'

The room is silent.

'I believe there is no better test of character than when you're thrown into a crisis. That's when we see people's true colours. What we saw here earlier today was one of the hardest things you will ever have to face. Every one of you had a role this morning, and every one of you played your part. And even though the outcome was heartbreaking, every one of you should hold your head high. You did yourselves proud, and you did this organisation proud.

'None of us wants to see this morning's events repeated. No one wants to see a mother lose her life, or a baby lose its life. And yet in Nepal, the horrible facts are that a mother dies in this country every four hours. A baby dies every 15 minutes.'

Some of the volunteers look shocked as I say this. It seems they weren't aware of these appalling statistics.

'Louise just expressed her burning desire to stop any more mothers and babies dying, and I know she speaks for all of us. A few days ago, Louise asked me to consider adding another arm to our organisation – she wants us to provide maternal care in Nepal to work at preventing these needless deaths. I waved Louise away because we barely have enough resources to treat all these women with their severe genital prolapse. "Nice sentiment, Lu Lu, but entirely impractical."

'Let me say this now, and let me say it with absolute conviction.' I take a breath and face Louise. 'Lu Lu – you were right. You were absolutely right. We *can't* let this keep happening. Somehow, some way – we *will* create a new arm to our organisation. We will provide pregnancy care in Nepal to do whatever we can to overcome these maternal and perinatal deaths.'

All at once, cheering and whistling and clapping erupt from the floor, and the sudden elation catches me off-guard.

'I don't know exactly how we will do this,' I'm shouting now to be heard, 'and I have no idea how we will fund our Maternal Care arm. But we will do this. With your help, we will do this.'

Heads nod eagerly and volunteers hoot and yell in support.

'The worst thing we could do now is to let the loss of these two lives this morning to amount to nothing. Don't let this happen. Don't waste this. Let's use this atrocious experience to motivate us. When we return home at the end of next week, we need to rally as many people as we can. We're going to need a lot more funding than we currently have, and we need to do whatever we can to raise that. Spread the word; let everyone see your passion. We will raise the funds we need; we will find more volunteers to help us out. We can do this.'

The frenetic noise erupts again, and it's so totally uplifting. It's hard to describe the unbridled energy in the room, the lifting of the spirit, the exaltation. I close my eyes to savour the charge of emotion of this moment. This will get me through. This will get me through the multitude of challenges and setbacks to come. This day, this moment, this extraordinary group of volunteers.

*

Louise stands again and walks over to me. When she reaches my chair I stand up and she gives me her second hefty hug for the day. It's almost as powerful as her first.

The commotion from the volunteers continues while Mack, who sits to my left, shakes my hand firmly. 'I'm with you all the way on this,' he shouts.

The noise finally subsides and Norman wanders over to join our end of the table. 'You know, Ray – I enjoyed our Summaries tonight more than any other night on the camp. I felt so inspired by what people were saying. After the crisis this morning, this was exactly what we needed.'

'Great to hear you say that, Norman,' I reply. 'It's my firm belief that everything happens for a reason. And I feel something good will result from this.'

'Ray,' Norman continues, 'do you know the Chinese word for *crisis*?'

'Ahh – no, Norman, I don't. I'm struggling enough with Nepali right now.'

'I don't know how you actually say the word,' Norman continues, 'but the Chinese use two brush strokes to write the symbol for *crisis*. One brush stroke stands for danger; the other stands for opportunity. I think what you're doing is using the crisis of this morning as an opportunity, and I think that's just brilliant.'

'If I knew that interesting fact before, I would have snuck it into my Summary.'

Norman smiles absently as he lumbers back to his seat.

'Ray?' It's Mack again. 'You must have some idea about how we're going to do this. How do we stop so many mums and their wee babes from dying?'

'Yeah, I've been thinking a lot about this. It really started to play on my mind after I visited Jyoti a few days back. And then of course the dramas this morning made me more determined than ever. There are so many factors that put the mums and babies here at high risk, and they're all intermingled. If we're going to make pregnancies safer, we have to tackle most of these issues.'

'What sort of things, Ray? We can't run a labour ward here. You said this yourself; even if we manage to ramp up our funding, there's no way we could find enough volunteers to manage a labour ward 24/7.'

'No, I know that Mack, but if we can find the right *local* people, they can run the labour ward. Just like we train doctors in prolapse treatment, we can train them to manage major pregnancy complications. We can train them to do caesarean sections. It will take time, but we can do this. And there are midwives in the area; we can train them more, too. You know, we can run workshops in emergency obstetrics so they get back their confidence. I know it won't be easy to organise all of this, but we should start planning this as soon as we can.'

Mack smiles his wonky smile again. 'But you know the women won't come. We talked about the cultural barriers here, and they're so entrenched. You can set up your labour ward, and you can get well-trained staff to run it, but how do you get the women to come?'

'Culture does change, Mack. You know that as well as I do. We shouldn't just sit back and wait for that. We need to find ways to give those changes a prod, push them along a bit. I've got a few ideas that I'm working on. And education is a big part of that.'

'Education, cultural change, training doctors, training midwives – you're not biting off too much are you, Ray?'

'Possibly I am. And I think if we try to tackle the whole country at once we'll be overwhelmed. But I reckon if we just focus on these things in one area of Nepal at a time we'll have a much better chance of winning. Let's get the problem sorted out in this little corner of the world first, and once we've mastered that, we'll use this model to fix the rest of the country.'

Mack smiles again and nods his head slowly. 'And the prolapse problem?'

'Full steam ahead. No slowing down there. Mack, there's so much overlap with the problems of prolapse and maternal health. Poor education, poor general health, patriarchal cultural practices, limited medical resources – all these things contribute to genital prolapse here, but they also cause the high maternal and perinatal mortality. It makes sense to me to attack both problems at once.'

The Man with the Scarred Face

Day #18. 7:00am, Dining Hall

The volunteers are scampering down the stairs to take their places at the breakfast table. Mack takes a seat across from me.

'Morning, Ray,' he says. 'I meant to ask you last night – what's the latest with Gorham and the infection?'

'Morning, Mack. It's bizarre, isn't it? We've got a potential public health disaster, and with all of the dramas of yesterday, I've hardly given it a thought.'

'I think we all had a few very understandable distractions yesterday.'

'We've got Gorham's HIV and hepatitis B tests back, and they're both negative, thank God. Or Lord Shiva, or whoever it is around here who runs the show.'

'It's good news, but I guess she's not necessarily in the clear?'

'No, you're right. There's a window period of 12 weeks. With the kit we use, it can take this long before an infected person will test positive. She and Suntil could still both be infected.'

'And it didn't go so well with Suntil the other day?'

'Not even close to well. I had this brilliant plan to get him tipsy on *Rakshi* so he'd spill the beans about has behaviour in India and agree to being tested. But he didn't bat an eye. He must have had seven or eight cups of Riken's finest, and he seemed more sober than I was – and I only had the single drink.'

'What will you do, Ray? If there is a viral infection there, this could devastate this whole area.'

'Do you know about Voluntary Counselling and Testing Centres?' Mack shakes his head.

'They started in Africa years ago, and now they've been running in quite a few countries. The centres use HIV test kits similar to ours, but the workers don't just test for the presence of HIV – they give really important advice about safe behaviour and prevention. Nepal has a few of these centres scattered around the place, but the closest one to here is a few days' walk.'

'That's not going to help your cause, Ray,' Mack says. 'Your chances of getting Suntil to walk for a few days to undertake a test he doesn't think he needs? What was Liz's phrase? A Himalayan snowball's chance in hell.'

'Yeah. It's all a bit depressing really. I need some more time to think this one through, Mack.'

The other person I have most concern for is Poppy. Thankfully she's here serving us again this morning. She seems her normal busy, carefree self, but we don't get a chance for a decent conversation before we must leave and start our work for the day.

All seven of us are rugged up once again as we begin our morning walk to the hospital. Paul falls in beside me. He skips his feet and adjusts his stride to keep in time with mine. It's as if we're marching together along the hospital path.

'So, how's it going?' he asks.

'Charged up and ready for another big day,' I say.

'Dr Ray,' he says, 'mind if I say something? It's about yesterday.'

'I'm all ears.'

'Well, you know that back home I work with the volunteer bush fire brigade.'

'Yeah, I knew that you were a Firie. Hope you weren't expecting that sort of work over here. We don't get a lot of bushfires in these parts. In fact, I hate to disappoint you, but I don't think there's ever been a bushfire recorded in this part of Nepal.'

'Damn. Well, if one ever sneaks up on us, I'll be there ready to strike it down.'

'So reassuring. I already feel so much safer having you with us, Paul.'

Paul's smile soon falls away and his face tightens to something more serious. 'When we do fight bushfires back home, it gets really tough sometimes.'

'I know a little bit about the work you do, Paul, and I've gotta say, you guys do some pretty amazing things.'

'We lose fights sometimes, too, Dr Ray. I haven't been involved in any fires where people have lost their lives, not yet anyway. But with some of the fires, we've certainly lost properties. And when people lose their home or their farm, it's totally devastating.'

'What happened yesterday reminded you of that?'

'Well, yeah, it did. But not only because there was a massive loss, and there was so much sadness and stuff. When the fire beats us and someone loses a home and that, it really hits us Firies, too. We kind of need to stick up for each other. We need to band together and help each other out, you know, emotionally.'

I look at Paul more closely now. 'You know, I'd never really thought of that. When you see those awful news reports with the footage of the houses destroyed and in ashes, all you really think about is the tragic people who have lost their homes. But those losses must affect you guys, too.'

'Yeah, and girls,' Paul reminds me. 'But there's something else I want to say, Dr Ray, and I couldn't really find the words for this yesterday. It wasn't 'til later when I was lying in bed that it kind of all came to me. When I watched the team in action yesterday, and the way everyone put in and helped each other out – not just during the emergency, but afterwards, too – well it reminded me so much of the 'spirit of the Firies'. That's what we call it back home – the spirit of the Firies. I was really impressed with the team yesterday. I'm proud to be part of this group. Thank you.'

'Wow, Paul. That was awesome. I can't tell you how good that makes me feel to hear you say those things.' I pause for a moment. 'There is one thing I want you to do.'

'Let me guess – you want me to find more coffee?'

'Okay, two things to do. Apart from finding more coffee, tonight I want you to take everything you just said just now and put it in your Sixty-Second Summary.'

'Done deal, boss.'

Norman approaches us. He tries to fall into step, but tangles his feet and trips in the process. He collects himself and says, 'Um … Don't turn around, but I think we're being followed.'

Predictably, despite Norman's advice, Paul and I both turn to look. A lone Nepalese man I don't recognise follows several metres behind us.

'Lots of people use this path,' I say to Norman. 'This guy's travelling in our direction, but what makes you think he's following us?'

'Well I noticed him yesterday as well. When we walked back home from the hospital last night he seemed to be waiting on the side of the path. And then when we walked past him, he came out and followed just behind us. I don't mean to be paranoid or anything, but he kind of looks a bit shady.'

Paul and I look at each other and raise our eyebrows. 'Well, here's a radical plan,' I say. 'Why don't we ask him what he wants?'

'Brilliant,' Paul says. 'No wonder you're the boss.'

We turn around and walk back towards the Nepalese man. As we approach him, he stops walking and looks down at his feet. I wonder if this may be another Shaman who wishes to perform one of those weird bellowing blessings. As we come closer, we see that the man's face is horribly distorted from multiple jagged scars. The craggy skin surrounding each of the grisly defects is an angry shade of pink. The scars look longstanding, and it's clear that this pitiful man must have suffered enormously for a number of years.

'*Namaste*,' Paul says.

The scarred man raises his head uneasily, and in a soft voice replies, '*Namaste*.'

'Do you speak English?' I ask.

As the man's eyes lock onto mine I try to read his expression. There is distress in there. Perhaps even torment. He brings his palms together and responds with a single word. '*Aushadhi*.'

Paul and Norman and I all look at each other.

'Medicine,' Norman says, '*Aushadhi* means *medicine*.'

'How do you know that?' I ask.

'I've been studying a few extra Nepali words. You know, not just the ones Poppy teaches us, but other words, too. I thought maybe they'll come in handy one day.'

'Norman,' I say, 'you continue to amaze me.'

The man continues to stare at us, and simply repeats the word, '*Aushadhi.*' It becomes clear to us that he understands no English at all.

'Do you think he wants us to fix his face?' Paul suggests.

'I hope not,' I reply. 'There's not much we can do there, poor man.'

Even though our day ahead is full, using various simple hand signs we encourage the man to follow us to the hospital. Nabin should be there by now, ready to interpret.

8:30am

'This man say he will die,' says Nabin.

Nabin and I are sitting in the assessment room of the hospital across from the man with the terribly disfigured face. At our request, the man has waited here until we completed this morning's ward round.

'Why are you going to die?' I ask the man.

'My friend, me – we die from infection,' he replies through Nabin. 'I no want this death.'

Suddenly I realise what is going on, and as I grasp the importance of the conversation my heart begins to race. 'Your friend's name is Suntil?'

'Yes, Suntil.' He tilts his head in a look of slight confusion.

'And your name is Badal?'

'Yes.'

'Badal,' I say, 'I promise we will help you as much as we can. If you have an infection we will find you the best medicine – the best *aushadhi* – to fix this. But we can only help you if you answer my questions truthfully and completely. Do you understand?' Enthusiastic nodding from Badal.

'On most of your trips to India, do you pay women for sex?'

A slight pause. 'Yes, is normal go to red-light district. Work very hard in day. Night time is for relax.' There is no obvious shame or embarrassment in Badal's response.

'Are there many different women you have sex with?'

'Not many. Fifteen, twenty in trip. Next trip – different women. Every trip different women come in red light district.'

'And when you return here to Nepal, do you have sex with other women?'

Badal looks downcast now. 'No red-light district here. Women here not good for me. Nobody want Badal with this face.'

It's such a poignant moment. Even though I deplore his reckless sexual exploits, I feel a burning pity for Badal that he believes the only way he can find intimacy is to pay for it.

'Your face was damaged in an accident?'

'Yes. Now four years. Work on roads in India. Hot tar from truck fall onto Badal. Make much pain.' He rolls up his right sleeve to reveal equally hideous scars over most of his forearm.

Working conditions among Nepalese migrant workers in India and a number of other countries are appalling, with widespread exploitation and unsafe workplaces.[93] Every year thousands of these migrant workers suffer severe injury or death from occupational accidents.[94]

'You received compensation? Did you get paid for your accident?'

Badal scoffs. 'No pay. No pay for four months because too sick for work.'

As with the large majority of migrant workers to these areas, there is no work compensation and there are no sickness benefits.[94]

'Badal, do many men from Nepal pay for sex in India?'

'Yes, doctor. Most men go to red-light district once in visit. Some go many time.'

I want Badal to confirm my strong suspicion that Suntil also visits prostitutes, but I fear if I ask Badal this question he may not betray the confidence of his friend. Instead, I decide to give the impression that Suntil has already disclosed his indiscriminate sexual activity.

'And Badal, when Suntil is at the red-light district, do you both see the same women?'

Hesitation now with Badal's response. He runs his fingers through his unruly hair and looks troubled.

'Badal, I cannot help you, I cannot stop your infection if you are not honest with your answers.'

But if I'm being honest with myself here, these intimidating threats to Badal are essentially verging on blackmail. The ethics of my interview are extremely dubious, but right now I'm so desperate to avoid an outbreak of major infectious disease in this area, I justify to myself this dodgy line of attack.

After a long stretch of silence, Badal replies, 'Sometimes we see same woman. One woman with two man – cheaper.'

I fear the response to my next question. 'Do you wear condoms?'

A look of distaste on Badal's scarred face. 'Condom is like put plastic on tongue with eating. No taste food. No good.'

I try to disguise my dismay at these revelations. More than 40% of HIV cases in Nepal occur in seasonal migrant labourers[95]; 26% are wives or partners of HIV-positive men.[96] Among the men in this village we know of at least two who put themselves at high risk of serious STIs, including HIV.

Badal claims he is not sexually active in Nepal, and he is probably being honest. But who knows what Suntil is up to in this area. And on top of all of this, even if we can somehow contain any outbreak of infectious disease in this immediate area, there must be thousands of other villages in Nepal where communities will remain dangerously vulnerable.[97–102]

What can be done about this potential epidemic in Nepal? In particular, how can we prevent the possible scourge of HIV? In most countries throughout the world, the mainstay of HIV prevention and management is Voluntary Counselling and Testing (VCT). VCT has proven to be an effective strategy for the containment of the disease and the care of those suffering with HIV/AIDS. However, in rural and remote areas of Nepal, these services are scarce and their utilisation is poor. Despite the Nepal Government's efforts to improve the provision of VCT services to high risk populations, there are many rural areas where access to VCT remains grossly inadequate. It's clearly unfeasible to set up a VCT service in every village or Health Post within the high-risk regions of Nepal. It would be far more practical to set up at entry and exit points of border regions of Nepal and India.

But more than that, there are other important areas that need to be addressed to improve the poor utilisation of VCT services. There remains a lack of knowledge and awareness of the problem.[103] As in most countries, stigma and discrimination play a major role in the barriers to the uptake of the service.[104] Unsafe sexual practices in migrant workers, both abroad and at home need to be addressed urgently. Prevention programs focused on the general population are ineffective.[105]

Our organisation and our group of volunteers are not formally trained in VCT, and we don't pretend to be qualified HIV counsellors. But here, in an isolated village where at-risk men live, where the nearest VCT centre is a few days walk away, it would be irresponsible not to offer advice and testing.

'Badal,' I continue, 'do you know about HIV?'

Colour drains from Badal's face. It's as if I have told him this is his diagnosis. 'Mumbai Disease,' he says slowly. 'This what I die from?'

HIV is so prevalent in those migrant workers who spend their time in Mumbai, in some parts of Nepal it has taken on the name of the city. Studies show that the prevalence of HIV in seasonal workers from this area of Nepal is up to 8%.[98]

'There is a chance you have HIV. If you wish, we will test you. You need to know that the test is not always correct. If we confirm that you do have the infection we can treat you with medication that will usually control the disease.'

'You stop me die?'

'You may not even have HIV, Badal. But even if you do, with medicines – with *aushadhi* – we can usually contain the disease for many years.'

Colour rapidly returns to Badal's face and it lights up with excitement. 'Doctor, this wonderful! Badal live! Badal live!'

He gives several chaotic *Namastes* to both Nabin and me. I begin to wonder if Nabin's translation of my last sentence was entirely accurate; perhaps Badal has been given a more encouraging outlook than the one I described. Despite this, for the moment I decide to take advantage of his extreme gratitude.

'Badal, there is something else I want you to do for me.'

'Yes, anything, doctor.'

'I want you to speak to your friend, Suntil. I want you to convince him to be tested, too.'

'I see Suntil tomorrow, early.'

'Tell Suntil that I will be in the operating theatre of the hospital in two nights' time, as soon as the sun goes down. I wish to see him there. I will be alone. It is important that you tell him I will be alone.'

The World Health Organisation does not support coercion of HIV testing in any circumstances[106], and yet there is no doubt that right now I am doing just that as I persuade Badal to pressure Suntil into undergoing assessment. I have now lost count of the rules I've broken today.

Poppy's Special Place

Day #20. 7:25am, Dining Hall

Sunday, and at last another rest day. We've all worked for ten days straight now, our longest stretch on this camp. Now that Fazi and Laya have gone, our days are stretched even thinner.

I look around the main table to the weary faces of the volunteers and wonder if I've done the right thing to push them so hard. We want to treat as many women as possible on each camp, but at the same time we need to look after the welfare of each volunteer. There is always a challenge to get this balance right. No one has complained – not to me, at least – but over these last couple of nights the buoyancy of our dinners each evening has lost some of its zeal. The few laughs this morning over breakfast sounded hollow and the conversation seemed listless.

I make a promise to myself that in future camps we'll work no more than seven consecutive days before we have a break. But at the same time, I begin to I wonder if something other than overwork is ailing our tired team.

Most of the volunteers have planned to simply stay in the camp today to rest and chat and read their books. I've decided to meet up with Poppy after breakfast so we can have a long talk. Since the tragic loss of Arpan and her baby a few days ago Poppy has been present at most of our meals. She doesn't seem to be suffering; in our eyes she seems to be her same easygoing self with no obvious signs of distress. But I want to try to understand her more. Why is she so different to other girls? Where did she get this strength of character and intriguing spirit? And is it possible that somehow she could pass this on to embolden other girls in Nepal?

When breakfast is finished, Mack and Jayne and I grab our jackets and head off towards the hospital for our morning ward round. But we hardly need our jackets today; the chill of the past few days has eased. The heavy coat of ice that draped the paths and trees has gone now; the frost has lost its crippling grip. I'm surprised that the vivid greens of the grass and the leaves have returned so quickly. And next to our path the narrow stream flows freely once more.

Mack looks around. 'I thought the winter was here to stay.'

'I guess the *Winter Spirit* guy has changed his mind. For the moment, anyway,' Jayne responds.

'Whoa,' says Mack, '*Winter Spirit*? This culture here really is getting to you, Miss Piggy.'

'It kind of does sweep you up a bit,' says Jayne.

'Actually, Mack,' I say, 'the *Winter Spirit* and I were having a heart-to-heart chat just last night. He said he'd be back really soon. Right now, I'm really glad he's having a little break.'

Mack blows out a breath that rattles his lips. 'Well, all I can say is I'm glad you and Jayne are having your own little break from work today – I think you've both gone a wee bit loopy.'

Jayne and I give each other a playful wink as the three of us continue our stroll to the hospital.

*

There are no outstanding problems on the ward, and after we finish our hospital round we return to the Dining Hall to find Poppy wiping down the tables.

'Hey Poppy,' I say, 'did you remember you and I are going to have a long talk today?'

Poppy pauses her cleaning and smiles. 'Of course, Dr Ray. Do you think I will forget this? I will soon be ready for talk.'

'Would you like to go for a walk while we chat? It's not so cold outside today.'

Poppy looks up to the Dining Hall windows, and then back to me. 'We can walk to my special place. It will take not long to get there.'

Not long, I think to myself. This was the term Milu used to describe our walk to his school. That walk (or the 'trek', as Jayne called it) lasted well over an hour. But today it won't matter if Poppy has the same loose interpretation of the words *not long*. We have most of the day to savour.

When Poppy finishes her morning tasks the two of us head off and join the trail that leads to the local village. It's market day, with more locals than usual walking to and from the village. As usual nearly everyone we pass greets us with a gentle smile and a humble nod of the head. Once again I marvel at the easy grace of these peaceful people.

Today the locals share the trail with trains of toiling pack mules. As is customary for this region, it's largely the women and the mules who carry the supplies on their backs. Most of the men we see sauntering along are unencumbered by any of the grinding loads.

We're stopped by one woman who labours under the weight of two hefty sacks of rice that are tied to her back. She breathes heavily as she chats to Poppy. I recognise this woman from our clinic. Like so many others, she suffers with fairly severe genital prolapse, but her lung disease has made it too hazardous for her to undergo surgery. Instead, a few days ago we inserted a ring pessary in an attempt to hold her pelvic organs at bay. But as I watch this woman strain under the load of rice I fear the pessary won't be strong enough to support her failing tissues.

'Poppy,' I say, 'could you ask this woman if she minds if we discuss her medical problems?'

Poppy talks briefly to the woman in Nepali. As the woman replies she looks across to me and smiles.

'This lady is very happy to talk about her problems, Dr Ray.'

'Thank you, Poppy.' I turn to the lady. '*Kasto Cha?*' I've recently learnt this phrase, which translates to 'How are you?'

Poppy laughs at my attempt at Nepali, but I'm encouraged when the woman responds to my question with another smile and a '*Thik Cha*' (I am fine). Unfortunately, this is the end of my useful Nepali for this conversation. I must rely on Poppy for the more detailed questions to come.

Through Poppy I ask the woman if she's experiencing any pain or other problems.

'Yes, Dr Ray,' Poppy translates. 'This lady still has much pain and urine still comes many times in the day by mistake. Pain is little bit better than before ring is put inside, but when she walks pain is still bad.'

While Poppy describes these most unpleasant symptoms, I study the woman's face. She still smiles despite her obvious discomfort and her continuing shortness of breath. This doesn't make sense to me. Is this some form of stoicism that disguises her more tender emotions? But her smile doesn't seem forced or false; she appears to be genuinely happy. How many others in this country who smile their warm smile each day are in fact hurting inside and out?

'I am sorry we have not made you better,' I say. 'We will come back to this part of your country next year. Perhaps we will have some better treatment for you then.'

But as I say these words, I chastise myself for probably giving this suffering woman false hope. We *will* return to this part of Nepal next year, but in the absence of a larger hospital with more advanced medical equipment we cannot hope to provide the safe prolapse surgery that women like these so desperately need.

'Is it possible for you to avoid carrying these heavy loads?' I hear the futility of my own question, and I know its hopeless answer.

'My family must eat. There is no other way.'

I wonder if I'll ever get used to these peculiar customs that are prejudiced against women and so clearly harmful to their health. Even when women are made aware of the injustice of their mistreatment, they often feel powerless to bring about changes that are needed to eliminate the gender inequity. To have any chance of eliminating these damaging traditional practices these women must somehow be empowered.

*

Before we reach the village, Poppy directs us away from the trail and onto a narrow forest path I've not seen before. As we progress along the path, terraces of crops are gradually replaced by natural greenery.

We begin a gentle descent into a deep, winding gully lined by massive rhododendron trees that soar above us. I stop to admire their beauty. Their ancient limbs are gnarled and knotted and strangely haunting. Dozens of timeless trunks clutch the earth with dogged roots – a stoic army to guide us down our rambling path.

'Poppy, these old trees are beautiful. This is a spectacular trail.'

'Yes, Dr Ray.' Poppy pauses and looks a little troubled. 'But please do not be thinking I am rude. Sometimes it is nice to have no words in beautiful place. If you do not mind, we speak later, but not now?'

Yet again, I'm astounded that a person so young can sprout such wisdom. Poppy is so right. There are times when words cannot do justice to sublime beauty. Sometimes the impotence of words can almost blemish the entrancing sight they attempt to portray.

We walk slowly, and in silence now, through the mystical beauty of the rhododendron forest, stopping frequently to admire the exquisite shapes and silhouettes of the ancient trees. At first the silence between Poppy and me feels uncomfortable, but soon the stillness brings a delightful meditative tone.

Old, fallen branches lay scattered along our path. I pause to pick up one and study its timeworn detail. Slowly I realise where I've seen this before. It was the first time I visited Poppy's father; several of these tangled craggy logs lay in the far corner of Poppy's home.

After several more minutes into our walk the rhododendron forest slowly filters out and our path is flanked by dark green scrub. A series of granite rocks of various shapes and sizes appear, and in silence we follow the narrowing path as it zigzags between the solid blocks. Finally we can walk no further when the path is blocked by dozens of enormous glistening granite boulders. Some are as big as houses.

We stop at the base of the rocky cliff face and I take in the enormity of the striking structures that surround us. I try hard to push aside any technical thoughts that would explain their presence, and to simply appreciate the wonder of the nature before us. But annoyingly my left brain wins this battle, as I explain to myself that these boulders are no doubt the product of major tectonic thrust faults in this geologically unstable region. As I consider these technical thoughts I can't help wondering what the little Milu would make of these masses of solid rock.

'Stones, sir,' would be Milu's earnest response. 'Angry monsters throw these stones in fights.'

The imposing boulders enclose us on three sides, and it's clear to me that the only way out of here is the narrow path that led us in. I assume we've reached the end of the walk.

'This is it, Poppy?' I ask. 'This is your special place?'

Poppy laughs. 'Dr Ray – we are not yet close to special place.'

'I don't understand, Poppy. This is a dead-end. Our path is completely blocked by these massive rocks.'

Poppy smiles and slowly shakes her head. 'Poppy's path to special place is not blocked.' She points out coarse steps that have been carved into some of the boulders, and without hesitation she begins to climb the steep escarpment. She climbs quickly and assuredly.

I shout out to her, 'If I lose you, I will never find my way back to camp.'

Poppy stares down at me with her engrossing eyes. 'But I will not lose *you*, Dr Ray.'

I follow Poppy up the cliff face and over several of the monster stones until we reach flat land on the other side. As we continue our walk among a series of smaller boulders and trees, another trail gradually takes shape. This is less distinct than the earlier trail; the only suggestion of a path is a gentle disturbance in the damp earth. It's clear there are far fewer who come this way.

The woodland thickens again with a rich forest of cedar trees and others I don't recognise. Poppy and I weave between the trunks, often stooping low to avoid the broad sweeping branches. The forest is now so dense that little light reaches us through the heavy canopy above. And although it's late morning, the faint filtered light forges an air of nightfall. As I look down at the leaf mould on the forest floor below me, there is now no obvious path at all, and I wonder, how does Poppy know the direction to follow.

We continue our absorbing journey and eventually I hear ahead of us the faint sounds of rushing water. The light around us gradually brightens and eventually dapples of sunlight begin to pierce the thinning canopy.

'We are close now, Dr Ray,' Poppy says.

I look up to see another cliff face of huge granite boulders that confront us. We walk towards two of the boulders and Poppy points to a narrow fissure that separates them. 'Please go through here,' she says, 'but be very careful. You must not to go too far.'

The towering boulders must be ten metres high and lean ominously towards each other. The gap between them looks ridiculously small.

'Seriously?' To me, the boulders look precariously poised, ready to crush any who enter their dangerous clutch. Reluctantly, and very slowly, I enter the fissure first. The only way I can fit through the narrow gap is by turning my body sideways. Uneasily, I inch my way forward and follow the fissure as it curves slowly to one side.

I can hear Poppy as she follows closely behind. The noise of running water is louder now and the light ahead becomes suddenly bright. I can feel that I've entered a larger space, but I'm blinded by the glare. I stop and close my eyes to allow them to adjust. When I open them, I'm treated to a breathtaking view.

Fifty metres below us, a winding river cuts a giant corridor through a heaving complex of blue-green mountains and hills. And in the distance, the transcendent soaring Himalayas keep vigil in their sacred bright white quilts. I turn back to Poppy, who looks at me and beams her sparkling smile.

We've arrived at a wide granite cave on the edge of the mountain forest. The cave is perched on a rocky ledge, high above the deep river that flows forcefully below. The chamber of the cave is no more than two metres deep with a roof that curves closely above our heads. It's as if one of Milu's giants has carved out a narrow notch with one of his massive fingers.

Poppy and I sit down on the floor of the cave with our backs to the smooth rock wall. We stare ahead in silence and drink in the spellbinding view. The effect of the striking vista and the powerful running water below is hypnotic. In this hidden corner of the treasured wilderness of remote Nepal, it's easy to see why this is Poppy's special place.

After a long time, Poppy finally says, 'Thank you, Dr Ray. Thank you for not saying too many words.'

'I'm so used to talking that I found it difficult to stay quiet,' I reply. 'But I'm so glad you asked for silence. That made it even more special.'

Poppy smiles warmly once more, and we both continue to look out at the captivating scenery before us. After some time Poppy says, 'Dr Ray, when you go walking in your country, what is it like?'

'Well, where I come from it's not like this at all. I live near the beach, and rather than looking at mountains and valleys, we look at water and waves.'

'I have seen beach in book pictures. Many grown people stand on very small boats. It is strange to see.'

I laugh. 'Surfboards! They are surfboards, Poppy. This is a way of having fun.'

'But where do they go on surfboards? What is purpose?'

'I guess the answer is for relaxation and excitement – much like the reason we have walked here today.'

Poppy nods, but her eyes show uncertainty.

'Perhaps one day I can show you,' I say. 'Poppy, how often do you come to your special place here?'

'In past, many times. But now, only few times in a year.'

'Too busy with all your chores?'

'Yes. Most days now very busy.'

'And what do you think about when you come here?'

Poppy takes a long time to answer this question. 'School, friends. But many times, not much thinking at all.'

'Have you been here in the last few days?'

'Only one time, Dr Ray.'

'Do you think about the mother and baby we lost last week?'

'Yes, of course, Dr Ray. It is very sad.'

'Poppy,' I say, 'it is normal to think about this, and to feel sad. You know this, right?'

'I do not know what is normal.'

'Do you have someone you can talk to about what happened?' I ask. 'Your family, your school friends?'

'Not family. Sometime some friends.'

I realise that I should have spoken to Poppy's father about the tragic incident and the intimate role his daughter played in the events that unfolded. I make a mental note to speak to Uttam as soon as I can.

'Do you think you're okay, Poppy? Are you still able to do your schoolwork and your chores the way you want to do them? Do you sleep at night?'

'Yes. This does not change, Dr Ray. Sometime I am sad, but not with tears. And I know this – what spirits bring into life, spirits must always take back. Dr Ray, you try very hard to make spirit wait for mother and baby, but spirit not wait.' She pauses again and continues, 'Also, I feel good to make mother peaceful.'

Hearing these reassuring words from Poppy is so desperately heartening. I'm no post-traumatic counsellor, but in my eyes she is coping very well with the disastrous events of that fateful day. I think Poppy could even teach some of our own team a thing or two about grieving.

'Poppy, with the loss of the mother and baby, please understand that you can talk about this to any of our team, including me. Anytime, anywhere.'

'Thank you, Dr Ray. You can talk to me anytime about this, too.' There is no sarcasm or impudence in Poppy's tone. I'm sure she is genuine in offering her own 12-year old support to our adult grief.

Poppy's Plans

'Do you ever think about your future, Poppy?'

'Sometime, yes, Dr Ray. Sometime I think about when I am grown woman.'

'And what do you see, Poppy? What is Poppy's future?'

I've been eager to ask this question for some time now, but I'm painfully apprehensive about Poppy's response. What if she answers, 'When I grow up, I want to have five children, and be a good wife to my husband'? If this is her answer, I would applaud Poppy having children and being a loving wife, but I would be crushed for her to waste her prodigious talents.

She turns her head to face me. 'Teach,' she says simply.

'What?'

'I want to teach. Be teacher. School teacher.'

'Oh Poppy – that is fantastic!' I shout. My heart races in both excitement and relief. 'I think you will make a brilliant teacher.'

But Poppy's enthusiasm does not match mine. She even looks sad now. 'But is not possible I can be school teacher.'

'This is because you father does not want you to have much more education?' I ask.

'This only part reason,' she says. 'To be teacher, must leave village to learn. Even if father let Poppy go to learn, no one is left to help family.'

I had been thinking that all I had to do to secure Poppy's further education was to convince Uttam that she should be given the same opportunities as her brother, Nerum. Of course, persuading Uttam would be no mean feat, but now I realise there is a crippling financial hurdle as well.

Poppy and I sit in heavy silence as we contemplate the hopelessness of her situation. The cultural and financial barriers to her future are overwhelming. I look out from the edge of our cave to the cliff face that surrounds us, and notice for the first time that more rhododendron trees grow out from the cliff face above. Their roots grow in the narrow crevices between the rocks. Some of the roots emerge from small cracks in the floor of our cave. My eyes follow the contorted roots and trunks as they wind their way around the side of the cave and cling desperately to the giant rock outcrops of the sheer mountain face.

These trees are as old and gnarled as those we passed earlier in our journey, but they are considerably smaller. The solid rock that imprisons the rhododendron roots stifles their growth. And now, as I stare at the twisted, toiling tree trunks, I realise with some sort of forlorn acceptance that these trees will never reach the grandeur of the free-growing magnificent specimens.

And then a thought comes to me – a scholarship. A scholarship for Poppy. Why didn't I think of this before? If some of us could sponsor Poppy's further education, perhaps then we could convince Uttam to allow her to continue her studies. Maybe there is a chance she could achieve her dream. And if this was successful, the flow-on effects to other girls could be enormous.

Should I mention this to Poppy now? Should I tell her that we will pay for her education to secure her future? If I do, there is a danger I may give her false hope. I think for a few minutes about what I will say next. And when the thoughts have formed in my head, I deliberate on whether they will be deemed wise or reckless. And then, I plunge ahead.

'Poppy,' I say, 'do you mind if we talk more about Arpan and her baby?'

'No, Dr Ray. I am happy to talk about them.'

'Okay,' I begin, 'the spirits decided to take this mother and baby. But, Poppy, if Arpan had come to us early in the labour, you know that she and her baby would not have died. You know this, right?'

Poppy looks at me and nods her head slowly.

'And you know there are many other mothers and babies who die in this country because they try to deliver their babies at home where it is often not safe.' I look for signs of pain in Poppy's eyes but still there are none. She simply nods again and says nothing.

'So why do women try to deliver their babies at home where it is not safe? Why do they not come to hospitals like ours, and clinics like Jyoti's to have their babies?'

'It is not the way for people in our country,' Poppy replies.

'No, it is not the way for most women, at least not here, and not in most parts of Nepal. But how do we change that? What can we do, what could you do – so that it *is* the way for women in this country?'

Poppy remains silent at first, and instead looks away again at the distant view. My eyes follow her gaze to the lush forest valleys and the surging river below. The sun is lower in the sky now and the reflected turquoise colours of the water have changed to a vivid golden yellow. After some time, Poppy looks back at me and gives me a glowing, incisive smile.

'Teach them. You want me to teach them.'

I grin proudly. 'Yes, Poppy. Somehow we must make you a teacher. But of course you can't do this alone. There must be others who teach, too. Education for girls in most parts of your country is terrible, you know this, too, don't you?'

'Not many girls go to school after 12 or 13 years,' Poppy says.

'Do you know what the word *inspire* means?' I ask.

'I do not know this.'

'Ah,' I reply, 'You have taught me so many Nepali words, now is my chance to teach you an English word. When you inspire a person, you make them feel like they want to do something. And it's usually something that's valuable or worthwhile. They watch you do something good and this makes them want to do something good themselves.'

Poppy's face lights up. 'I watch Miss Liz teach, and I want to be teacher, too.'

'Yes. Exactly, Poppy. I think that if someone like you became a teacher, you would inspire many other girls to learn. And we need to teach the many thousands of girls and women in Nepal the safe way to have a baby.'

It's a delightful moment to see Poppy's face full of wonder now as she considers her possible future and how important her role could be.

'And the operations we do each day on women, you know why we need to do these, don't you?'

'Yes, Dr Ray. Things fall out. You put things back inside with operations.'

226

'Precisely. And let me tell you why things fall out. Girls in your country have babies when they are very young. They carry very heavy things, even when they're pregnant. The married women go without good food so their husbands can eat well. All these things, and more. I know this is the *way* for people in your country, Poppy, but they are so *wrong* for the women here. People need to be taught this – girls *and* boys need to be taught – so that girls and women can live much healthier lives.'

Poppy gazes once more in the direction of the distant mountains, but she no longer seems to focus on the scenery. Her dark brown eyes, wide now as she contemplates my words. 'You think I can do this?' she says eventually.

'Oh, Poppy, I absolutely think you can do this. I *know* you can do this. You are intelligent, you have drive, and I've watched you in action while you teach all of us foreigners how to speak Nepali. You have a gift, Poppy, and it only seems right that you can use it. The only problem we have is getting you to have further education.'

Poppy grimaces again and the gloom quickly returns to her face. 'But Dr Ray, it is not possible to get much more school. It is not possible to leave village to learn to be teacher.'

'I know that right now this is not possible for you. But I have some ideas to try to make this possible. Poppy, I can't promise that we will get you further education or that you will become a teacher. I can't promise that. But I *can* promise that I will do everything I possibly can to make this happen.'

Poppy looks at me without speaking. A sad smile unfolds on her face. Her eyes are focused now as they begin to swell with silent tears. 'You and your friends from Australia,' she says eventually, 'you are all very kind to Poppy. I promise to you I will be my best possible.'

As Poppy and I sit in her cave in silence once again, other thoughts are bubbling away in my head. It's clear we will never overcome the major problems of gender equity in this country without improving the education standards among women and girls – and probably boys, too. But knowledge alone will not be enough. The cultural traditions of this country are so entrenched they will not change with the mere awareness that they are harmful to women. Women need to be empowered. And while feminist activism is beginning to form in cities like Kathmandu, equal opportunity is unlikely to spill over to rural areas like this, where the large bulk of the Nepalese population live.

As Jyoti pointed out, rural Nepal needs community-based programs, women's groups, and novel public health education. It needs strong local leaders to drive a women's movement. It's so clear to me now that Poppy has the potential to become such a leader. I don't want to lay too much on her plate right now, and so I hold back these thoughts. Now is not the right time; for the moment I will keep these rousing hopes to myself.

Poppy breaks my thoughts. 'There is something else, Dr Ray.'

'Yes, Poppy?'

'Many mothers die here because they have their babies at home?'

'Yes,' I reply. 'They do not see the midwife or a doctor during the pregnancy, and they have their babies at home without proper care.'

Poppy hesitates. 'Dr Ray, I need to know this.' She pauses once more.

I know the question that Poppy will ask now, and I dread its arrival.

'Did my mother die because she delivered me in home?'

'Oh, Poppy. That was so long ago. We don't know if she would have survived or not if she had delivered in a hospital.'

'Yes, but Dr Ray, I know you speak to my father. What is your guess? Do you think maybe she not die if she deliver me in hospital?'

There is anguish in Poppy's face, and she stares at me intensely for an answer. I so want to protect her from any more pain, but it's really important to me that I don't deceive her. I breathe in deeply.

'The honest answer, Poppy, my truthful answer – if your mother delivered you in a hospital that had good equipment and good staff, she would not have died.'

I search Poppy's face once again for signs of distress, but there is no hint of hurt or torment. Instead, this time I see a look of resolve and firm determination. Poppy no longer has the face of an innocent 12-year old girl. She has taken on the presence and poise of a single-minded young woman.

Waiting for Suntil

6:40pm, Operating Theatre

The theatre is empty. I watch the fragile rays of late afternoon sunlight flicker uncertainly through two stark windows – accusing eyes in the aftermath of the failures of the last few days. Inevitably, reluctantly, the autumn rays slowly yield to the seduction of the early evening gloom. But this is no hostile takeover; the darkness bears no duress. Though hesitant and unwilling at first, the light seems now to accept that this is the way of things; this is the natural order.

It's been three days since the deaths of Arpan and her son. In that time, we've completed 20 operations in this room. And I should be content that our team has restored so many lives. But tonight, in the silence and the gloomy light, the theatre takes on the same haunting feeling of the day Arpan's body lay here with her stillborn son. *Do you see us here? Do you both look down on us now? Are you at least somehow grateful for the futile attempts we made so save you both?*

Although I wait in hope for Suntil, I strongly doubt that he'll meet me here tonight. When we spoke at Riken's Teahouse with Nabin as our intermediary, Suntil was so determined to deny his infidelity and his risk-taking behaviour. But is it possible that Badal could have convinced him to now be more truthful with me? I decided to come here alone, without an interpreter. Perhaps at the teahouse the presence of Nabin may have prevented Suntil's openness and honesty in his response to my questions. Alone, he may be more willing to admit to his high-risk behaviour and undertake the HIV test. Maybe.

Just in case Suntil does show for a one-on-one conversation and considers the viral testing, I have with me a copy of our HIV counselling handouts. *HIV Pre-Test Counselling* is an information sheet we give to all women considering surgery to inform them of this preoperative blood test. The handout has Nepali translation of a number of phrases that are essential for informed consent prior to HIV testing. To date, every woman we've tested it this camp has had a negative result.

As well as the counselling handouts, I have at my disposal the Nepali translation of a number of other important phrases that Poppy taught me earlier today. On our way back from her special place, at my request Poppy was kind enough to translate several expressions that may come in handy – if not tonight, then at least with other patients in times to come. Once we finished our walk this afternoon and returned to the Dining Hall, Poppy was also sensible enough to write down the phrases for me; she knew that within minutes I would have forgotten almost all of them. It's strange to think that the person who may require these translated phrases is her own uncle.

As the room dims further I turn on the operating light and aim its beam to the shelves on the opposite side of the theatre. Under the glow of the single floodlit wall, I begin to contemplate the strange series of events that have taken place over the last week. The horrible loss of Arpan and her son; the painstaking postmortem caesarean section; my own unexpected meltdown; the wonderful camaraderie of our team; Jayne's amazing act to give away her famous red scarf; and now, the threat of HIV and other diseases pervading this endearing close-knit community.

Prior to each camp I sit down with all of the volunteers and give them a pep talk about the trip to come.

'This is International Aid,' I tell them. 'Be ready for unexpected events. I know it's cliché, but expect the unexpected, and try your best to go with the flow. Often there are last minute changes to well-laid plans, situations we weren't anticipating, conditions we weren't expecting to treat.' But even I was not ready for the extraordinary challenges of this past week.

I look across to the dwindling stock on the theatre shelves. We're really low on a number of medical supplies now, particularly swabs, sponges, and IV fluids. We've used quite a deal more of these supplies than we'd anticipated. Paul has ordered replacement stock, but it's unlikely this will arrive anytime soon. We still have another five operating days to go here, and I begin to wonder whether we'll be able to continue our surgery for all of this time.

I look down at my watch. It's been more than 30 minutes since the sun has set. I've almost completely given up hope of Suntil now. I'm wondering if I should leave when I hear noises in the next room. Footsteps, and then a male voice.

'Doctor?'

My heart leaps. But it is not Suntil who walks through the door. It is Badal.

Badal shrugs his shoulders and throws out his open hands in front of him. 'No Suntil. No Suntil.'

I'm disappointed that Suntil has not turned up, but I'm also surprised that Badal has made the effort to come here to tell me this. No doubt he feels that he's let me down. It's possible he that now thinks we will not treat him. With my very limited Nepali I try to reassure him. '*Thika cha* – It's okay. It's okay.' I do my best to give an encouraging smile.

'*Aushadhi?*' he asks with eyes full of hope.

'Yes. *Aushadhi* – medicine' I assure him. Badal's HIV test results came through this afternoon. He will be very relieved to learn that his results are negative. He still has a very high risk of harbouring a bacterial STI, and it will be sensible for him to receive a course of empirical antibiotics.

It was not my intention to give Badal's test results to him tonight. My plan was to contact him tomorrow to give him the good news, plus the post-test counselling in the presence of an interpreter. But it seems too cruel to withhold his test results any longer.

I pick up an *HIV Post-Test Counselling* handout with its Nepali translations, and point to the sections that apply to Badal:

Your tests show that you do NOT have HIV.

I wait for this information to sink in. Badal looks at the handout, and then up at me, then back to the handout, then back to me once more. A look of radiant joy spreads over his scarred face.

'Doctor! Doctor! Doctor!' he screams again and again. He grabs both my hands and falls to his knees in front of me. He tosses his head from side to side and repeats, 'Doctor! Doctor!'

You would think I'd just saved his life. Even though there is some slightly more sobering information to come, I find it impossible not to break out a big smile myself at Badal's unbridled delight.

Once he calms down, I return to the handout and continue this most basic form of post-test counselling:

If you have had risky behaviour in the last 90 days it is possible that the test is wrong.

If it is possible you have been exposed to HIV in the last 90 days, it is recommended you undergo another test 90 days following that exposure.

If you take part in risky behaviour in the future, you may still contract HIV.

There is no point spending any more time here waiting for Suntil. I move my arm in the direction of the recovery room to indicate to Badal that we should leave, '*Jaaum* – Let's go.'

The huge grin still has not left his face as I grab one of our theatre torches and turn off the operating light. By torchlight we walk through the recovery room towards the small external door. But as we open the door to the blackness outside, we're both startled by the dark figure of a man who looms in the doorway. Badal and I both jump back in fright, and in the confusion my torch falls to the floor.

Slowly, uneasily, I stoop down to pick up the torch and move the light towards the shadowy figure. It illuminates the unmistakable face of Suntil.

*

'Suntil. *Namaste.*' Right now I can think of nothing more to say. I look across to Badal, who appears as shocked as I am to see Suntil.

Suntil does not address me, but instead turns to Badal and begins an aggressive exchange. Badal, who less than a minute ago was euphoric at his good news, is now as enraged as Suntil. Their argument is in Nepali, and I can only guess the meaning of their heated words.

Eventually Badal turns to face me. He joins his hands in the classical prayer position and gives me a gracious *Namaste*. He then walks through the door and disappears down the hospital path. Suntil and I both watch him as he walks away, then turn to face each other. Neither of us speaks, and I wonder how on earth this is going to unfold. Suntil's face is still stormy, but there is also an air of deep contemplation.

Our silence continues until Suntil finally breaks. He says one word. 'Test.'

'Test? You want me to test you?' I'm so relieved I feel like shouting. But I do my best to remain calm and professional; I don't want to do anything that might further unsettle Suntil and to lead him to change his mind. I direct him into the theatre and turn on the operating light once more. We sit next to the table where, in hope, I'd set up the test kit and paperwork. I pick up the sheet of useful phrases that Poppy has translated earlier today.

'It is very sensible that you have come,' I read in Nepali.

There is no response from Suntil.

'This may save your life.'

Still nothing.

'It may also save the life of other people who are close to you.'

Suntil raises an eyebrow at this. At least some sort of response.

I pick up the translated *HIV Pre-Test Counselling* sheet and point to the first question.

Do you understand HIV and how this virus is transmitted?

Suntil takes the handout from me and scans it. He then turns it over and places it face-down on the table. He says firmly, again, 'Test.'

I pick up the handout again, turn it back over and point to the first question, but Suntil snatches it and throws it forcefully to the floor. I consider my next move. I'm determined to find out Suntil's HIV status, but I know that before performing this test, ethically I should give him quite a deal of information and advice. But I'm fairly sure that if I persist with my attempts to give him this information, he may well end up refusing the test altogether.

I leave the handout on the floor and pick up Poppy's sheet of translated phrases. Suddenly, I realise that the words on this sheet are written by Poppy herself. Is it possible Suntil recognises her handwriting? If he does and he's seen this sheet, he may mistakenly believe I have confided in her. This would be disastrous.

233

Hurriedly, I pull the sheet up to my chest. Suntil doesn't seem to have noticed the handwriting. I lift the sheet away and bring it towards my face, covering the sides with my hands to prevent any further chance of Suntil identifying the writer. I read the next phrases in Nepali.

'You have my word that I will not tell anyone you have come here for this visit. You have my word that I will not tell anyone of your results to this test.'

Suntil simply nods and holds out his arm. I put on my protective gloves, apply a tourniquet to his arm and collect the blood into a standard pathology tube. The only HIV test kits we have available on our camp are the ELISA‡ assays which will take at least two hours of laboratory work before a result is obtained. We'll need our pathology technician, Suman, to perform the test, and as it's now well into the evening, it will be unreasonable for him begin this until tomorrow morning.

I read from Poppy's sheet again. 'Your result will be available tomorrow.' Another curt nod from Suntil.

'It is important that you now receive some medication.' Suntil stares without expression. 'This will treat other infections you may have developed. There are two tablets and one injection.' A slow nod, and to my pleasant surprise, when I hand Suntil the antibiotic tablets he swallows them without protest. He rolls up his sleeve further to expose his upper arm and surrenders to the sting of the deep, penetrating jab.

Suntil and I sit in silence once again. There are so many things I desperately want to tell this man. I want to tell him that the test we will perform on his blood is not 100% accurate. If it returns as positive tomorrow, we would need to perform a second, confirmatory test. As I tried to indicate to Badal two days ago, I want to tell Suntil that if it does turn out he has HIV, this is no longer a death sentence. With medication he could have a near normal life expectancy. But wait: 'With medication' – how in the world would we get HIV antiretroviral medication here? In this remote area, how could he undergo long-

‡ ELISA, or the Enzyme-Linked Immunosorbent Assay was the first screening test commonly employed for HIV. In more recent years the primary screening test has shifted to the Rapid Diagnostic Test (RDT), particularly in resource-constrained settings. The RDT can be performed on a drop of blood or saliva. This test can provide a highly sensitive result in 15-20 minutes.

term monitoring of his condition? I have no idea how we could tackle this predicament. If it turns out he has the virus, I tell myself that somehow we'll work out a way he can gain access to the continued assessment and drugs.

But there is so much more. I want to tell Suntil that regardless of his test result, he needs to tell Gorham that he is at risk of HIV. He needs to sit down, be honest with her, and let her know that he has almost certainly given her a bacterial STI. He needs to avoid further unprotected sex until his HIV tests are back. And even then, even if his results return as negative, he must still avoid unprotected sex until the test is repeated in several weeks' time.

HIV counselling is challenging at the best of times, but I have so little experience in these techniques; I'm really feeling out of my depth. Making things worse, Suntil refuses to read the counselling handout or show any desire to know more about his risks and the dangers of transfer. There are so many other barriers to getting across this crucial information to Suntil: I can't speak his language, and it appears he does not want to share his secrets with any others, including an interpreter; it's unethical for me to break Gorham's confidence; and if Suntil finds out Gorham has been to see me with an STI, this could be disastrous for her. There have been strong hints of domestic violence, and from what our nurse Mani has said, there is a distinct possibility that this brutality could deepen.

With these disheartening thoughts I stand to leave. As I did with Badal about half an hour earlier, I wave my hand in the direction of the recovery room and say the words, '*Jaaum* – Let's go.' But Suntil does not move.

'*Jaaum, jaaum.*' I repeat.

Suntil remains seated, and now shakes his head.

Okay, I think. *What now?*

Suntil stares at me, stone-faced. 'Gorham,' he says soberly.

Wow. Does he actually have some concern for the welfare of his wife? I desperately hope so. Or, wait – does he think I know she has an infection, and that she's been to see me? I so desperately hope not.

I sit back down next to Suntil and force the best poker face I can muster; I must continue to do everything I can to maintain Gorham's confidence. But how can we continue this 'conversation' without a common language? There are none of Poppy's translated phrases that can help here. Once again Suntil and I sit in silence.

After a few very uncomfortable moments I reach down to the floor and pick up the discarded handout and begin pointing to some of the translated sentences. This time there is no protest from Suntil.

When I point to the last sentence – *If it is possible you have been exposed to HIV in the last 90 days, it is recommended you use condoms or avoid sexual intercourse until the second HIV test results are shown to be negative* – Suntil speaks.

'No. Gorham think bad me.'

It's the first time I've heard Suntil string English words together in some form of sentence, and it takes me by surprise. Has he been holding out on me? And what does he mean? Is he saying that if he begins to use condoms Gorham will suspect him of infidelity? Sadly, this makes sense.

I look at the words on the counselling sheet once again, and with a pen I cross out the Nepali word *kondoma*, which I assume refers to the English word *condoms*, but leave the rest of the sentence untouched.

Suntil looks deep in thought again. After several more awkward moments he says, 'Gorham test?'

I continue my charade that Gorham has not come to see me for treatment.

'Yes, we must test Gorham,' I say, as I pick up Poppy's translation sheet. 'Gorham, test *voli* – test tomorrow.'

Suntil's face is bitter, but he nods and stands. He takes in a deep breath and looks into my eyes. His own eyes are fierce now, and the effect is chilling. In English, he simply says, 'Thank you.'

I release the breath I had no idea I was holding, and beam a huge grin of both relief and delight. This has been a really difficult exchange, and although I greatly fear for the result of Suntil's HIV test, I feel like a big part of the battle has already been won.

There is no *Namaste* from Suntil, nor joining of his palms. He simply turns his back and leaves through the door he entered. Like his brother, Uttam, Suntil is clearly a proud man who is profoundly affected by the powerful patriarchal domination of this part of the world. And I wonder: would I have been any different had I been raised with such a potent cultural sway? If the only exposure in my upbringing was this bigoted gender discrimination, would I be any less sexist? I think the honest answer to that is no – I would probably be no different to these two men.

Even though dealing with Suntil and the outrageous sexism and cultural restrictions has been exasperating at times, tonight I saw at last some encouraging seeds of concern and compassion for his powerless, and most vulnerable wife.

The Scourge of HIV

I am so very late for dinner, but I walk to the Dining Hall slowly as I consider the massive problem of HIV and AIDS. Our issues here in a village in remote Nepal are a miniscule component of what is an overwhelming worldwide pandemic. But once again, it's the developing world that is tortured most.

While there is still no cure for HIV and AIDS, in the last several years there have been massive advances in treatments that have dramatically improved the lives of those infected with HIV. The introduction of combination antiretroviral therapy (ART) has been one of the great public health success stories of the past 40 years. People receiving treatment are living far longer than was thought possible.[107] A 20-year old HIV-positive adult on antiretroviral medication in the USA or Australia has a life expectancy approaching that of the general population.[108,109] Along with these outstanding public health developments, early treatment of HIV can dramatically reduce the odds of passing on the disease to others. And this critical protection persists for years.[110]

Regardless of these great strides made in HIV treatment in the cocoon of our Western world, there are massive inequities in the treatment of HIV and AIDS in developing countries. The vast majority of people living with HIV live in low- and middle-income countries, with two-thirds living in sub-Saharan Africa. At last count, worldwide, over 36 million people currently live with HIV[111], but 30% are unaware they even have the virus.[112]

Here in Nepal there is a concentrated epidemic of HIV among high-risk groups including seasonal migrants and their wives, and female sex workers.[113] Of those registered as living with HIV, only 49% receive treatment.[114] Why such a low proportion, when the disease can be so effectively held at bay?

If Suntil has HIV and does not receive treatment, his immune system will be progressively destroyed. He will eventually develop overwhelming infection and ultimately die a premature, and horribly undignified death. And in the years prior to his death he will risk spreading the infection to any of his sexual partners. What would prevent Suntil from receiving essential life-saving therapy, when the ART medicine and the main HIV monitoring tests are provided free of charge in this country? Tragically, there are a number of reasons why Suntil would probably never undertake treatment.

HIV/AIDS is probably the most stigmatised disease in the world[115] and this social scorn also stains Nepal.[116-18] Suntil's pride almost led to him to avoid even being tested in the first place. Treatment of the disease would require a massive escalation in his commitment. He would require protracted monitoring and contact with multiple health workers over many years. The unrelenting stigma and discrimination that would shadow this long-term treatment would be even more repressive.

Nepal's political instability has resulted in nominal government support for national HIV and AIDS programs.[119] But despite this, the country has made some progress with the control of HIV infection in recent years, with now 67 treatment centers throughout the country. However, these health stations are often great distances from those living in rural and remote areas. Suntil would need to walk for at least three days to reach the nearest ART centre, and he would need to do this on countless occasions for ongoing care. Although ART and the most common maintenance tests are free, he would still need to pay for doctors' consultations and numerous other medical tests, transport, food and lodging. And added to this there are crippling costs of lost income – the opportunity costs – for the six-day round trip. These are major constraints for the majority of HIV sufferers who live in rural and remote Nepal.[119]

If Suntil is infected with HIV, he could easily be the conduit for the disease spreading to this region of Nepal. It's difficult to know whether or not he's having sexual intercourse in this area with anyone other than his wife. Once home, a large proportion of seasonal migrants do have extramarital sex in their villages, and most do not see any reasons for using condoms with village women.[120,121]

And what about Gorham? If Suntil is infected with HIV, what chance does she have of avoiding the disease? Mani told me that despite Gorham's very limited education, she is aware of the risks of contracting HIV with unprotected intercourse. But, like the wives of most seasonal migrants, she is too scared to ask her husband about his potentially risky sexual behaviour while abroad.[120,122] Condoms are readily available and free of charge, but if women in this area of Nepal ask their husbands to use a condom or if they refuse sex, many, like Gorham are physically and verbally abused by their husbands.[9]

If Gorham was to finally conceive, but was infected with HIV, without treatment during her pregnancy the baby is also at high risk of HIV infection. And in neonates, HIV infection progresses even more rapidly than in adults.[123]

In Nepal, females are the fastest growing HIV-infected population, especially in the rural areas.[9] And in the hardest hit countries, girls account for more than 80% of all new HIV infections among adolescents.[124]

Of course, my mind now flashes to Poppy. Oh my God, Poppy. A horrible image of Suntil staggering home with too many *Rakshis* under his belt, to find an adolescent Poppy at home alone. The scene that unfolds in my mind is utterly repulsive. I stop my walk, turn to the bushes beside me, and begin to dry retch.

The way I read it, we have a recipe for a public health disaster here; not just in this immediate community that surrounds us, but also in the multitude of other villages and regions of rural and remote Nepal.

I finally reach the Dining Hall. The warmth and the vibrancy inside the room are a stark contrast to my cold, morose frame of mind.

'There you are, Ray,' Mack says with his distinctive smile. 'We've been concerned for you. You've missed dinner, but we got Poppy to put some aside for you.'

'Sorry, Mack. Had a patient to see. Took longer than I thought.'

Mack's smile suddenly abandons his face. His eyebrows approach each other with concern.

'What's wrong, Mack?'

'Well, when you didn't turn up for dinner we sent Paul looking for you. He checked the hospital, and you weren't there. I don't wish to be rude, Ray, but we know you weren't with a patient.'

I'm cornered here. I've given my word to Suntil that I will not tell anyone he came to see me tonight. 'Mack, you've just gotta trust me on this one. I'm sworn to secrecy.'

Mack nods slowly, but doubt and distrust linger on his face.

Jayne looks across and shouts. 'Hey, you dirty stop-out!'

'Me, dirty?' I reply, 'That's a bit rich coming from you, Miss Pig in Mud.'

'Ooh, got me,' Jayne laughs.

Steph chips in, 'Our surgeon and our main scrub nurse – now they're both up to their necks in mud!' Her smile slowly softens as she turns her head to the side. 'You okay, Ray? You look, kind of … flat.'

'Sorry, Steph. Just a few things on my mind.' I curse myself for being so open-faced with my concerns, and look across the rest of the table, searching for something to change the subject. 'Guys,' I yell, 'I can't believe you all started your dinner without me,' I say with mock indignation. 'You would've only had to wait a couple of hours.'

'We would have waited,' Paul laughs, 'but you're just not that important.' He picks up a small piece of leftover naan bread and throws it in my direction. 'Here you go, Dr Ray. We saved you something.'

I catch the bread awkwardly and begin chewing on it. 'So touching,' I say, with crumbs escaping my mouth, 'I knew you wouldn't let me down.'

Louise comes over. 'Ray, there's someone here to see you.' She points to the other side of the room where a middle-aged man sits in conversation with Norman. 'He's been waiting here for nearly an hour now.'

A Welcome Visitor

I walk over to meet the stranger. Norman addresses me. 'Ray – at last. Let me introduce you to Dipak. He is a doctor who's travelled from eastern Nepal. He's keen to spend some time with us at our camp here.'

As Dipak stands to greet me, I'm immediately struck by the intensity of his eyes. They are crystal blue – an eye colour so scarce among the Nepalese race. He looks to be mid-forties, and the luminous blue eyes light up as he smiles and shakes my hand.

'Hello, Dr Ray. I've heard so much about the work you're doing in Nepal. It's great to meet you.' His English is excellent.

'Dipak, you're most welcome. You've come to do some surgery with us?'

'I'm so sorry,' he looks almost embarrassed as he laughs softly, 'I am not that sort of doctor, I'm afraid. I'm not a medical doctor at all. You see, I am a doctor of Philosophy; I have a PhD.'

'Oh,' says Norman, 'so you're a *real* doctor then.'

Dipak doesn't appear to understand Norman's quip. Neither of us chooses to explain.

'I'm sorry,' I say, 'we've been expecting two medical doctors from Nepal. They were supposed to arrive here two weeks ago. We'd planned to help teach them the surgery we perform at these camps.'

'Yes, I know all about them, Dr Ray. They were to come from my hospital. Their placements fell through. You did not get any message of this?'

'First I've heard,' I reply. 'And it's such a shame, because our organisation's approach is to teach as many local doctors and nurses as we can on these camps. I'm sure you understand – this is the best way to get long-term improvement here.'

'Oh, I completely understand. Sustainability – that is the key. I know it is a late time in your camp, but tomorrow evening there will be one other medical doctor arriving from my hospital. Will it be possible for you to teach him some of your work?'

'Of course. We'll be delighted to help. And we're happy for you to be here, as well. I assume you've come yourself to see how we run these camps?'

'Yes. I have a strong interest in Community Medicine. My PhD was centred on the problems of medical care in the rural areas of my country.'

'You have researched medical care in rural Nepal?' I ask excitedly.

'Yes, sir. This was my thesis.'

I look across to Norman, who grins broadly.

'Dipak,' I say, waving Mack over to join us, 'we have so much to talk about. How long did you say you were staying?'

*

We learn from Dipak that he originally came from a village only about 40km from here. He left the area to study public health at Kathmandu University, and for the past year he's worked in the Department of Community Medicine at Dhulikhel Hospital in eastern Nepal. Dipak's main focus is the supply of doctors in remote areas of the country.

'I suppose it's like most countries,' Mack says, 'hard to get doctors to work in rural regions?'

'Absolutely, Dr Mack,' Dipak says, 'Do you know, in Kathmandu they have one doctor for every 850 people, but in remote areas like this there is one doctor for every 150,000 people. This imbalance is disgraceful, sir.'

By contrast, the doctor to patient ratio in Australia is one for every 300 people.[106] The scarcity of health professionals in rural areas is a problem that plagues most countries of the world, but as usual, the deficiencies are greatest in developing countries like Nepal.[125, 126] Nepal's ratio of doctors to patients is improving, but the proportion of doctors remains the lowest of all the Asian countries.[127]

'Why is it so bad, Dipak?' Mack asks. 'Why are there so few doctors in Nepal?'

'What is your term for this? *Greener pastures*? Nepal has a number of medical schools now, but every year, nearly half of the young doctors leave the country as soon as they graduate.[128] They work in countries where they can earn much higher incomes. And for the doctors who remain in Nepal, the cities like Kathmandu can offer them more money than the rural areas. Most of the doctors who do work in rural areas leave their posts prematurely.'

Norman jumps in. 'In the meantime, the health of the people in these parts of the country really suffers.'

'I'm afraid so.' I follow Dipak's glance to the volunteers across the room. 'May I ask you about the work you are doing at your medical camps, Dr Ray?'

'Yes, of course.'

'You treat the epidemic of genital prolapse we have here in Nepal, I understand that. And you try to teach the Nepalese gynaecology doctors how to manage this problem.'

'Yes, we teach Nepalese specialist gynaecologists, and specialists-in-training, but we're not making major inroads yet.'

'Are there other areas of health you wish to improve in our country?'

'We've identified the main two areas of women's health problems in Nepal – prolapse and pregnancy care. At this camp we've been providing occasional emergency obstetrics, but we plan to do a lot more than that.'

'We had a tragedy here just a few days ago,' Norman says. 'We lost a mother and her baby here in this very room.'

Dipak scans the room again. 'Deaths of mothers and babies are far too common in my country.' He looks troubled. 'May I be open with you Dr Ray?'

'I prefer that you are open, Dipak.'

'The treatments you and your teams are providing at your camps in Nepal – these are extremely valuable to our people. All around Nepal, the word is spreading of the excellent work your teams do to improve the health of many women.' Dipak's powerful blue eyes narrow, ever so slightly, and I know he is about to deliver a blow. 'Dr Ray, despite everything you do, you will never overcome the medical problems in Nepal. Not with the way things are.'

I look across to Norman and Mack. They both stare at Dipak with looks of disbelief. None of us speaks as we absorb the impact of Dipak's crushing words. Eventually I respond. 'We realise that we face some enormous challenges, Dipak, but we are not so fatalistic. Can you explain why you feel so … negative?'

'Dr. Ray, your work is honourable, and I am most pleased you choose to teach Nepalese doctors how to carry on this work when you are gone. But I am sorry I must say to you, most doctors you teach these skills for surgery – nearly all return to the city with these skills to do operations only in city. They do not stay in the rural areas where the surgery is so much needed.'

In previous camps, every one of the doctors we trained to perform prolapse surgery had told us they wished to continue their new surgical skills in rural areas. I was aware of only one of these doctors who changed his mind and returned to Kathmandu. But now we're hearing that in fact only a small minority of the trained doctors have stayed in the rural areas. If this is true, it's devastating news.

'The two doctors from our hospital in Dhulikhel – the ones who were to join you two weeks ago – our administrators stopped them coming when they learned that, after their training here, they were also planning to live and work in Kathmandu.'

'If it's just the money thing,' Mack says, 'can't the Nepali Government simply pay them more to work in the rural areas?'

'It is more difficult than that. There is more for them to do in the cities where they have trained. Over the years of their study they've developed friendships, they often meet their wife or their husband, the schools are better for their children.

'Some of the doctors in Kathmandu say, "the city is so much more exciting place for us. Even if more money came for country work, what is point of having high wage if there is nothing to spend this money on?"'[129]

'It seems so harsh,' I say. 'All this time we've been trying to work out ways of overcoming the genital prolapse problem here, and ways to stop all the mothers and babies dying. Having more competent doctors here is a crucial part of that, but what you're saying is that we have no hope of improving the local doctors' skills, because the few surgeons we do train don't stay here anyway.'

'That is it, I'm afraid. Unless we can overcome the shortage of doctors here the health of the people will remain very poor.'

'But you've studied the literature on medical services in rural Nepal, and you've written a thesis on the subject. You must have some ideas as to how we can overcome this manpower shortage.'

'Yes, I have a number of ideas, and I am not sure you will be happy with them. But if you do not mind, I have been travelling since early morning to get here, and I am very tired right now. Would you mind if we continued our conversation tomorrow?'

'How rude of us. We've been so absorbed in our conversation we hadn't even considered the long day you must have had. You will stay here in the lodge with us?'

'You are very kind, but I have relatives who are not far from here. They have agreed to provide accommodation for me. May I join you for breakfast tomorrow?'

Dipak says his farewells, and we're left to mull over the hopeless predicament of women's health in rural Nepal. Right now, it feels like we're surrounded on all sides with barricades that thwart every one of our attempts to improve the plight of these desperate women.

Binod Arrives

Day #21. 6:30am, Dining Hall

As Steph and I skip downstairs to enter the Dining Hall for breakfast, we're surprised to see another stranger at the main table. He sits alone, staring into the potbelly fire, and appears oblivious to Steph and me, who have stopped at the base of the stairs. We pause here to study the new visitor.

'Okay, Steph. What's your hunch? Who is our latest guest?'

Steph puts her finger and thumb to her chin as she ponders. 'Well, I haven't seen him before. He looks to be Nepalese, 16 or 17 years old – high school age, fairly well groomed. Can't have come too far to be here so early in the morning – I'd say he lives in one of the villages around here. Hmm, but why would he come here? Something to do with his school, I'd say. He's got a notebook with him. Maybe a school project on hospitals or some health topic. Yeah, that's it – he wants to interview us for his school assignment.'

'Wow. Impressive stuff, Sherlock. But I think you're way off. Didn't notice his shoes, did you? He's wearing hiking boots. None of the locals in this area have got boots like that. It's clear that this boy is from the city. Probably Pokhara. I'd say he's from a well-off family there, and he's having a hiking holiday. He's so young and raw – it's probably the first time he's left home. I reckon he's stopped here for a feed before he continues his trek.'

The boy looks up to see us staring at him. He stands immediately and walks towards us. He's surprisingly tall for a Nepali, and for one who probably hasn't completed adolescence. Steph and I walk in his direction and we all meet at the edge of the main table.

'Hello. My name is Binod.' He presses his palms together and bows his head.

'Hello Binod,' I reply. 'This is Dr Steph, and I am Dr Ray. I'm sorry we were staring at you just now, we were trying to guess where you are from. You are from Pokhara? Or another big city in Nepal?'

'No, Dr Ray. I am from village perhaps 20km from here.'

Steph gives me a smug look. 'And you are doing some work for your school? A school project of some sort?'

'School?' Binod repeats. 'No, Dr Steph. I finished medical school nearly two years ago.'

Steph and I look at each other, astonished. 'Medical school? You're a *doctor*?' I ask redundantly.

'Yes, Dr Ray. I am honoured to be here. I have come here to learn pelvic surgery.'

I shake my head and give an embarrassed smile. 'I am so sorry. Please do not be offended. You look so very young, and we were expecting a doctor to join us much later today. You are most welcome.'

Binod smiles. 'There is no need for apologising. There are many people who think I am younger.' His English seems nearly as good as Dipak's. 'I decided to leave earlier yesterday so I can spend more time learning with you. I was told your camp has only has one more week left.'

'Your village is in this district of Nepal?' I ask.

'Yes, but I have been studying for some years in east Nepal – in Dhulikhel Hospital. This is where I leave from last evening.'

Mack and Jayne arrive and join us. 'Morning, guys,' I say. 'This is Dr Binod. He'll be with us for … the rest of the camp?' I look to Binod who nods eagerly. 'Binod decided to come 12 hours early to get in an extra day with us.'

'You're a *doctor*?' Jane asks. 'When did you start medical school? Like, when you were like 12 or something?'

'This is Jayne,' I say, smiling. 'Please don't mind her candid comments. She really does mean well. Jayne will be our scrub nurse for most of the surgical cases. I bet you can't wait to start working with her.'

Binod doesn't appear to understand the gentle sarcasm.

'Welcome to our camp, Binod,' Mack says. 'I will be providing your anaesthetics while you're here. How far through your gynaecology specialty training are you?'

'Ah ... there may be another misunderstanding here. I am not training to be gynaecologist. I am training to be general doctor.'

This totally surprises me. It's not something I've contemplated before – a general doctor who performs pelvic surgery.

'You're keen to learn about the management of genital prolapse?' I ask.

'Yes, sir. Very, very much.'

'You want to be a general doctor who performs surgery for prolapse.'

'Yes, that is correct.' Binod's eyes dart from me, to Mack, and back again.

'Are there other sorts of procedures you wish to learn?'

'Oh yes, Dr Ray. I wish to perform caesarean sections – I have already assisted with several in my hospital in Dhulikhel, appendectomies, perhaps hernia surgery. I wish also to fix broken bones and other trauma cases.' Binod looks at Mack now. 'I even want to give spinal block and other regional anaesthetics so that I may treat many more people. I have much passion for being a General Practice doctor.'

We all fall silent as we comprehend this idea of a general doctor who also performs surgical and anaesthetic procedures. Decades ago, this was the nature of General Practice in Australia and other Western countries. There are pockets of remote areas of these countries where these procedures are still the domain of the general doctor. Why couldn't this be the model for these remote regions of Nepal? There would be many rural areas where the small numbers of patients could not justify having a full-time specialist on hand for most days of the week.

'Not complicated cases,' Binod adds, 'not complicated operations or anaesthetics – of course I will transfer these patients to specialist doctors.'

'Binod,' I ask, 'when you eventually qualify in General Practice, where do you intend to practise?'

'It is my intention to return to this area, sir.'

'We heard last night from your colleague, Dipak, that very few doctors choose to work in remote areas like this. What is it about you then? Why are you planning to work in this isolated part of the world when most of your colleagues won't?'

'Well, largely it is because I am from here. Well, near here. I want to help the people I grow up with. I feel this for a long time now.'

'Are there many doctors like you, Binod?' Steph asks. 'Are there many new doctors who choose to work in remote areas of Nepal?

'No, Dr Steph. Not so many. Most doctors who come to remote area do not stay for long. Government makes it compulsory for new doctors to spend some time in rural areas, but very few stay.'

'Binod,' Mack says, 'may I be so bold as to ask you what it costs to become a doctor in Nepal?'

'It is very expensive to attend medical school. The total fee is approximately 60,000 lakhs.'

'That's a massive fee,' Mack says, clearly surprised. 'That's around $70,000 Australian.'

'I don't mean to be rude,' I say, 'but how do you pay $70,000 when you come from this part of the world?'

'This is not rude question, sir. This amount is very high, but government pays some of this fee as scholarship. For remainder, my family and the community all save to help pay this amount over six years. They are very good to me.'

The more I think about this prospect, the more I begin to warm to the idea. Although it seems Binod is one of only a very small number of Nepalese medical graduates prepared to live and work long term in remote areas of the country, his attitude and his enthusiasm hint that it can be done. Is it possible that a general doctor with minimal gynaecology experience could be trained in pelvic floor surgery and emergency obstetrics procedures to reach a safe level of expertise? If so, it just may be that this is the model that will fit the critical need for trained doctors in these regions. Just like we need to nurture and cultivate precious girls like Poppy to tackle cultural barriers, we need to promote passionate people like Binod to live and work in remote Nepal.[§]

---

§ An MD in General Practice (MDGP) is now a three year Nepalese Graduate program available after passing MBBS.

'I see you have met our recruit.' A voice from behind us now. Dipak has entered the Dining Hall. As he removes his thick coat he says, 'Binod, I did not expect you would arrive here until tonight. You must have travelled through the night.'

'*Namaste*, Dipak. Yes, I hope you do not mind. There are so few days left on this camp, I wanted to see as much as possible.'

Dipak smiles warmly, with the air of a proud father. 'Dr Ray, everybody – good morning. I was planning to introduce you to the idea of generalist training before you met Binod. But I see I am too late. Binod has explained our proposal? A general doctor who performs a wide range of surgeries.'

'It's a novel idea,' I say. 'I gather this is your PhD thesis?'

'Oh, one small part, sir. There are a number of things we can do to attract doctors to these remote parts of Nepal. I did not have the energy last night to put forward the arguments, forgive me. And to be honest, I was a little nervous that you would not be happy with this idea. But you would consider the idea of training doctors other than those specialising in gynaecology surgery?'

I look to Mack, Steph, and Jayne, and then to Binod. Prolapse surgery and caesarean sections can be quite complicated at times. As much as I want Dipak's strategy to be successful, I do have doubts that a general doctor could safely provide this treatment. But it seems right now we have no reasonable options. If we're cautious and we put safeguards in place, I see no reason why we couldn't explore the training of general doctors.

'I believe that we can consider this idea. As you would be aware, surgery is not for everyone; some people don't have the innate practical skills – and this includes some specialist gynaecologists. But I don't believe you have to be a specialist to be competent at certain surgical procedures.' I look back to Mack, Steph, and Jayne. 'Do you guys agree? Is it reasonable to try a different approach here?'

'I think it's elementary, Ray,' Mack answers. 'I think with the right person, if they practise something often enough they can become quite capable and safe.' Steph and Jayne both nod in agreement.

Breakfast arrives as Louise, Paul, and Norman appear at our table. We introduce Binod and explain our plans to cautiously begin training him in pelvic floor surgery. If this is successful, we would consider training other selected general Nepalese doctors.

'But the most crucial thing in all of this,' I say, 'is that the treatment is safe. This is new ground, and every one of us must keep telling ourselves – "first do no harm".'

Poppy arrives at the table and distributes our roti curry. But this morning she doesn't appear to be herself. We've all become so used to her light-hearted, mischievous spirit, but right now she looks troubled. I try to catch her eye, but she doesn't look up from the plates she sets down. Mack also senses the heavy air.

'Our Little One is not quite right today,' he whispers to me.

'I guess this is all catching up with her,' I say. 'I'll speak to her before we start work this morning.' I try to put Poppy's unsettling mood out of mind by returning to the conversation with Dipak. I want to learn more about rural medical care in Nepal.

'So, Dipak,' I say, 'tell us more about your thesis; what else can we do to attract more local doctors to rural Nepal?'

'There are many things. Did you know that a few years ago, the doctor density in Kathmandu was 25 times more than in rural Nepal?[130]. The World Health Organisation says "one of their most complex challenges is to ensure people living in rural and remote locations have access to trained health workers."[131]

'Binod has shown you that when you are raised in a country region, then as a medical graduate you are far more likely to return to live and work there. And there is good research in Nepal to confirm this happens with other doctors who come from country areas. We need many more medical students to be chosen from rural and remote regions, rather than city.

'The medical education in this country must be overhauled. We must meet demands of rural medicine. At the moment, medical students learn about complexities of things like lung transplants – but how many will need these skills when they graduate? Why not teach them how to prevent and treat chronic airways disease? There are so many modern methods to teach. We must change to these[132].

'At the moment, the role models and the heroes of the medical students are the people who taught them, and these are mostly doctors who work in city hospitals. It's no wonder that when they graduate, the new doctors want to stay in the city. We must change to have many *rural* doctors provide teaching, and teach *rural* diseases. These people, these rural doctors can be role models. This will bring new doctors to rural areas, not because it is compulsory, but because these doctors want to come.'[133]

It's inspiring to see Dipak so enthusiastic with his ideas. And they make so much sense. In our own country, rural doctor shortages have been well recognised, too, and our rural doctor training programs have been shown to make a significant improvement[134,135].

'But are there currently enough rural doctors to provide this teaching in the first place?' asks Mack.

Dipak frowns. 'This is big problem for us. Not enough rural doctors, and not enough rural hospitals to teach. I believe if we can have more doctors and hospitals in country area, and change selection and teaching, many more rural doctors will come. I believe this very strongly.'

Dipak's stirring words spin in my head, over and over. And as we all sit in the penetrating silence that follows, I feel some sort of powerful surge. It's a sense that we've just heard something momentous, something pivotal to our dogged efforts to improve women's health in this compelling country.

Poppy's Plight

7:20am

'Is there something I can do, Poppy?'

'No, Dr Ray.'

'You remember that I said you can talk to us anytime about the awful things that happened here in this room.'

Poppy does not reply. She continues to collect the leftovers from this morning's breakfast. The volunteers have left for the hospital with Binod and Dipak, and only Poppy and I remain in the Dining Hall. I sit at the main table as she clears the plates and food from around me. A full minute passes in uncomfortable silence before I speak again.

'It's okay, Poppy. I won't push you to tell me what's bothering you. But if you change your mind, I am here as your friend to listen. I must get to work now.' But as I stand to leave, Poppy finally responds.

'You forget so quickly, Dr Ray.'

'What did I forget, Poppy?'

'I told you I am okay with the death of mother and baby. No problem here.'

'Then what is it that makes your face so sad?'

Poppy stands in front of me and sighs. She draws in a big breath and says, 'Just not much sleeping last night, Dr Ray. Too much fighting in home.'

'You were fighting? With your father?'

'Not me fighting. My uncle fights with my father. All night. Not fighting. Arguing.'

254

'Oh, Poppy, that's terrible for you. You work so hard all day, and you can't even rest at night?' As I try to console Poppy my mind races. Was this argument connected with Suntil's behaviour in India, and his subsequent infection? Is Gorham at further risk? 'Do you know what the argument was about?'

'I am not completely sure. My father shout to my uncle many times, "It is *your* fault. *You* bring this here. You act like Western pig". What does my uncle bring here, Dr Ray? What is it that make my father so angry?'

What do I say to this innocent, fledgling child? What can I tell this young girl who has no idea of the frightful things that are inflicting some of the members of her family? Nothing, of course; I can tell her nothing. Her uncle's sinister secrets remain sheltered by the code of confidentiality; but for once I am glad of the existence of this ethical decree. And I remind myself that today the result of Suntil's HIV test will come through. But if this is positive, the conflicts in Poppy's household will crash to a massive new disastrous dimension.

'Did you feel unsafe, Poppy? Did you or Gorham feel in danger during the arguing last night?'

'Not much. Once Gorham is thrown to ground, but no hurt. I am just sitting in corner with crying.' Poppy's eyes moisten as she continues to stare. 'Why is my father so angry, Dr Ray? Why is he angry with my uncle?'

I look into Poppy's wide-eyed face, and struggle to find something close to an appropriate response. 'Adults are complicated creatures, Poppy. Don't try too hard to understand them. Sometimes we never find reasons for people's behaviour.'

Poppy screws her mouth to suggest she is not happy with my answer. Noisily, she collects the remaining dishes and carries them into the kitchen. I sit back down at the table alone and reflect on the mounting number of stresses that must be gnawing away at this endearing young girl. Recently, I've been so caught up with the challenges in my own precious world that I've hardly given Poppy's conflicts a thought. What torment must she be facing? Each day she works such long hours and struggles to squeeze in a basic school education. She knows that at any time her father is likely to put an end to her school attendance, destroying any hope of a fruitful working career.

And now, as if all of this was not enough for one young person to bear, she has to somehow cope with fierce hostility in her own home. Her own small, crowded, single-roomed home with nowhere to hide.

I feel helpless at Poppy's miserable plight. Every one of us volunteers would love to pick her up and take her away from all of this and the painful burdens that surround her – adopt her if necessary. But this will never be. The very most we could ever possibly do is support her financially and, with the unlikely agreement from Uttam, sponsor her to complete her schooling and tertiary education.

7:45am

I make my way alone along the hospital path and try to clear my cluttered thoughts. The mountain stream that follows the path is full and unsettled today as it thrashes against the rocky outcrops. The water – normally so sparkling and clear – is now the colour of slate. It rushes ahead in torrents of confused rapids and swirls. I look up to the distant snow-capped peaks and try to picture the melting source of the frantic flow.

My team will be waiting for me at the hospital by now, and I know I must get to them soon. But I pause for a few moments in an effort to still my flurried mind. I sit down on a large, flat boulder and watch the rush of the bustling stream.

My eyes follow the watercourse as it snakes its way through the forested foothills and beyond, and I ponder its final course. Wherever this churning flow leads, whatever its final form, the water is clearly impatient with its surging tide.

I'm lost in my rambling thoughts when a voice springs up from behind me.

'*Namaste*, Dr Ray.'

I turn around to see the young face of Nerum.

'Nerum!' I call, '*Namaste!*'

I haven't seen Poppy's brother since my first visit to his family's home nearly two weeks ago. Nerum's eyes seem jaded; their spark of our first meeting is absent today.

'I was not expecting to see you here, Dr Ray.'

'Just taking a few minutes of time-out,' I reply. 'You're not going to school this morning?'

'No, sir. I am too much tired.'

'Nerum, may I ask you about last night in your home?'

Nerum gives a short squint before replying uncertainly. 'Yes?'

'I must tell you, Nerum, I have spoken to Poppy. I know there was some fighting in your home. Can you tell me what you think it was about?'

Nerum takes a long breath before he responds. 'It was just my father and my uncle. It is not rare thing for them to be having strong arguments, sir. My father does not like some things that Suntil does.'

'Do you know why you father was so angry last night?'

It's a long time before Nerum answers. His expression is heavy now. 'Yes, I do. But my father make me promise to keep this secret.'

'Okay. I'm sorry to put you on the spot like that. I won't ask you any other questions about last night.' I try to give a convincing smile. 'May I ask you something else though?'

'Yes, Dr Ray?'

'I want to ask you about girls and women.'

'You have problem with your love life, Dr Ray?'

'Ha!' I laugh. 'No, but thank you. I want to know what you think about girls and women. What role do they have in Nepal?'

Nerum smiles for the first time. 'You mean, should they be only mothers and home keepers?'

'Yes, I guess I do mean that. Do you think they should be able to do more than those traditional things? Should they get the same education as boys and men? Can they have careers and assets?'

Nerum sighs again. 'It is difficult, sir. At Intermediate School nearly all students are boys. Nearly all teachers are men. But some teachers tell us that we must be fair to girls, and we must give them same chance as boys. But they also say we must respect our father and mother. How can I respect my father if I am different to his thinking of girls?'

'Yes,' I say, 'this is difficult, but I do feel it is possible to have a different opinion to someone and still respect them as a person.'

'No, sir. When I tell my father that Poppy should go for more schooling, he is angry and says I do not respect him as father.'

I shake my head slowly. 'And your school friends, Nerum? The boys of your age? What do they think about the role of women in Nepal?'

'Many boys say they are happy for girls to be equal. But Dr Ray – when I watch them with girls, very few have action that shows this.'

Another kick to the guts of gender reform in Nepal. Discrimination against women and girls is so deeply entrenched in the traditions of this country, it seems it will take generations before we see positive change.

'Nerum, when you are married and have a daughter, will you wish her to be educated and have a career? Will you wish her to progress in the same way as a son?'

Nerum looks across to the ancient rocks that surround us before looking back to me. 'Sir – yes – this is my thinking. But if I am to be truthful, I would have fear if I am only man in village who allow his daughter to have this ... this freedom.'

'Thank you, Nerum. I appreciate your honesty. It was a pleasure to speak to you. And now I must get to the hospital to start the day's work.'

'Goodbye, Dr Ray. Please come to visit us at our home again. Perhaps in a few days when the home is more happy.'

I bring my palms together and bow my head to Nerum. I turn to resume my walk to the hospital, and then stop. 'Oh, Nerum. This stream here – where does it flow? Into which river does it run?'

Nerum smiles. 'They do not teach us this at school, Dr Ray. What we learn is this – all flowing water surrenders to a greater force.'

A Student of Surgery

9:45am, Operating Theatre

After a tour of the hospital and the operating theatre, Dipak informs us that he will leave our camp today to attend some meetings in Pokhara. Binod will share accommodation with Dipak's relatives in the village near here. Dipak plans to return to our camp in a few days' time to check on Binod's progress.

As he's about to leave, Dipak look around once more at the primitive facilities in the theatre. He pulls me aside. 'It can't be easy for your team to work in these conditions. You need to know we fully appreciate what you are doing here.'

'It's strange, Dipak, but in a weird sort of way, the limited equipment and supplies kind of add to the fulfillment here. Don't get me wrong – we would totally embrace a lovely modern hospital with up-to-date equipment and supplies. And if we had that we could operate on many more women than we currently do. But as it is right now, it's not all doom and gloom; we do all get a buzz out of these extra challenges.'

After Dipak leaves we decide that it would be best for Binod to simply observe the first prolapse operation of the day. He stands behind my right shoulder during the case, and watches with a keen interest; each time I glance around he appears to be in intense concentration. He asks intelligent, probing questions about the procedure, and about surgery in general.

'Dr Ray, what makes a good surgeon?'

I think about Binod's question for a few moments before I reply. 'I guess we all tend to focus on the technical side of surgery, you know,

259

being adept with your hands, fine motor skills, and so forth. But there is so much more to it than that. It's knowing who needs surgery, and choosing the correct procedure. There is that saying: "a good surgeon knows *how* to operate; a better surgeon knows *when* to operate. The best surgeon knows when *not* to operate."[136]

'I think that sums it up well. There are masses of women here who have terrible genital prolapse, but so many have such poor health it would be too risky to attempt to operate on them.'

'And Dr Ray, these women with poor health – could we do surgery on them in a hospital that had more advanced equipment than the hospital here?'

'Most of them, absolutely. But we have no means of transferring these women to more up-to-date hospitals. For now, all we can do is treat them conservatively with ring pessaries.'

'But the pessaries do not always work, do they?'

'Unfortunately, no. And even when they do manage to hold things up, there is always the risk of long term complications from the pessaries..'

We complete the first operation, and Binod turns to me. 'Dr Ray, I would like to scrub and be assistant with the next operation. Would this be okay?'

I look across to Steph, my usual assistant. 'You're okay with this, Steph?'

Steph grins. 'Oh, I'd be very happy to have Binod step in and take my place. Now that Fazi and Laya have left there are a few things piling up on the ward; it'll give me a chance to sort those out.'

Binod is a good surgical assistant. He provides a clear operating field and quickly learns to anticipate my movements. By the end of the second case together we've developed a synergy that's almost on par with the interaction between Steph and me.

During the first of the cases after lunch I decide to allow Binod to tie some knots. We exchange places and I become his assistant for a few minutes.

'Where did you learn to tie knots like that, Binod?' I ask.

'Goats, sir. And some chickens. I take leftover sutures from hospital and practise on animals, and then we eat them. Very similar to human.

Not eating human, I am so sorry – I mean stitching human.' Binod looks embarrassed as we all chuckle at his unfortunate choice of words.

'Your knots are very secure, Binod,' I say, 'but you need to be gentler with your hands. In this area of the body, the tissues of most patients are delicate. One of the secrets to good surgery is to be kind to the tissues. Too much trauma and they can tear and bleed and lead to breakdown following the surgery, not to mention more postoperative pain. Treat the tissues firmly, but treat them with respect.'

I watch Binod's reaction to my criticism. He simply nods firmly and slowly with a look of resolve. Many students of surgery react poorly to criticism. They make all sorts of excuses for their errors in an effort to protect their fragile pride. But Binod's response is reassuring.

As the afternoon progresses, I allow Binod to perform a little more of the operating. By the end of the day it's clear that he's already begun to understand some of the important surgical principles. He still has a long way to go before he would be competent and safe to operate without supervision, but his comprehension and his basic surgical dexterity are showing really promising signs.

We're removing our gloves and gowns after the final case of the day when Steph returns to the operating theatre. 'Ray, Sunam, the pathology technician is here. He says he has a very important test result for you.'

My heart sinks once again. Last night, to avoid suspicion, I simply placed Suntil's anonymous blood sample among the preoperative patients' samples in the pathology collection area of the Assessment Clinic. I made no mention to Sunam of any 'special test'. In the two weeks of this camp, Sunam has never come to the theatre to give me any specific result. I know what this means.

'Thank you, Steph. Please tell Sunam to wait for me in his lab. I will get changed and meet him there shortly.'

Horrendous News

6:15pm, Sunam's Pathology Lab

Sunam works in a tiny, windowless room next to the assessment clinic. It's still light outside when I arrive. Sunam doesn't appear to notice me walk through his open door. He sits with his back to me, his tattered chair facing a narrow timber bench that's scattered with bottles and tubes, and a messy assortment dog-eared tables and charts. The soiled sink and walls in the corner of the room are stained with splashes of strange grimy fluids. I look around the lab and wonder how Sunam finds the stamina each day to work in these dismal conditions.

'Sunam – you wanted to see me?'

Sunam jumps up quickly and turns to face me. He looks startled. 'Yes, Dr Ray. I am sorry, but now I just doze off.'

'You have a result you wanted to give me?'

'Yes. Not good result. One of patients – HIV positive.'

Even though I expected this grim news, my heart sinks further with the crushing sounds of Sunam's words.

'This is bad result,' Sunam continues. 'I check twice, and do second test to confirm. Is definite positive. You will not operate on this woman?'

Sunam assumes the result is one of our patients we're working up for surgery. He has no idea of the identity of the person with the positive result. In order to protect patient confidentiality, each of the blood samples collected for HIV tests is identified with a number rather than a name. I ask to see the result that Sunam has recorded in his log book.

Patient ID: 300555. HIV Ab: positive.

I recognise the ID immediately as the number I assigned to Suntil's blood sample.

'No, Sunam. We will not operate on this patient.'

I stumble out of Sunam's lab, sick in the stomach at the thought of the news I must now give Suntil. I try to block out the thoughts of all the horrible implications of this devastating result, and walk next door to the Assessment Clinic. Inside, I pick up a copy of the *HIV Post-Test Counselling* handout and look down at the chilling words:

Your test results are positive. This means that you have HIV infection.

I know I must speak to Suntil as soon as possible and hand him this horrifying statement with its Nepali translation. There is no point delaying this confrontation; I decide to leave right away to find him.

In the cold and growing gloom of the impending bitter night it's a miserable walk along the narrow paths towards Suntil's home. After several minutes I come to the shallow stream and its strange, stony altar. Only the faintest of twilight shines through the leaves in the trees above. The colours around me are muted, and the green shrubbery is now almost black.

My eyes drift to the solid surface of the altar that also seems much darker than the last time I was here. On closer inspection I see the stone slab is now stained heavily with dark blood. The murky crimson fluid taints most of the slab and side of the sacred edifice. It seems that an animal has been recently sacrificed.

In the close silence and the darkening shadows I stand and try to picture the slaughter that must have taken place here earlier today. Judging by the blood loss, the sacrificed animal was clearly fairly large. A goat? A pig? To the satisfaction of the onlookers from the village, the terrified animal would have had its throat slit on this sacrificial altar. Did this doomed animal know its fate? Could it smell the blood of the animals that went before it? With the slaying of this ill-fated animal, *Naga*, the local water spirit will somehow be appeased, and in the eyes of these villagers, this sacrifice will protect their community from harm.

*

It's almost dark by the time I reach Suntil's home. I was hoping that I'd find him outside alone, smoking his *bidi*. But the front of the small home is empty. When I knock on the front door and call out, I hear shuffling from inside before the door is opened. Gorham appears, and looks surprised to see me.

'*Namaste*, Gorham,' I say. 'Is Suntil here?'

'*Namaste*,' Gorham whispers. She avoids my eyes as she whispers, 'No.'

'Will he be home soon?'

Gorham shrugs her shoulders and wobbles her head. I'm not sure if she understands my question, so I rephrase. 'Suntil?' I ask as I move my pointed finger in a long arc towards their home. Gorham looks at me now and gives me the same response. I take this now to mean that she has no idea of when he'll return.

And as we stand in silence outside Gorham's home, I wonder if there is anything I can say to her about Suntil's HIV status. I look down to the *HIV Post-Test Counselling* handout that I'm holding, but remind myself that it would be unethical for anyone to learn of Suntil's positive result before he does.

And yet, it's more important than ever that he does not have unprotected intercourse with Gorham – or anyone for that matter. Holding the handout away from Gorham to prevent her seeing its contents, I flick through the pages until I find the section I want. Then, carefully shielding most of this page, I show Gorham the relevant sentence and its Nepali translation:

It is essential that you do not have unprotected intercourse under any circumstances.

This is the advice I gave to Gorham verbally when she first presented to us a few days ago with her bacterial infection. She reads the words of the handout and looks up at me soberly. Does she assume I'm simply repeating this advice to reinforce the risks of her original infection? Or does she now guess the positive results of Suntil's HIV test? I study her face.

Her sad, knowing eyes tell me that she now understands this impossible, perilous situation.

Binod's Bluetooth

Day #22. 10:20am, Operating Theatre

I have to push myself harder than usual this morning to concentrate on the work at hand. I have not been able to find Suntil, despite leaving a message with Poppy last night at dinner for him to contact me. At breakfast this morning, Poppy told me that Suntil did not come home last night at all, and no one knows his whereabouts.

Earlier this morning in the clinic, I spent some time instructing Binod in the art of preoperative assessment. He needs to learn how to choose which patients are suitable for surgery, and, also how to choose the most appropriate form of surgery. Again his grasp of clinical management was really encouraging.

'When we're assessing women with prolapse, Binod,' I said, 'you must be willing to learn not only the surgery that's needed, but also your own limitations. Eventually, when you're operating without supervision, it's crucial you don't get tempted to tackle cases that are too complicated.'

'I understand, sir. I must not make the patients sicker than before they had treatment. If I have doubt, I will not perform surgery.'

We're about to scrub for the first case today when Binod says, 'Dr Ray, you and your team have been very kind to me already, but I wish to ask a special favour.' He looks at me sheepishly.

'Yes, Binod?'

'If you don't mind me to say, it is very quiet here in the operating theatre. Would it be permissible to be playing some music during the surgery?'

I chuckle. 'I'm sure we'd all love some music while we're operating, but sadly, Binod, we didn't think to bring any equipment to play music.'

'It is no problem, sir. I have music in my phone, and, also Bluetooth speakers.'

Mack calls out, 'It will sure beat listening to Ray's voice drone on all day.'

Binod sets up his phone and speakers to play his music. I'm keen to hear the sounds that appeal to modern Nepalese youth. As we start to operate, the theatre fills with the distinctive melodies and the ritual drumming of traditional Nepalese song. The voice-like hum and cry of sarangi strings arrive, and soon they're joined by the haunting tones of a Nepalese vocalist. And as the rich harmonies of Nepalese music begin to echo throughout the theatre, I think to myself that even among the younger generation, the classical musical styles don't seem to have advanced in this country. Right now, we could be listening to a cultural production at the local Village Hall.

Suddenly, mid-track – an aggressive burst of electric guitar. The amplified screams are piercing, and seem grossly out of place. I look across to Mack who contorts his face in confusion. I'm about to speak when, bizarrely, the softer strains of Nepalese song return. Somehow, they manage to meld with the surge of modern guitar. Eventually, the electronic music fades, and the track returns to the traditional Nepalese score. After a few moments the music shifts again, and I'm sure I hear something approaching the soulful sounds of rhythm and blues. The strange music continues with its amalgamation of several musical styles. I shake my head and put down my scalpel and forceps.

'Okay, Binod. What on earth is going on here?'

'Sir?'

'What is this music?'

'Remix, Sir. This is trend in Nepal now. Many studios mix this music.[137] With next track, we will hear jazz and reggae fusion with Nepalese folk song.'

As the curious combination of sounds continue throughout the morning, I slowly begin to appreciate this extraordinary musical style. The shifting backdrop of Western music somehow adds intrigue to each track, and yet, despite the transformation, the traditional Nepalese flavours are sustained.

As we continue to operate to the blended sounds of the remix medleys, I begin to feel a budding surge of optimism for this country. To improve health and equity in Nepal, many elements of the traditions here need to change. But it would be devastating for the Nepalese culture to be quashed, to be swallowed up by our own Western ways. Change is desperately needed here, but like the music, the culture needs to retain its heart. Binod's Bluetooth gives me hope that this may well be possible after all.

Trust and Distrust

Day #23. 7:10am, Dining Hall

'No, Dr Ray. Uncle still not come home.'

It's been two days now since we received Suntil's positive HIV result. I have still been unable to find him. Without warning he appears to have left the village, and no one seems to know his whereabouts.

'Poppy, does Suntil disappear like this very often?'

'He go to India many times, but not at this time of year, not with winter coming. He always tell us before he go away. But this time he does not say anything.'

'Poppy, you must tell me the moment he returns.'

'Yes, Dr Ray. I already promise this.'

I wander over to the main dining table where Dipak has returned from his stay in Pokhara. He's chatting to Louise and Mack and he catches sight of me as I approach.

'Dr Ray, good morning. How's our lad doing?'

'*Namaste*, Dipak. Well, I must be honest with you. Binod means well, and he has a heart of gold. It's really clear that he *wants* to perform surgery, and we've been watching him and operating with him for three days now. But the thing is … well,' I frown and pause for dramatic effect. 'Binod has been superb.'

A sigh of obvious relief from Dipak. 'You had me so worried there for a moment. Binod has been our shining light among the trainees.'

'So cruel, Ray,' says Louise. She turns to Dipak. 'Dr Ray was teasing you just then. Please ignore him when he does that.'

'I'm sorry, Dipak,' I say. 'That was unfair. I must admit though, I was sceptical at first about a general doctor performing this sort of work; I did need some convincing. But from what I've seen, Binod has the makings of a very good surgeon. He still needs a lot more training, but in my opinion he's got all of the important qualities you need to safely perform basic prolapse surgery. And I'm sure he can also be trained in the techniques of caesarean section.'

'You think this model has merit? Generalists performing basic surgery?'

'Binod demonstrates that the system could work. Of course, we've only seen one such generalist – and from what you have just said, he is not your average doctor. But I think that with the right training, the right attitude, and the proper safeguards in place – yes, this model has merit.'

Dipak picks up his cup and looks into the hot tea. He smiles warmly and says, 'This means so much to me. This means so much to this country.'

*

Breakfast is finished and the volunteers are collecting their various bags and papers as they prepare to leave for the hospital.

'Dipak,' I say, 'May I speak to you in private about an important matter?'

'Of course, Dr Ray.'

I ask the volunteers to head off to the hospital to meet Binod and start the ward rounds without me. I explain that I'll catch up with them later in the morning.

Mack is the last of the volunteers to leave, and as he reaches the Dining Hall door he turns and gives me an unnerving look of suspicion before he exits the room.

I turn to Dipak once more. 'Can this conversation be confidential?'

'Yes. What is wrong?'

'You are an authority in Community Medicine, and you specialise in the rural areas of this country.'

'Yes, but please tell me the problem.'

'I have a patient with HIV, and I'm at a loss to know what to do.'

'Your colleagues are not aware of this patient? You must tell them immediately.'

'No, it's not like that. This is not a patient we have treated. This is not a patient we *will* treat. This patient is a man.'

'Oh, I see. A migrant worker, no doubt.'

'Yes. It's the first case we've found in this village, but I'm alarmed that the disease will spread.'

Dipak looks into the fire of the potbelly, and frowns. 'HIV and AIDS are big problems in this part of Nepal. I believe many people in areas like this die from HIV/AIDS without even knowing they have the disease.'

'That's terrible, Dipak, but how would they not even know they've been infected?'

'I am sure you know some of the most common expressions of AIDS – fevers and sweating, muscle wasting, chronic cough, and so forth. All of these symptoms occur in people suffering with other conditions, like malnutrition and tuberculosis and pneumonia. And all of these other conditions are very common in remote Nepal. It is the poverty in this part of the country that brings all of these things together. Poverty leads to malnutrition. Poverty leads to poor health. Poverty leads to these men chasing work in foreign areas where they contract these diseases. And poverty-stricken areas like this have the lowest access to medical help. It is like – how do you say it? The perfect storm.'

'Yes, the perfect storm, precisely. And I have another dark cloud to add to this storm. We have identified the man involved, but we've not been able to find him to give him the grave news. He seems to have left this village. My concern is for his wife, once he returns. Even when he does return and he receives his positive result, I doubt very much that he will notify his wife or any other sexual contacts.'

'You have tested his wife?'

'Yes, and at this stage she is negative. But here is my dilemma, Dipak – without this man's permission, do I have the right to tell her of her husband's disease?'

'Ah – individual rights versus the collective rights. This is a tough question, Dr Ray. As you imply, confidentiality is crucial in doctor-patient relationships; it's essential for sound medical care. However, I believe there are exceptions when it is reasonable to override this principle. But I would stress – these exceptions should be a last resort. It is far better to persuade the patient that he should inform his sexual partner himself. Apart from the muddy ethics of informing contacts without the patient's consent, if confidentiality is broken we risk future patients not coming forward to undertake HIV screening.'

'What do you suggest?'

'This gentleman trusts you?'

'I think so. As much as I can tell.'

'You must do everything you can to track down this man. Find him, give him his terrible result, and do whatever you can to convince him of the importance of telling his partner of his disease.'

'But there is another problem, isn't there, Dipak?'

Dipak looks at me again with his extraordinarily blue eyes. 'Yes. Treatment for the disease.'

'It's true, isn't it,' I say. 'The nearest Voluntary Counselling and Treatment centre is days from here.'

'Yes, this is another big problem. He will need regular trips to VCT centre. Nearest from here is at Indian border – perhaps three days' walk. And as I'm sure you know, he will need regular testing of his CD4 count, to measure his immunity. Currently there only 13 testing centres in this country. Nearly all of these centres are in major urban areas.'

There is a long silence between us now as we both stare into the piercing flames of the fire.

Finally, I speak. 'He's not going to get treatment, is he?'

Dipak looks at me. 'It is most unlikely.'

'And if I don't find him, or he refuses to tell his wife? I really don't know what to do, Dipak. We are only in Nepal for six more days before we must return home.'

'Dr Ray, I am happy to help you if I can. I can contact the Nepal Health Authorities if this is not resolved before you leave here.'

I look across to Dipak now with a new sense of respect. I stand and shake his hand. 'You would do this for me?'

He smiles softly. 'I would do this for Nepal.'

9:15am, Operating Theatre

Mack and I are alone in the anaesthetic bay as he draws up his medications for the first spinal block of the day.

'So, Ray,' Mack says. 'There were problems you needed to sort out with Dipak?'

'Yeah, Mack. Just a few hassles.'

'Nothing you want to share with your team?'

'Oh, Mack, I'm sorry. It's just that I'm sworn to secrecy.'

'It's connected with the issues you had with Suntil?'

'Mack, I really can't say anything. Please just cut me some slack with this.'

Mack puts down the syringe he's holding. 'Ray. You and I are friends. But what I am going to say, I say as a working colleague. We have all been cutting you a lot of slack lately. We are a team here; we work together. You brushed us with the postmortem caesarean thing, and that was a near disaster. Don't brush us again.'

I stare at Mack, my mouth open in disbelief. There is anger in his delivery, and it sounds so out of character. I am lost for words.

The rest of the morning remains strained as we push ahead to complete our cases for the session. The theatre is quieter than usual, and I sense that Jayne and Louise have picked up on the uneasy tension between Mack and me. Binod seems oblivious to the friction in the room.

Eventually, Jayne says, 'You know what's missing here? The stimulating sounds of Binod's Bluetooth.'

'Excellent idea,' Louise replies. 'Binod, would you mind?'

'No, sister. I will be happy for my music to be played.'

Louise connects Binod's speakers to his phone, and once more we hear the lively blends of Nepalese remix.

Binod continues to impress us with his enthusiasm and his grasp of surgical skills. I continue to quiz him on various possible complications. 'What would you do if this artery here was to bleed? ... How would you fix the bladder if it was damaged? ... What if incontinence was this woman's main symptom? ...'

While Binod and I continue our teaching through the morning, Jayne and Louise chat to each other.

'Jayne,' Louise asks, 'tomorrow is your last day here. What's the thing you're most looking forward to when you go home?'

'Oh, that's easy – a long, hot shower. I had no idea I'd miss those suckers so much. What are you looking forward to?'

'Well, I can't wait for a hot shower either, but there's one other thing I've really been looking forward to.'

'A steak and chips? A Big Mac?'

'No, no. I miss all those things, of course. But there's something *here* that I really can't wait to see before we leave. It's Jumari. We're going to operate on her tomorrow, at last. She's been here for two and a half weeks now. Her infection is almost better. It's been so cruel for her with all the horrible time she's had with the prolapse, and her husband abandoning her and everything. When we fix Jumari, this will be my highlight of all the prolapse cases we've done here.'

The Search for Suntil

6:35pm

After we finish our final case for the day I tell the team that I may be late again for dinner. I change out of my theatre gear and head directly to Riken's Teahouse. Perhaps someone there will know of Suntil's whereabouts. Nabin is kind enough to join me again for the visit.

In the dying light of the long surgical day, Nabin and I approach the distinctive mud brick building and pause at the front door.

'Nabin,' I say, 'this is very serious. We need to find Suntil as soon as possible. I want you to ask everyone here if they know where he might be. If they ask why we want to see him, tell them … tell them we have some important work for him.'

'What is real reason for finding Suntil?'

'We really do have some important work for Suntil.'

As Nabin and I enter the teahouse, it's noticeably busier than the first time we were here. Tonight, most of the tables are full. Live music plays, and rowdy conversations compete with the colourful noise. A small group of men sing along to the sounds of a stringed instrument I can't identify. Others smoke *bidis* that add to the room's hazy cloud.

As Nabin and I approach the bar, we're greeted by a cheerful Riken. The deep bass tones of his booming voice soar above the background clamour. He laughs heartily as he looks from Nabin to me. Nabin translates the thundering words.

'Riken say he *knew* you love his *Rakshi*. He say, he knew we will come back for more. Riken *Rakshi* – best in country.'

I force a painful smile and nod slowly to Riken, who laughs again and slaps me firmly on the back. As he wanders away, I lean towards Nabin's ear. 'What would happen if I refuse to drink *Rakshi* tonight?'

'Dr Ray, this not good idea. You make insult if you do not drink Riken *Rakshi*.'

Okay, I say to myself. *Toughen up.*

We sit down at one of the few remaining tables, and Nabin yells, 'Dr Ray. You will make shouting again for *Rakshi*?'

'Yes, Nabin. I will be shouting.'

I scan the crowded room. There must be 25 or more people here. Every single one of them is male, but it's no surprise that Suntil is not amongst them. And sadly, I realise that all of the women will be at home right now, cooking and cleaning for their revelling men.

Nabin stands. 'I will start asking for Suntil now?'

'Thank you, Nabin. Also, ask where he goes when he's not here and when he's not working.'

As Nabin begins to circulate the room, I look up with dread to see Riken returning to our table. He holds three cups and a long jug, no doubt full of his famous, powerful brew. Dramatically, and from a great height he pours the liquid into the three cups, and immediately begins to drink his own. I stare at Riken as I begin to sip my own *Rakshi*, but this time I'm ready for the searing onslaught. I hold his gaze as I swallow the fiery liquor, and do everything in my power to avoid a reflex scowl. Riken grins wildly, and then proceeds to talk in Nepali. His words are animated, and I have no idea what he's saying. I shrug my shoulders and open my palms, but Riken continues to ramble. Without a pause, he refills his cup, and even though I'm only a few sips into my own, he poises to fill my cup, too.

'*Pugyo, dhanyabaad,*' I say. 'Enough, thank you.'

Either my Nepali is still defective, or Riken simply chooses to ignore my remark; he continues his lively banter while he fills my cup once more.

When Riken finally pauses for a breath, I shout to him, 'Suntil? Suntil?' and again open my palms to the ceiling. He pauses for a moment, as if to think. He looks to speak again when mercifully Nabin returns to the table.

'Sorry, Dr Ray,' Nabin says. 'Nobody see Suntil for some days now. Nobody know where he go for other times.' As Nabin sits down, the music breaks between songs, and in the relative quiet he begins to sip his own drink. He and Riken begin a brief conversation. Riken laughs loudly once more and I ask Nabin to translate.

'Riken ask, "Suntil is in trouble with the ladies again?"'

'More like the ladies are in trouble with Suntil,' I murmur.

Nabin and Riken recommence their conversation, and Nabin turns to me once more. 'Riken wish to know what you mean by "ladies in trouble with Suntil".'

I'm surprised that Nabin could hear my muttering over the remainder of the noise in the room. 'Nabin, that was not for translation. I was only thinking out loud.'

Nabin and Riken both look confused.

'Please ignore my comment about the ladies and Suntil. What about Badal? Has Riken seen Badal?'

We learn that Badal has not been to the teahouse for a few days either, but we manage to get the directions to his home from Riken.

'Nabin, we must find Badal now. Will you kindly come with me?'

Riken resumes his babbling and follows us to the door, *Rakshi* jug in hand. It's clear he wants us to stay longer, but we thank him for his hospitality and his famous *Rakshi*, and step outside into the cold and darkening night.

*

Under the faint white light of my mobile phone, Nabin and I follow Riken's directions towards Badal's home. As we edge our way along the empty village paths, I begin to consider the futility of this whole exercise. Even if somehow we do find Suntil tonight, I can't really give him his horrifying test results – not with Nabin here with me. To do this would break Suntil's confidence. In addition to the breach of ethics, I've given Suntil my solemn word that I will not discuss his consultation and his medical condition with anyone. But even if I can eventually get Suntil alone and somehow let him know of his HIV infection, he is so very unlikely to seek treatment in any case.

And all the while, all throughout this covert attempt to track down this miserable man with his destructive disease, the secrecy of this whole affair is causing such damaging distrust among my team. It's so important for the function of our camps that the volunteers have confidence in their leader. But right now, after a number of secret meetings and dodgy disappearances, their trust in me seems to be at an all-time low.

So – what's the point of all this? Why bother? I toss over these demoralising thoughts, and eventually tell myself that the reason I choose to push on with this pursuit is that there is still a possibility Suntil may change his ways. If he learns of his infection, there is a chance – a slender chance – Suntil may practice safe sex with Gorham – and with any other of his sexual partners. There is a chance that we could limit the spread of disease in this region. Despite the slim hope of success, despite the deterioration in trust, this pursuit seems right somehow; it would be wrong to not even try.

As we continue our slow walk, I look across to Nabin. 'Do you feel cold?' I ask.

'No. Not cold. And you, Dr Ray?'

'No. I don't feel the cold either.' And yet, as we speak, the whirls of white vapour escape our mouths to declare the outside chill.

Nabin puts out one hand to stop me and smiles as he rubs his belly with the other. 'I think Riken's *Rakshi* work magic from inside.'

Badal's home is a small mud block building, similar to many others in the village. A stone statue of Shiva sits at the front door, as if to guard the vulnerable souls inside. Nabin knocks and calls out, and Badal's scarred face appears at the door. In the craggy shadows that forge from the light of my phone, his deformities seem even more grotesque.

'*Namaste*, Badal,' I say. 'I am sorry to disturb you. It is very important that we find Suntil. Do you have any idea where he might be?'

Nabin translates, and immediately Badal contorts his damaged face in a glaring stamp of disgust. He spits out his response. 'Suntil no longer friend. No speak since night in theatre.'

'Okay,' I say, 'I understand you are no longer friends, but where are we likely to find him? Where does he go when he's not at home, and he's not at work?'

'I not know. I not care.'

This is getting nowhere. With an infuriating sense of defeat, I thank Badal and tell Nabin that we should call it a night. Badal's door closes with a crash and we turn to leave. As we look up we see the outline of a large man approaching us. The bulky frame reminds me of Riken's.

'Dr Ray! Nabin!' The voice that calls out to us is rich and seems to echo along the narrow path. It *is* Riken.

As he reaches us, I shine my light towards Riken's face. He booms some words in Nepali, and Nabin translates immediately.

'Riken say no need for new fancy light. Best light come from sky.'

Nabin and I both look up to see a near full moon emerging from behind a heavy cloud. How did I miss that? I turn off my phone light as Riken continues to talk through Nabin.

'You want to stop darkness so you can find your way? Sometimes solution is in front of you.'

'Thank you for the advice,' I say. 'But, Riken, why did you come here?'

'Suntil is my friend. He is in trouble, yes?'

'What makes you say this?'

'I see in your face tonight, Dr Ray. I see worried face. Suntil tell me stories before. I know what things happen in India. I know about Mumbai Disease.'

Mumbai Disease – the term is the same in English and Nepali, and as soon as Riken utters these words, Nabin's head jerks back. I look from him and back to Riken, and slowly shake my head.

'Riken, I say, 'if Suntil or anybody had a sickness, I could not tell you of their disease until I had their permission.'

As Nabin translates my latest sentence, Riken gives me a cagey smile.

'We must help Suntil, yes?' Riken says.

'Yes, Suntil needs our help.'

Riken frowns now and stares at me intently. 'Dr Ray, you must tell us what to do.'

'The most important thing is for us to find Suntil as soon as possible. He must see me alone to talk. This is all I can tell you right now.'

'Is very important?'

'It is extremely important.'

Riken looks in the direction of the village path and gives a curt nod.

'Riken,' I say, 'you *do* know where Suntil is, don't you.'

Riken turns his head back to me. 'Yes. Suntil stay with me in my home now.' At last a breakthrough.

'Please persuade Suntil to come to the operating theatre. Tonight, if possible. Can you do that? Tell him I will be there, alone. No interpreter, no Badal, no one else.'

'You do operation on Suntil tonight?'

'No, I will not operate on Suntil. The theatre is a place where we can be alone. But please, do not mention any illness. Do not mention Mumbai Disease or any other disease. Can I have your word on this?'

'Of course, Dr Ray. I give my word – Suntil come tonight.'

*

On our walk back to the Dining Hall, Nabin sounds troubled.

'Dr Ray,' he says, 'Suntil has HIV?'

'Nabin, I cannot answer that question.'

Nabin continues, 'In first time in teahouse, you tell Suntil if he has infection he can die. Now you must see him with urgency. Why you must see him alone? Is not too late for me to come. You need help for translation, Dr Ray.'

'Nabin, that is very kind of you. You have been extremely helpful, and I know you wish to help more. But you must understand – I gave Suntil my word that I would see him alone.'

But as we continue our walk, I consider this next challenge with Suntil. Assuming he turns up to the theatre tonight, I must give him the most dreadful news. And even though I will have with me the translated sheets of the *HIV Post-Test Counselling* handout, what Nabin suggests is correct – without an interpreter present, our communication will be painfully inadequate. Suntil is likely to have so many questions that I'll have no chance of understanding. Yet, he's made it painfully clear that he wants no one else to be present during our 'consultations'. I feel like I've been backed into a corner with a hopelessly implausible task.

We walk in silence for the next few minutes before I speak again. 'Nabin, there is something else you can do. I need you to write down the Nepali translations of a few sentences for me.'

*

8:10pm, Dining Hall

The team are all eating their dinner as I enter the room. My eyes scan the main table and find Mack. He sits between Louise and Steph. Decisively, I approach Mack and stand directly across from him. He looks up from his plate.

'More "patients" to see, Ray?' His tone is sarcastic.

'Yes, Mack. And I haven't finished yet. I have come here to see you guys only briefly. I'll need to leave again now for some really important business. I apologise that I will need to miss dinner again, but what I am about to do is crucial.'

'And let me guess,' Mack says. 'You can't tell us where you're going, or what you're doing.'

'At this stage, no.'

There's an uncomfortable silence, and I realise that the rest of the room is also hushed. There is no eye contact from any of the other volunteers; all seem intently focused on the food before them.

I try to raise my voice to allow all the volunteers to hear. 'I hope that soon I'll be able to explain this whole grueling affair.'

There is no response from any of the team, but as I make my way back to the operating theatre, I hear someone at the table whisper, 'Did he say something about an affair?'

Delivering the News

It's another lonely, wretched walk to the theatre. The building is empty when I arrive. Once inside, I turn on the main operating light, sit down, and contemplate the daunting situation in store. How did this get so crazy? Here we are, in a really remote part of the world, working in a team to improve *women's* health – and yet, somehow I've managed to isolate myself to deal with the medical problems of a *man*. In a few minutes' time I'll be having a secret meeting with this man, who does not speak my language. And I must tell this man he is infected with HIV.

From a public health point of view, it's crucial that Suntil shows up tonight and learns of his infection before any more time is lost. We must do everything humanly possible to limit the spread of this disease. On these grounds, I deeply hope he comes.

But if I'm being honest, a big part of me does not want Suntil to turn up tonight. With all the recent dramas and conflict and misunderstandings, I feel totally drained right now; I don't feel up to this. I'm not sure I have the energy, let alone the counselling qualifications to deliver Suntil's devastating result in the most appropriate way. So much easier to hand this over to the Nepalese Health Authorities and let them deal with it after we've gone.

But as I sit here, trying to think of every conceivable reason why it would be better to avoid this confrontation, I slowly accept that right now, there is no better option; this strategy to tell Suntil myself is the right one. Some sort of thorny bond has developed between Suntil and me, and although I am his reluctant confidante, it's best he hears the shattering news from me.

I look down at the sheets of paper before me and shuffle through each galling page. Among the paperwork are the notes entitled *Delivering a Positive HIV Test Result.* These are the guidelines we collected from a Sexual Health Clinic in Australia. We included these in our medical supplies for the unlikely event that we came across the disease in any of our preoperative patients.

DELIVERING A POSITIVE HIV TEST RESULT

1. *HIV test results should be given in a calm, safe, non-judgmental manner.*
   » Okay.

2. *For patients who are not proficient in English, results should be given through a professional interpreter.*
   » Yeah, right.

3. *If the patient expresses fear about disclosing the result to a partner, it would be best to explore those issues prior to testing.*
   » I have so missed the boat here.

4. *The focus is to provide appropriate emotional support to the patient.*
   » Fat chance of that.

5. *Offer immediate reassurance that HIV does not mean AIDS and is not a death sentence. Tell the patient 'People with HIV who receive the care they need can live long and healthy lives.'*
   » Absolutely. But how on earth does Suntil *get* the care he needs?

6. *Let the patient know that a number of auxiliary and support services exist for people with HIV. Link him or her to a social worker or case manager to assist with health services in your area.*
   » Yeah. As if.

7. *The more active the referral, the better for the patient. Preferably, pick up the phone and make an appointment while the patient waits in the*

office. Ideally you, or another member of your staff can take the patient to the treatment clinic, make introductions, and help the patient get an appointment before he or she leaves.

» Dream on.

8. *Persuade the patient to inform all sexual partners and give him or her instructions on how to prevent further transmission of HIV.*

» And this will be the biggest challenge of all.

I shake my head at the hopelessly inapt guidelines, and rehearse the steps I'll take when Suntil arrives. Keep the tone neutral and direct. 'Your result is positive, Suntil. This means you have HIV.' Point to the translated version of this on the handout. 'No – there is no doubt about the result.' Maintain eye contact. Be firm. Not too much sympathy; not too little. Suntil is often highly strung, and I know from his interaction with Badal he can sometimes be ferocious; be ready for fireworks when the weight of his diagnosis sinks in …

I hear a voice coming from outside and walk to the recovery room door. As I slowly open the door to the night air, I'm both relieved and afraid to see Suntil standing there. Neither of us moves or speaks, and as we both wait there in uncomfortable silence, I'm taken back to the moment a few nights ago when Suntil stood in this same doorway. Badal and I had suddenly confronted Suntil's dark frame, and as a result my heart leapt in fear. Tonight, even though I am expecting him, I can feel my heart racing even faster.

'*Namaste*, Suntil.' I finally say.

A simple nod in reply.

I gesture Suntil inside and close the door. We both sit under the operating theatre light, and I fumble through my papers. Before I can find my place on the HIV handout, Suntil speaks.

'HIV, yes?'

I look into his dark, weary eyes. 'Yes, Suntil. You have HIV.' And to remove any doubt of his understanding, I point to the sentence on the HIV handout. Suntil reads the sinister words.

Your test results are positive. This means that you have HIV infection.

He looks across to the scattered stock on the shelves on the opposite wall. His eyes remain fixed there for some time, until he looks back to me and simply stares.

I try to read his eyes. There is no shock in there, no anger, no fear or sadness … What is in there? Mild bitterness, perhaps. It's as if I had simply said to him, 'Dinner will be an hour late tonight,' or, 'I'm afraid we've just drunk the last of the *Rakshi*.'

Surely Suntil cannot understand the significance of contracting HIV infection here in this remote part of the world.

'I … die?' A simple, heart-wrenching question, still unfettered by any hint of emotion.

'No, Suntil. Not with treatment. Not with *aushadhi*.'

I search my translated pages until I find the sentence I need.

With the right treatment and care, you can live a long and healthy life with HIV.

And then I find an appropriate passages in Nabin's translated pages. *Your treatment will require a great deal of travelling, and many visits to other clinics.*

It is important to start treatment in those clinics as soon as possible.

There is no reaction from Suntil. I point to another translated passage.

Do you trust me?

A short pause. 'Yes, Dr Ray.'

I try to generate as much sincerity as possible in my face before I point to the next sentences.

We cannot cure this disease, but we can keep it under control. The only way we can do this is for you to have treatment.

I search Suntil's face again for a hint to his reaction to all of this, but his expression remains inscrutable. I realise that I'm not going to get a response tonight. But it's still crucial that I explain the dangers of spreading his disease to others.

'Gorham,' I say loudly and firmly to catch Suntil's attention. He flinches, and appears to focus once again. I insert his wife's name on a selection of the translated pages.

[Gorham] NOT have HIV.

If it is possible [Gorham] exposed to HIV in the last 90 days, it is recommended [Gorham] undergo another test 90 days following that exposure.

It is essential that you do not have unprotected intercourse under any circumstances. You must use condoms or avoid intercourse with any person.

And from Nabin's pages:

This is extremely important, [Suntil]. Do you understand?

He gives a sour look now, but nothing more. Unlike last time I advised safe sex practice, at least there is no protest. But I have no idea how likely it is that he'll follow this advice.

We sit in silence for a few more minutes while I allow the magnitude of our discussion to settle. Suntil is very still, and stares at the shelves opposite once again. He must have so many questions building up, but with our language barrier and my limited stock of translated phrases, I doubt I'll be able to provide anything near satisfactory answers. And yet he's made it clear that he doesn't want Nabin or anyone else to be involved with his medical issues. Surely he must be aware that people in the village will learn of his infection. Badal must be highly suspicious, and Nabin and Riken seem to already have guessed. I must try another tact.

Searching through Nabin's translated sheets, I point to another sentence.

Will you trust me to share your results with one other person? He can translate for us.

Suntil spins his head towards me. 'No Nabin.'

What is the problem with Nabin? Clearly there are issues here.

'Okay, not Nabin ... Gamika? What about Gamika?' I'm not even sure if Suntil knows our other translator.

'No woman.'

No, of course. No woman. What about a different doctor – a doctor from another village? What about Dipak? He's not a medical doctor, but I'm not going to even start to explain that. I find the Nepali word for 'trust' on the translated sheets: *bharosa*.

'*Bharosa*, Suntil. *Bharosa* Dr Dipak – I trust Dr Dipak.'

A suspicious stare, and then a classic Nepalese head wobble – the first I've seen from Suntil. Yes? Maybe?

'Tomorrow night,' I say. '*Bholi rati* – here.' I point to the floor. 'Dr Dipak, Dr Ray, Suntil.' I point to him. Finally, I get a sharp, grim nod in response.

*

1:15am

It's no surprise to find the Dining Hall empty by the time I return; all of the other volunteers would have gone up to bed some time ago. It's only marginally warmer in here than outside, but I decide to stay downstairs a little longer. I sit before the dying potbelly embers, and reflect on the past few hours. What sorts of torture must be going through Suntil's head right now? And how will he react to this? Have I really done the right thing pretending to be some sort of counsellor? I have probably overstepped the mark, and if I've bungled this, Suntil may be even more likely to do something inappropriate, and less likely to undertake treatment.

Maybe I should have tried to be less like Superman, and left this HIV counselling to the proper authorities. Just like the dying fire here, my confidence – which at best was modestly warm earlier tonight – is now nothing more than tepid.

Some Priceless Support

Day #24. 7:05am, Dining Hall

'You must have gotten back late last night, Ray,' Louise says. 'I was the last one here to go up to bed. That was after midnight, and you were still weren't back.'

'Yeah, it was a long meeting,' I reply. 'Lu Lu, you know this is important stuff, don't you?'

'Ray, I've worked with you for years now, and of course I trust you. Some of the team are a bit confused, though. I think it would be good if you could tell them what's happening, you know, with you disappearing a lot lately.'

'Thanks, Lu. I really hope I can explain everything soon.'

'No pressure, Ray, but you know that most of the team will be leaving tomorrow.'

I look around the room and take in the rest of the volunteers who chat freely amongst themselves. Tomorrow morning, several of them will begin their long journey back to Kathmandu. They'll stay overnight in the bustling city and try to catch their breath before flying back to their homes in various parts of Australia. Steph and Jayne will only travel as far as Pokhara. There they'll begin their trek though Annapurna Circuit. Louise, Mack, and I will remain at the camp for three more days in case any complications develop in the women who recently underwent surgery.

I walk over and sit next to Binod who has joined us again for breakfast.

'*Namaste*, Dr Ray,' Binod says. 'This is our last day of surgery together.'

'Well, our last together at this camp, Binod, but I feel very strongly that we will work together in the future.'

'I will be very happy to work together again, sir.'

The Dining Hall door opens and Dipak walks in. He removes his hat and coat, and as he approaches, Binod and I stand to greet him.

'*Namaste*, Dipak.'

'*Namaste*, Dr Ray, Binod. Ray, you must be relieved to have reached your final day of operating here.'

'There are mixed feelings,' I reply, 'and relief is certainly one of them. Dipak, let me give you an idea of how Binod has progressed.' I turn to Binod. 'Today, we have five patients who are being prepared for surgery. I want you to assess all of these women this morning without me. Once you've done this, I want you to present each case to our operating team. You'll need to confirm that each woman is fit for surgery, and describe the type of operation she will require. Are you up to this?'

'Yes, sir. Very much up to this. I will go now and commence assessments?'

'Excellent. I will see you in about one hour.'

Dipak grins with palpable pride.

I turn to him, now. 'May I speak to you in private again?'

I ask Poppy to bring out some tea as Dipak and I move away from the other volunteers to one of the smaller side tables.

'You found your HIV man?' Dipak asks.

'We did, last night.'

'And you gave him his results?'

'I did, but I'm not sure I did the right thing. The man speaks very little English and his desire for secrecy was so great that he refused to even have an interpreter present.'

'I see. This would be most difficult.'

'Giving him the positive result was fairly straightforward. It was after that I struggled. I found it so very hard to give him any sort of decent counselling.'

Dipak nods slowly in thought.

'Dipak, let me ask you this: is it possible that what I have done will drive this man to suicide?'

Dipak moves his head to one side. 'Yes. This is possible. Suicide is not a rare response among Nepalese when people learn they have HIV infection.'

I heave an anguished sigh. 'I was hoping for something a little more positive.'

'We do not know the numbers, Dr Ray. Nepal does not have reliable data related to suicide and attempted suicide. Available data are based on police reports or on specific populations, so there is possibility of gross underestimation.'[138]

'Dipak, I am not a trained counsellor in these matters. I fear I have not served this man well.'

'Dr Ray. Forgive me, but you do not think this through. If you did not tell this man of his infection, who would do this? Yes, VCT clinics have counsellors who are trained in these matters, but why would he go to such a clinic in the first place? You told me this man trusts you. The chance of someone in these parts of Nepal travelling to VCT for proper treatment is very slim. But without getting advice from someone he trusts, the chance is zero.'

Dipak makes a very reasonable point. And to be fair, my main motivation in informing Suntil was to prevent him spreading his infection to others. Surely our interaction last night will have had some positive effect on this.

'Dipak, I need to ask you a favour.'

'Yes, if I can help.'

'I do feel strongly about giving this man better counselling than he had last night. And I want to reinforce some of the important information. I think the man has agreed to meet with you and me together for more discussion. Would you be free tonight to help counsel this man further?'

'Dr Ray, I would be delighted.'

8:20am, Preoperative Assessment Clinic

It's so much quieter here today. Only thirty or forty women queue for assessment. After so many days of frenetic clinical checks, it's such a relief to have a much smaller lineup. The word is out that after today's cases there will be no more surgery at this camp. If any of the several women presenting today require an operation they'll have to wait until we return here for our next camp. This will probably not be for 12 months because we've organised our two remaining camps this year to take place in other regions of Nepal.

Louise, Mack, and I walk past the Assessment Clinic and into the ward where Guna, the ward nurse, and Binod wait for us with the patients who have been prepared for today's surgery. The five women sit and lie in various positions on mattresses that will become their postoperative beds later in the day. Binod reads from a clipboard as he runs through his preoperative assessment of each of the women.

'First case: 31-year old with four children. Severe prolapse of uterus and bladder. Main symptoms are pelvic pain and not able to pass urine properly. Surgery is needed, and patient is medically fit. The operation required is a vaginal hysterectomy and bladder repair. Preoperative blood tests are all satisfactory. Patient is consented, fasted, and ready for surgery.'

We follow Binod as he moves around the room and stops before each bed to present the woman's clinical history. Finally, he reaches the woman who will be our last surgical patient for this camp – Jumari.

'Fifth case: 20-year old who has delivered one child – a stillborn. Severe prolapse of uterus, bowel, and bladder. Extensive necrotic infection over prolapsed tissue requiring several days of local cleansing and systemic antibiotics. Main symptoms: pelvic pain and incontinence of bowel and bladder. Infection cleared over first several days, but has recently returned. Due to infection, this patient is not fit for surgery today.'

'*What?*' Louise exclaims in disbelief.

'This patient is *not* fit for surgery today,' Binod repeats, this time with some hesitation.

'You can't be serious!' Louise yells. 'Ray, he can't be serious. If we don't do her surgery today …'

'I know, Lu Lu, I know,' I say as I hold up my hand. 'Let's reassess before we jump to any conclusions.'

Jumari has been steadily improving since the day she arrived here. There were no signs of infection a couple of days ago, and we had almost decided to perform her surgery on that day. Instead I decided we should wait two more days to give her body a little more time to build up some strength.

Binod speaks to Jumari to gain permission for another examination. She shows no modesty as she casually lifts her sari to reveal her extensive prolapse. I reach for a curtain screen on wheels, but none is present.

'Sister,' I say to Guna, 'where are the screens?'

Guna gives a strange, startled expression, and turns to Louise. Louise shrugs her shoulders and looks at me.

'Okay,' I say, shaking my head. 'Don't worry then.' Instead, we hold up a blanket to shield Jumari from the other patients in the room. Louise and I re-examine the extensive prolapsed tissue, and with piercing alarm we see immediately that the widespread redness and swelling are back. Tragically, heartbreakingly, the infection has returned.

I look at Mack, and then to Louise. 'Lu Lu, Binod is correct; we cannot safely operate on Jumari.'

'No, Ray!' Louise pleads. We *promised* Jumari. We can't let her down now. Please don't do this.'

'Lu, I know this is extremely disappointing. But you know we can't operate like this. We could cause major complications.'

'Yes but … she won't get it done … and it will be another year … we *promised*!'

'Lu, with respect, you're being emotional. We can't take this risk.'

'Why didn't you operate two days ago? I knew we should have operated then. This is so unfair.'

And with that, Louise turns her back and storms out of the ward.

I turn to Binod. 'I'm sorry. It's been a long few weeks. Everyone's a little on edge right now.'

'She is simply concerned for the patient,' Binod says. 'It is understandable.'

'What are your thoughts, Mack?' I ask.

'Yes, Louise had her heart set on this one. I can see why she's upset. But this is your call, Ray.'

'Binod,' I say. 'Can you explain to Jumari that we cannot operate on her today? Please explain that we want the best for her, and the best management is not to operate.'

And as Binod speaks solemnly to Jumari in Nepali, I kneel down beside her and hold her slender hand. Tears well in her eyes as she grasps Binod's wrenching words, and she moves her head slowly from Binod, to me, and then directly ahead to nothing. As her shoulders slump and her stare becomes more vacant, she takes on the precise appearance she had two weeks ago when she arrived at our camp.

Binod continues to talk to Jumari, but she no longer appears to absorb his grim attempts to explain. We all want to restore this helpless woman's life as soon as we can, but I can think of no reasonable alternative to waiting until her infection has completely cleared. There are no other surgical teams in the region, so it will be another 12 months before we can treat her.

Louise returns to the room and sits on the edge of the Jumari's bed. She leans forward and gives Jumari a long, heartfelt hug.

'I'm sorry,' Louise says. 'I'm so sorry.'

Hope and Hopelessness

11:45am, Operating Theatre

Thank goodness for Binod's Bluetooth; again it's a very welcome distraction from the dark mood that swamps the theatre room. I had been looking forward to this last operating session, anticipating a sense of achievement as we completed our final few cases for the camp. But right now, as we begin the first procedure, the overwhelming feeling is of apprehension. The team are professional as they go about their usual work, but the tension in the room is even tighter than yesterday. Mack and Louise are little more than civil. Jayne tries some light-hearted humour, but today this raises nothing more than flickers of unconvincing smiles.

Despite the diversion of the music while we operate, Binod clearly picks up on the agitation. 'Everybody is sad today, sir. I am very sorry that we cannot operate to fix *Didi* Jumari.'

'Thank you, Binod,' I say. 'We're all disappointed that we can't operate on Jumari. But this is nobody's fault, and your assessment and your advice were absolutely correct.'

As we progress through our first case, Binod speaks again. 'Dr Ray, may I ask you a question?'

'Of course.'

'What will happen here when you and your team are gone?'

'When we leave here in a few days? I guess this little hospital will go back to the way it was before we came.'

Binod gives a faint frown and then looks deep in thought. 'You will not be back for one year?'

'It looks that way. Tell me what's on your mind, Binod.'

'Sir, please do not be thinking I am rude. When your team are here, many people are treated. There are operations for prolapse, babies are born, even sometimes caesarean sections; when you are here this hospital is *real* hospital. When you are not here, this is only Health Post.' Binod's brow furrows, but not with a look of grievance; he appears more determined, almost driven as he speaks.

'I have been thinking for few days now,' he says. 'Why could not this hospital become real hospital every day, even when you are not here?'

I put down the instruments I'm holding, and slowly shake my head. 'I would love this to be a 'real' hospital all the time, but this cannot be. Who would run the hospital? How could we pay for the hospital? Where would we find the trained doctors and nurses?'

'I know this is not possible in this year,' Binod says. 'But when I have more training, I can be the doctor here. We can find nurses, and I speak to Mr Paul yesterday, sir. He tells me soon your organisation will give treatments for mothers and babies. You need *hospital* for mothers and babies. Let *this* be hospital for mothers and babies.'

I'm silent as a torrent of tangled thoughts stream through my head. Don't blindly dismiss this idea, I tell myself. We do need to focus on one area of this country at a time, and we do need a base. Why not here? The buildings are really dilapidated, but we could gradually renovate these. Doctors? Binod is very promising, but we would need to train at least one other, and we'd need more nurses and midwives. But funding – it's one thing to find and train medical staff, but how much to run a hospital? Is this idea even realistic?

I think back to my words to the team on the night we lost Arpan and her baby boy. *The worst thing we could do now is to let the loss of these two lives amount to nothing. Don't let this happen. Don't waste this...*

I look directly into Binod's eyes. 'Binod, this may well be worth considering. I don't want to build up your hopes; I can't promise anything right now. But we will give this some serious thought. I'll put this idea to Dipak, and I'll discuss this with the rest of my team.' I look up at Mack, and across to Jayne and Louise. None appear to have overheard the conversation between Binod and me.

Challenges and possibilities dart around in my head for the rest of the operating day. Since we first started our organisation, we've been traipsing around the country running camps to do our bit to improve women's health. But if we're being truthful, we've hardly made a dent in the massive problem. Maybe it *is* time now to target one place and work on a better model of care. Maybe we should build up this little hospital here to provide year-round care. We could turn this place into a teaching centre, a major teaching centre, a hospital to train doctors, and nurses and midwives …

But *funding*. It always comes back to funding. It's one thing to acquire donations to set up a hospital, but it would be unrealistic to rely on this funding for its continued activity, for its operational costs. If we were to venture into building up this place to become a year-round, fully-fledged hospital, our model would need to be *sustainable*. If not – if instead we were to rely on continued donations for the running of the hospital – the moment funding stalled we'd be in all sorts of strife; the hospital would simply collapse. So how could we make this sustainable?

The next few cases flow more easily than I'd expected. Far from languishing in the gloom of today's theatre, I feel charged as I consider the remote possibilities of developing the hospital here. Even though I can't think of a way around the sustainability problem, it's invigorating to contemplate all sorts of expansion ideas. Maybe this could also become a base for Community Medicine programs, to provide education and research into public health.

Inevitably though, as the afternoon progresses my thoughts return to the struggles of this current camp. Uneasily, I remind myself that I have at least two of my team very much offside right now. Mack and Louise have both been such supportive colleagues and friends. How painful to see their support come crashing down. And so quickly. It was only a few days ago that the bond between us seemed so sturdy.

I can see things from Mack's point of view. In his eyes, the leader of the team has stopped being a team player. When Mack eventually learns why I needed to be so secretive, I'm fairly sure he'll come around.

And Louise – she's has been a really good friend for decades now. I understand her frustration, because in her eyes, we've failed Jumari. We could have operated two days ago when the tissues appeared clean. But it's highly likely that at that time some latent infection remained beneath her superficial flesh. To have operated then would almost certainly have led to widespread dissemination of the infection. Louise is not only loyal, she's professional. Once the heat of this disappointment settles, I'm sure she'll accept that what led to Jumari's corrective surgery being cancelled today was not mismanagement; it was simply fate.

We reach the final case for the day. Binod and I are preparing to scrub when Jayne walks over to us. 'Where's Mack?'

'I just assumed he was putting in the spinal block,' I reply.

'Nope. Patient's here, but no anaesthetist. He's been gone for at least 15 minutes.'

'This is not like him. I hope he's alright. Paul, would you mind checking for Mack in the ward? He can't be too far away.'

Another 15 minutes pass.

'What do you think's happened, Ray?' Jayne asks.

'My guess is that there's a problem with one of the patients on the ward. Strange that he hasn't sent us a message through.'

Paul returns to the theatre. 'Not in the ward. No one's seen him. This is so weird.'

'What do we do now, Ray?' Louise asks.

'We'll just have to wait, and hope everything's okay.'

Another 20 troubling minutes pass before Mack finally returns.

'I'm sorry everybody. Pressing business. Can't tell you where I've been, but it was ... *crucial.*' Mack glares at me before he turns to prepare his next anaesthetic.

Ouch.

It's dusk as we finally complete our last case of the day – most likely the last case of the camp. Somehow we've managed to stretch our very limited surgical supplies to last the distance. And there *is* a sense of relief as we stand and remove our gloves and masks. In acknowledgement of the end of our surgical work, I shake hands with Mack, Louise, Jayne, and Paul.

'Well done, guys. Excellent effort, and not just today, but for the whole of these last three weeks.' I look at Louise. 'I know it would have been even more rewarding to have done one more case on this camp, but it was just not meant to be.'

Louise bites her top lip and says nothing.

'Binod,' I say, 'you and Dipak return to Dhulikhel Hospital tomorrow?'

'Yes, Dr Ray.'

'You both must join our team for dinner tonight.'

'That is very kind, sir.'

The theatre is cleaned and everyone is about to walk back to the Dining Hall for dinner. I ask the team to go ahead without me and explain that I'll soon be meeting Dipak for a discussion here in the theatre. I tell them that once more I expect to be a little late for our meal. There's no surprise, and no argument from the group as they leave. It seems they're getting used to my evening forays.

As the team leave the theatre building, I'm pleased to see Dipak arrive. I'm keen to have a few minutes alone with him before Suntil joins us. Dipak walks into the theatre and sits with me next to the operating table.

'When your man arrives, Ray,' Dipak says, 'what is it you wish to get across to him?'

'His name is Suntil. There are two things I want to be sure are absolutely clear to him: that he must practice safe sex, and that his treatment is essential. I'm fairly sure he understands these points, but I want to reinforce them. He is likely to have quite a few questions.'

'Do you think he will undertake all the rigours of treatment? There will be so very many difficulties with travelling and multiple visits to clinics.'

'I know you and I both feel the odds of him accepting treatment are slim. But I'm sure you agree – we need to give it the best chance.'

Dipak gives a wistful smile. 'Yes, of course.'

'While we wait, Dipak, can I ask you another question?'

'Please do.'

'Binod has come up with the idea of developing this hospital here into a larger centre, a hospital that is staffed throughout the whole year with experienced doctors and nurses. Do you think this is feasible?'

'Well I must admit, the idea has also crossed my mind. No doubt Binod would be keen to work here?'

'Yes. But if we could train Binod further, and perhaps one or two others, and if we could find more nurses and midwives – do you think it would be possible to expand this place?'

'This would be the perfect area to have such a medical centre. This region so greatly needs a proper hospital. Could we find the staff to work here in this capacity? In time, I am certain we could. But Dr Ray, I am sorry to say that the Department of Health of the Nepal Government would not be interested such a project. As you know, their budget is very limited.'

'Dipak, I am not proposing a *government* hospital here – I am wondering about a *private* hospital. Well, not exactly private, but a *not-for-profit* hospital.'

Dipak's ridiculously blue eyes expand with either delight or surprise, or perhaps both. 'You could *do* this? You could *fund* such a hospital?'

'We've got some really passionate supporters out there who will help us raise funds. The team here are rather exhausted at the moment, but I know that once they get home and charge their batteries they'll put in a big effort and rally support.'

'And you would incorporate teaching at this hospital? Not just teaching doctors, like Binod, but medical students, and nurses?'

'Absolutely. This would be a major thrust of the hospital.'

There is a lull in our conversation now as Dipak concentrates. We both stare down at his fingers on the table while they tap to a frenzied, soundless beat. Abruptly, his fingers stop their curious dance and Dipak looks up at me. 'Dhulikhel,' he says. 'Dhulikhel Hospital.'

I'm confused. 'Yes, you return there tomorrow.'

'Yes, Dr Ray. But Dhulikhel Hospital is also a not-for-profit hospital. And very, very successful. It can be done. Like Dhulikhel, it can be self-sustaining.' He beams with obvious delight.

'That's wonderful to hear, Dipak. But … how? How do they pay for all those wages and medical costs?'

'Much of the funding comes from the fees of the medical students, but there are other sustainable sources. Dhulikhel Hospital would be happy to share their successful model with you, I am sure of that. In fact, I expect they would support you setting up a hospital here. Part of their philosophy is to extend medical care to remote regions of Nepal.'

I struggle to believe that I'm hearing this. It's as if so many pieces in a grueling puzzle are finally falling into place. It's so obvious that we need to make a much bigger impact on the prolapse crisis here, and we need to stop the senseless deaths of so many mothers and babies.

Earlier in the camp, I told my team that it's crucial we confront both of these problems, and make a major difference. But I had no idea how we would do this. Now I think we have a strategy where we *can* make a major difference. I so want to share my excitement with my team – I just hope they're over their hostility.

I close my eyes and allow my mind to wander over all the appealing possibilities of establishing our own hospital here. Regular medical training, improving surgery standards, safety in pregnancy, public health measures to control diseases like HIV...

A knock at the outside door tears me from my trance. I jump up and walk into the recovery room, but stop before reaching the door. I turn and walk back into the theatre. 'Dipak, could you start by reassuring Suntil that you and I will be totally confidential? He does seem obsessive about his infection staying secret. He's even desperate that no one knows he's come here to see us.'

'Of course, Dr Ray. But please understand – this is perfectly normal behaviour.'

I welcome Suntil into the theatre for the third time, and watch his face as I introduce him to Dipak. He has a fearsome look of icy hostility. Dipak does not appear perturbed, and begins a long conversation in Nepali. His speech is so rapid that I understand very few of his words. Suntil speaks only occasionally, but his fierce expression is fixed.

After several minutes Dipak turns to me and speaks. 'Dr Ray, are there specific things you wish me to say to Suntil?'

'Do you think he understands the importance of undergoing treatment?'

'Yes, but I'm not convinced he will accept treatment.'

'Can you explain to Suntil that it is very important that he tells his wife, Gorham of his infection?' Spousal or family support is critical for HIV sufferers to overcome obstacles to care and treatment.[139–141]

Dipak speaks in Nepali once more, but Suntil shakes his head emphatically. 'No. No.'

'Suntil,' I say, 'you need support from Gorham. And she is at risk of contracting the disease herself.'

Dipak translates, and a discussion then begins between Suntil and me.

'I not tell Gorham. I not tell anyone. Not even Nabin. If village hear I have HIV infection they not want me here.'

'Suntil, how do you know this?'

Suntil's jaw tightens and his nostrils begin to splay. He leans in and bores his stormy eyes into mine. 'Men have HIV because they be with sex worker, or they be using drugs, or they have sex with other men. All these things very bad. Village not want these people.'

I finally understand the reason for the profound stigma surrounding Suntil's infection. HIV is connected with behaviours that are forbidden or illegal in most Nepalese societies.[142] And yet strong social ties are crucial in promoting HIV treatment, particularly in resource-limited settings.[143,144] So how in Shiva's name do we tackle this? Right now, I am at a total loss. I look across to Dipak for some sort of guidance here, but he simply raises his eyebrows, and twists his head in an expression that suggests utter futility.

I turn back to Suntil. 'Riken. Riken is your good friend. You are sharing his home. You can tell him about your infection. A good friend will help you through a problem like this.'

Again he shakes his head. 'No tell Riken.' But gone is Suntil's defiant tone; there now is a defeated sadness in his voice.

'Suntil, why did you leave your own home?'

He seems to ignore my question, and instead looks to Dipak. The room is silent. He closes his eyes and lets out a tortured sigh.

'Too much fighting.' Suntil says eventually. 'With Uttam. And ... And ...' He looks to the floor now as he wrestles with his next sentence. 'When I am with Gorham ... is very difficult to stop sex.'

I'm stunned at this admission from Suntil; firstly, that he would share this information with us, but secondly that he has the strength for self-imposed exile. He rises a notch in my estimation.

'Suntil, what will you do now?'

As Dipak translates this question, Suntil looks away and sighs heavily. 'This village not for me. I go away. Maybe back to Uttarakhand.'

'Will you get treatment?'

Another heavy sigh. 'Not likely.'

'Suntil, if you take proper treatment, your life can go on; if you do not take treatment, your life will end early.'

Suntil looks urgently into my eyes once more. 'Dr Ray, my life already end early.'

He stands and shakes my hand, Western style. He gives a simple nod to Dipak, and walks out of the theatre. I suspect this will be the last time I will see this man. How many other men – and women – in this country suffer this vicious torment? How many perceive such powerful feelings of shame and rejection that they chose certain death over disclosure?

As Suntil disappears into the dark of the night, Dipak addresses me again. 'Ray, I know you are upset over this, but there is nothing more you could have done. Together, we have given far more important advice and encouragement to this man than most HIV sufferers would receive in rural Nepal. Now we must leave this to fate.'

'Thank you, Dipak. And I will keep telling myself that.' I grab the torch and turn off the theatre light as we make our way to leave. 'Oh, I almost forgot. This is your last night here, but it's also the last night for most of our volunteers. We would be very pleased if you would join us for dinner.'

'I would be very happy to join you. Let me tell my friends where I stay that I will not be eating with them tonight. I will see you in the Dining Hall a little later?'

'Yes. And I really appreciate you coming here to help me tonight. We probably haven't changed the outcome, but I'm satisfied in the knowledge that we've done our best.'

The Crush of Banishment

8:15pm, Dining Hall

Alone, I make my way back to the Dining Hall. Again I need no torch to see my way; the near full moon bathes my path and the verging trees. In the distance, the silver-white gleam highlights imperial Himalayan peaks to paint a scene that is stately, majestic. Regal white coats adorn the soaring summits and shimmer in the incandescent sheen. Scattered clouds nearby, themselves illuminated – sentries to this towering royal court.

As I enter the Dining Hall I'm struck immediately by the heightened energy in the room. Most of the crew will leave tomorrow, and I'm sure this is the reason for the extra buzz in the air. But things aren't quite right. As I circulate around the room and people gradually become aware of my presence, the mood chills. I walk up the end of the dining table where Norman, Louise, and Paul are in spirited conversation. When they spot me, their lively banter stops, and they begin to engage me in hollow small talk.

After a few uncomfortable minutes, I leave this group and join Steph and Mack at a small side table. Steph – normally so open and sincere - smiles and chats incessantly. But tonight she gives me no eye contact. She and the other volunteers seem happy enough, and they're certainly courteous to me, but tonight my links with the team don't seem genuine.

I refuse to believe that this is simply about my absence from most of this week's meals. Is there some other problem in the camp that hasn't been brought to my attention? If so, it seems that whatever this problem is, every one of the volunteers is aware of it except me. Is the issue so great or so grim that they're too frightened to confront me? I would so hate the camp to end like this, with some awkward conflict eating away at the wonderful bonds we've all developed over the last few weeks.

I've been so keen to introduce the idea of a Mothers and Babies Hospital here to everyone, and to share my excitement, but right now it doesn't seem a good time to bring this up. It's probably best that I wait for our Sixty-Second Summaries later tonight.

Poppy is here again. I expected that with this being the final night for most of the team she'd be a little sombre. But I'm surprised to see her bright eyed and perky as she serves us our meals.

'Poppy,' I say when she reaches my place at the table, 'won't you miss all these people when they leave here tomorrow?'

'Yes, of course, Dr Ray,' she says with a smile, 'I make many good friends here. I will be very sad when they leave.'

'But Poppy, you seem so happy.'

'Dr Ray, my friends are here tonight. Tomorrow will be tomorrow. No need for sadness now. Now, it is time for happiness.'

I consider Poppy's simple creed. She seems to be saying: live in the moment, don't waste time with concerns over future matters you can't influence. It's the sort of line you'd find on a self-help bookshelf, and it's sage advice. But how in earth do you know this when you're only 12 years old?

'You are so right, Poppy,' I say. 'But where did you learn this? Who told you not to think too much about tomorrow, and to be happy now?'

Poppy stops distributing the food and plates, and stares at me again with those bewitching brown eyes. She looks to ponder for a moment and then says, 'I do not know who teach me this. This is something I know for many years.'

'Do most Nepalese people know this? Do most people, say, in your school class know this?'

'It is not something that we talk about, Dr Ray. It is not secret, but people just happy when happy, sad when sad.'

We from the West like to think we're sophisticated and we so freely describe these people in remote Nepal as primitive. We run our camps to improve their health and educate them with our advanced Western knowledge. And yet, in so many ways these humble people are the sophisticated ones. It is they who are so often the teachers, and we the students. And the message is all the more potent when the lesson comes from a fledgling child.

I look around at the team of vibrant volunteers. Jayne is now sitting with Mack, and she hoots and laughs and slaps her thigh as they share some sort of sidesplitting tale. When she draws a breath and looks in my direction, she quickly turns away. Clearly, she and Mack are not keen to share their riotous joke.

I peruse the room again and I eat my meal in silence. The potbelly stove struggles away with its feeble flames as it has for every one of the 25 nights we've been here. I glance to the flickering light it casts on the ceiling and the high windows. On most evenings, the windows reveal nothing more than the inky blackness of the cold night sky. But tonight, the moonlight remains so lustrous that the outline of the Himalayas and surrounding clouds are still clearly visible. It's a framed prospect of my view from the hospital path on the way here this evening.

But as I study the commanding vista more closely, I see that the clouds have thickened, and now obscure all mountain peaks bar one. A single crest pierces the thick, white fleece, alone now in its quest to touch the impervious heavens above.

*

The meal is over now and our plates have been cleared. It's that time of night that I normally tap my glass with a fork to capture everyone's attention and announce the commencement of the Sixty-Second Summaries. I psyche myself up to hide the frustration of my sudden isolation from the group, but before I can reach my glass, Louise grabs a glass herself and firmly clangs it several times with her own fork.

'Okay, everybody,' Louise says in an officious tone, 'listen up. Before we have our Summaries tonight we've got something important to discuss.' Louise looks at me. 'Dr Ray, I don't wish to be rude, but could you please leave the room?'

Stunned, I look around at all of the volunteers. They stare at me in silence as I stand. I look to Louise. 'For the night? You want me gone for the night?'

'No, not for the night,' Louise replies. 'We just need about 10 or 15 minutes, please.' She speaks to me not as a loyal friend and colleague, but as a school teacher might rebuke a difficult student.

It's the worst I've felt for the whole three weeks. Slowly, and as bravely as I can, I walk upstairs to my bedroom.

An Extraordinary Evening

After at least 20 demoralising minutes, there is a faint knock at my door.

'Ray?' It's Steph. 'We're ready for you now.'

I try to read Steph's eyes, and get nothing more than uneasy sadness. I walk down the stairs ahead of her, and as I reach the lower rungs, I note with some confusion that the Dining Hall furniture has been rearranged. The main dining table has been moved away from its usual central position. Its long side is now adjacent to the far wall. The chairs are lined up to face the table. And where is everybody?

'Steph? What the hell is going on?'

'Can't really say, Dr Ray. But I think you might find your answer in the kitchen.'

I look across to the kitchen doors, and back to Steph. Bewildered now, and with a lot of trepidation, I slowly walk towards the paired doors that connect the Dining Hall to the kitchen. I pause in front of the doors, breath in deeply, and slowly push them open.

'SURPRISE!'

A fanatical roar of cheering, whistling, and hooting from the crowd of volunteers and staff who begin to pile out into the Dining Hall. I struggle to take this in. And ... there are others here.

'Nabin, Gamika, Liz ... Liz? – where did you come from?' I see Guna and Mani, and other nurses from the ward – even some of the patients. Two are carrying IV poles. 'Didn't we operate on you last week?' Even Riken is here, and other Nepalese people I don't even recognise.

A chuckling Mack and Louise pull me aside.

'Ray,' Mack says, 'that expression on your face – priceless.'

'But Mack, Lu Lu – what *is* this? What is going on?' Louise simply continues to giggle.

'How do they say this in the classics?' Mack says. 'Soak it up, Ray. Yes, that's it. Soak it up – this is the team's farewell for you.'

'But … you guys have the shits with me.'

'Ha-haaa. Got you a beauty there, didn't we?'

'You *don't* have the shits with me?'

'Well,' Mack says, 'I must admit it was a bit touch and go there for a while with all your clandestine activities. But today I learnt what you've been up to with Suntil and Gorham, and all of this business with the HIV. You were spot on with what you did, Ray. But let's talk about that later.'

Still perplexed, but with sprigs of relief beginning to sprout, I shake my head and turn to Louise. 'Lu Lu?'

'Oh, Ray, I was a total brat today. Mack took me aside and reminded me of that. I was so angry when we couldn't operate on Jumari, and I was wrong to take it out on you. Please forgive me.'

Right now, everything feels so powerfully surreal. Only a few moments ago I was floundering in self-pity. I look around the room and try to grasp how quickly things have changed. The large crowd appear to be very much in party mode. Some now sit in the chairs that face the table, and I notice portable lights, and the curtain screens – hey – these are the screens on wheels that were missing from the ward this morning.

'What's with all of this then?' I ask.

'Ah,' Louise says, 'you'll just have to wait and see. Oh, and Ray – do you mind? We need to postpone our Sixty-Second Summaries until tomorrow.'

Suddenly, the room begins to shake to the lively beat of local music. I look across to see that Binod has brought along his Bluetooth speakers. Laughter cascades throughout the room, and drinks flow freely as I begin to circulate among the festive guests.

'Liz!' I shout, 'You'd never miss out on an excuse for a party, would you?'

'Just try to stop me, Ray. And by the way, well done on running a very successful medical camp.'

'Oh yeah,' I reply, 'I have so got my finger on the pulse – I had absolutely no idea that this night was happening.'

'I could kind of tell that from your face just now.'

The music suddenly stops, and a loud voice comes from behind us. 'Ladies and gentlemen. Ladies and gentlemen, could I have your attention, please?'

We look around to see Paul standing on the dining table. He wears a dinner jacket – where did he get that from? – and holds what vaguely resembles a microphone. But when I look more closely, the object he holds is actually two pair of large artery forceps bound together with surgical tape. Paul holds the shaft of the forceps and speaks into the handles as if this were a real microphone.

'If you could all please take your seats … oh, right – we haven't got enough seats. Okay, first in best dressed. The rest of you will have to sit on the floor or stand. Sorry. Our performance will begin shortly.'

'Performance? Liz, do you know anything about a performance?'

'Ah, no, Mister Finger-On-The-Pulse.'

I look over to my team members, but they're all heading towards the curtain screens. I walk to the back of the room and, intrigued, I wait for the 'performance' to come.

The main Dining Hall lights dim and the two portable ward lamps are switched on to light up Paul, who remains standing on the dining table. A mobile curtain screen extends from each end of the table. Behind each screen we can hear frantic activity from the remaining team members.

'Ladies and gentlemen,' Paul continues. He really does give the impression of a seasoned compere on his theatre stage. 'Before we start tonight's performance, it's important you all know that this production is a dedication to the community here. It is an acknowledgement of our gratitude to the people who have helped us over the last few weeks.'

Paul pauses while there is generous applause from the audience.

'But I must also say this,' Paul adds. 'We have all been busy for these three weeks, but there is one member of our team who has been extremely busy. While we've been eating and drinking and relaxing at the end of each day, Dr Ray has been running around like a crazy man, doing all sorts of after-hours work. And this work has been vital for the welfare of this whole area.' Heads turn around to stare at me, and I give an uncomfortable smile in response.

"I speak for all of us now,' Paul goes on as he stares in my direction. *Okay Paul, you can stop now*, I say to myself; *they've got the message.* But he continues, 'This performance is also dedicated to Dr Ray, for his untold commitment to this organisation, for his leadership of our group, and his awesome loyalty to every single one of us.'

There is more applause from the room, and all I can think to do is to nod awkwardly and wave to those who look in my direction. I'm thankful the light that reaches me is dim; it's less likely the crowd can see my tragically flushing face. Is it possible to feel proud and embarrassed at the same time? Until tonight I would not have thought so.

The ward lamps are switched off, and the room quietens. In the darkness there is scrambling and chuckling in the area of the table.

'No!'

'That's *my* side. You're on *that* side.'

'Don't touch me there!'

'Sorry.'

More chuckling.

When the lights return, five of the volunteers appear on the table, all dressed in blue theatre gowns and caps. Attached to their fingers are long pieces of surgical adhesive tape. The lengths of tape hover from their hands to just above their ankles. The volunteers stand in a line and stare straight ahead, their faces intense and severe. The scene is a contorted image of the five red dancers with their finger ribbons in the Village Hall two weeks ago.

In the centre of tonight's group, Jayne clearly struggles to sustain her sombre stare. Her mouth twitches upwards and soon a smothered giggle breaks free. Her giggling spreads quickly and soon all five explode into wild waves of laughter. Their laughter soon spills over to the audience. Over the next few minutes, all five battle to recover their frozen faces. But as soon as they look to have control, there is another cackle, and chaos breaks out once again.

Finally there is calm, and music from Binod's Bluetooth restarts. It's remarkably similar to the drums and flute we heard at the production two weeks ago. It's clear now that our team are about to perform their own version of the cultural dance. Oh my God – anything could happen here.

The five remain motionless for a minute or two before they begin to wave around their arms and hands. The surgical tape follows their limbs, and swirls in vast flowing loops. I'm surprised and impressed that our group can look almost professional.

But something seems to be wrong. Norman jerks his arm towards himself, and Steph's arm follows firmly to his chest. She looks distressed. Norman lifts his arm up and down, and Steph's arm follows as if being pulled. They look at each other, and then across to the long tapes on their fingers. And becomes clear to them, and those of us watching, that their adhesive tapes have attached to each other's.

As they try in vain to separate the tapes, laughter erupts from the audience. Other tapes begin to snag, and within a short time all five dancers' tapes are doggedly stuck to the others'. With their hands bound now, they stop their movements and look at each other. But then, to the delight of the crowd, they simply shrug their shoulders and continue their dance.

I turn to Liz. 'This group really do dance as one.'

Liz smiles. 'They seem really united.'

The volunteer dancers are not quite as one as they arch their spines and tilt back their heads. In vain they try to coordinate their limited movements. Their arms look so awkward with a mishmash of tape binding all of their hands together. Seemingly unperturbed, they begin to slither and twirl around their long table. Their attempts at dancing are commendable, but not exactly elegant. And the crowd love it; they laugh and clap and cheer at the crazy performance.

Out of nowhere, Paul reappears on stage. He now wears a red wig and holds an ugly mask to his face. The mask is a cardboard drawing of the face of Lakhe, the flesh-eating demon. And even with this whimsical version of Lakhe – a demon in tuxedo – there are startled shrieks from locals in the audience. He prances around the hapless group of dancers, who do their best to ignore him. But as they continue their tethered moves to this most bizarre dance, Lakhe and the audience watch on as the tapes begin to attach themselves to the group's arms, legs, and bodies. With each twist and twirl their movements become more and more constrained, until finally, as one, they mould to a large, messy medley of blue body parts.

The audience roar in raucous, unrestrained laughter, some falling about the chairs as they hoot and screech. Behind the mask, Paul watches on as his own shoulders shake in fits of his own bubbling laughter. He finally doubles over and stumbles to his knees with a mighty guffaw.

The music stops to announce the end of the outrageous performance. The crowd are on their feet, cheering and applauding with gusto. Paul stands and bows humbly to the audience, and then looks across to his five very tangled colleagues. He whispers something to the group, and as one, they all bend their knees and lower their interwoven mass in their own effort to acknowledge the approving crowd.

Paul removes his wig and mask and speaks into his make-believe microphone. 'Thank you, Ladies and gentlemen, thank you. That didn't go quite to plan, but I think you can tell our team are very attached.' More spontaneous hooting and applause. 'We will now have a short intermission to allow our dancers to be freed from their, ah, captivity.'

Binod's sparkling music restarts as the guests all stand and resume their laughter and lively chatter.

One of the kitchen staff appears with a large bread knife and begins to slice through the multiple pieces of surgical tape that bind the dancers. I wander down to the front of the room to help, but by the time I reach them, most have been freed.

'Impressive stuff, guys,' I say. 'Must have taken you weeks to perfect those moves.'

Louise is panting. 'That was so amazing,' she gasps. 'Can you believe that, Ray? I know we should have practised with the tapes, but we didn't want to waste too much of our supplies.'

'We had no idea,' Jayne says. 'I was so not expecting us to stick like that. I reckon it was better that we didn't use the tapes in practice, because we all got such a surprise, it made the whole thing like, funnier.'

'And you've got more to come?' I say. 'You guys are amazing.'

Mack is still pulling off tape from his fingers and arms when I approach him. 'Have you got a few minutes to talk, Mack? Or do you need to get ready for your next skit?'

'No more skits for me, Ray. That's me done for the night, thank God. I'm sure I'm not designed for these sorts of things.'

We walk over to stove. 'Mack, how did you find out about Suntil and our secret meetings?'

'Well now, there were a few things, Ray. You see, Sunam told us he had detected a patient who was HIV positive. We checked, but this infected patient's record number didn't match any of the women who'd come through our Assessment Clinic. The only other people we knew had been tested were Badal and Suntil. We'd been told Badal was negative, so that left only Suntil.

'I knew you were concerned about Suntil's status – you had told me yourself. So this afternoon when I disappeared for a while from theatre, I sat down with Nabin and asked him what was going on. He told me everything. He said that he was almost sure Suntil was infected with HIV, and that you'd spent a lot of time trying to track him down. Nabin also told me that Suntil had asked for your word that you would tell no one about your meetings together. And I know you promised him you'd also keep his infection a secret. It wasn't too hard to work out the rest from there.'

I give a feeble smile and nod. 'Guess I wouldn't make a very good spy.'

'Huh – you'd be a lousy spy. Ray, I am sorry I didn't trust you for a while there. This must have been atrociously difficult for you. Your primary aim was to contain this infection; I understand that. But this man, Suntil – because of his stubborn resolve to keep his problem confidential, there was only one course of action open to you. The only chance you had to stop the HIV from spreading was to keep your meetings a secret from every one of us – and we gave you such a hard time for doing so.'

I smile more openly now. 'Mack, if our roles were reversed, and you were disappearing for clandestine meetings, I'm sure I would have given you just as hard a time. Sorry I had to be such a secretive bastard.'

'Well, I'm sorry I was a wee bit intolerant.'

As we shake hands warmly, I watch the quirky movements of his white moustache. It does its thing when Mack is cheery like this – half up, half down, it follows the fitful lines of his trademark wonky smile.

Jayne and Steph wander over to join Mack and me. Jayne is bubbling with excitement.

'You must have guessed, Ray. Did you guess?' Jayne speaks so quickly in her excitement. 'You must have known something was going on. It was so hard to keep this a secret from you.'

I smile and shake my head. 'Jayne, I had no idea. I thought something was seriously wrong, so this came as a total surprise.'

'We couldn't even look you in the eye tonight at dinner,' Jayne continues. 'I was sure if I did I'd spill my guts and spoil the surprise.'

I laugh. 'Spilling your guts at dinner – such a beautiful image, Jayne. So, how long have you guys been planning this, anyway?'

Steph answers. 'Around a week. We were going to include you in the show, but you just kept disappearing. So we decided to surprise you instead. Before you got here tonight, Mack sat us down and told us all about why you weren't here a lot of the time lately. I knew that each time you weren't with us, it would have been for something important, I just knew that. God, that must have been hard though, you know, telling someone they're HIV positive, when you can't speak their language.'

'Yeah, it was pretty challenging, Steph. But do you know what? I think I'd choose this HIV counselling stuff over that cultural dance thing you all just did. Man, that looked lethal up there. It did look amazingly funny though.'

Paul and Norman join us. 'So, Dr Ray,' Paul says, 'you liked our little performance? Very high quality dancing, wasn't it' His tone is playfully mocking.

'Highly professional,' I reply. 'That group of red dancers from a couple of weeks ago? You made them all look positively sloppy.'

'Yep. They'll all be nervous right now, knowing there's a classier dance troupe in town. We're calling our performance Dance of a Thousand Tapes. I doubt that anyone's gonna be able to reproduce that.'

'Oh my God!' says Norman. 'Let's hope not. No one told me tonight was going to be a massive big rumble. I swear to God I nearly suffocated in the middle of that mess.'

Everyone laughs, but Norman doesn't seem to appreciate the humour. I begin to circulate among the other guests. Liz is chatting to Dipak, and they look up when I approach.

'That's the most I've laughed in months, Ray,' Liz says. 'They could not have rehearsed that, surely.'

'They did rehearse, apparently, but not the tape binding thing. That was pure professional creativity.'

'Genius,' she says. 'Hey Ray, Dipak here has been telling me about your ideas to beef up this little hospital here.'

'It was Binod's suggestion first, Liz. I'm trying not to get my hopes too high just yet, but to be honest, I'm really excited about the idea.'

'If you could pull this off,' Liz continues, 'it sounds like you could do some amazing things here. I mean, I know your team's already done some great work and all, but a full-on hospital with a labour ward? That would be magnificent!'

'It would be, Liz. I've been explaining to Dipak that a major part of the work we'd do here would be teaching. And you and I both understand the importance of education. Did Dipak tell you he specialises in Community Health?'

Liz turns her head to Dipak. 'No. Not yet. And I imagine there's a lot of public health education going on with that.'

'It's crucial,' Dipak replies, 'and community research, as well.'

'Ah,' Liz says, 'Ray, that's just what you and I agreed on – that this was vital to improve the problems in these parts. And no doubt your revamped hospital will have its own Community Health department?'

'Absolutely essential.'

Dipak's rich blue eyes sparkle as he smiles broadly. 'Music to my ears, Dr Ray.'

'Liz,' I say, 'do me a favour, would you? Don't mention the hospital idea to any of my team yet. It's probably best to come from me.'

'It's a Mothers and Babies Hospital, right?' Liz says. 'Okay then – *mum's* the word.'

I look around at my team. They seem exhilarated as they wander about the room and mingle with the other guests. Looking back on the earlier part of the night, I feel childish to have felt snubbed from their group. It's been so chaotic here tonight that I haven't had a chance to put the hospital idea them. I'm so excited to tell them all, but I'll wait till later this evening when I expect things will settle.

Jyoti approaches us. '*Namaste*, Dr Ray!'

'Jyoti, I'm so glad you could come. *Namaste.*'

'Your team are very interesting Nepali dancers.'

'Yes, I think it will be better if they stick to their medical jobs.'

'This will be better than sticking to each other!'

'Ha! Brilliant. I will tell them that. Jyoti, can I ask you something?'

'Of course, Dr Ray.'

'After our conversation the other day, we're more determined than ever to improve pregnancy care in this part of the world.'

'You have some more ideas, Dr Ray?'

'Yes. There are so many barriers to caring properly for mothers and babies in this part of the world.'

'Yes, this is what we discussed.'

'Okay, Jyoti, hold onto your hat … how would you feel if we renovated these broken-down buildings here, we organised hospital staff *all year round*, and we provided ongoing teaching to midwives and doctors and the community?'

Jyoti makes no comment in return. She simply stares at me in silence. Her expression a carbon copy of the dancers' frozen faces ahead of their performance. Slowly she brings both palms to her cheeks. 'Dr Ray, this is *true*?'

'I really hope so. We will have many hurdles, but this will be our goal.'

'This will be *wonderful* for the women of Nepal.'

'*If* we can do this,' I continue, '*if* we can pull this off and make this a proper, full time hospital – would you be keen to join us and work here?'

'Oh my God, Dr Ray – this would be my dream.' Jyoti is beaming now. 'You know this area is region of my family. I always want to work in this area, but I always want to be treating more women. If proper hospital can be here, I will be happiest midwife in Nepal!'

'Jyoti, perhaps I have given you too much hope. I still need to put this to my team – the team here, but also others at home. We would need to raise a lot of funds. Right now this is only a vision, but it is very powerful vision.'

'What can I do, Dr Ray? What can I do to help you?'

'For the moment, just keep up the wonderful work you're doing in your Health Post. I will keep you up to date with our developments by email. After some time, I may need you to help me a great deal.'

After Jyoti walks off, I turn to Dipak. 'Do you think I overstated our plan?'

'Not at all,' Dipak replies, 'I understand you don't wish to disappoint people, but I feel you gave Jyoti important hope that is not unrealistic.'

He leans in to speak in my ear conspiratorially. 'Dr Ray, may I say something else?'

'Of course, Dipak.'

'This is what I believe – I believe that if you are walking a path you are meant to be walking, everything falls into place. The universe is telling you that.'

Fashion and Foolishness

A number of guests move aside as the dining table is repositioned. Four of our volunteers lift the heavy table and rotate it 90 degrees so that it now points away from the wall. Jayne and Steph move the two curtain screens to the end of the table that faces the wall. There is more bustling activity behind the screens now, where I assume some of the team prepare for the next part of the performance.

Paul takes the stage once more. 'Ladies and gentlemen, thank you for your patience. We are now almost ready for the second half of our performance this evening. If you could please take your seats – those who have seats – and the rest of you, please take your standing positions.'

The audience chat and laugh as they move leisurely towards the seats that have been arranged to line both sides of the table. Everyone else stands behind those seated. The babble slowly settles as we wait for the next performance to begin.

The room darkens again and the music restarts. Soothing, soulful sounds of traditional Nepalese song drift through the room and hush the final few murmurs. The ward lamps now light up to reveal Norman who stands alone at the back of the table-stage. He wears Nepalese clothes and a traditional hat – a *topi* – and stands poised while Paul resumes his presentation.

'Ladies and gentlemen, our first outfit this evening is displayed by Norman.'

Norman begins to walk along the length of the stage. His gait has the flair of a fashion model as he parades his costume before us.

'Norman wears the traditional knee-length daura. This hand-crafted classic shirt has a generous cut to allow a relaxed, unfettered fit – sporty elegance geared for the dynamic man about town.'

There are cheers and hoots and whistles as Norman struts the stage. As he comes closer to where we stand, I see the fit of his clothes are anything but 'relaxed and unfettered'. Norman's frame is colossal compared to any of the local Nepalese men. I guess this costume is the largest he could find, but it's at least two sizes too small for him. I'm impressed that despite the very tight constraints of his clothes, Norman somehow looks cool and composed. His swings his hips with self-assurance as he strides the length of his runway.

Paul raises his voice now to be heard over the boisterous crowd. 'The lightweight trousers and flaring hems have been handsomely tailored by the House of Mingu ... That's in the back room of our general store in town here.'

Liz yells to me, 'Handsomely tailored? You're kidding me. They barely reach his bursting calf muscles.'

Poor Norman. The trousers are so under-sized that his ankles and most of his calves are exposed.

'I think Norman is setting a trend,' I shout back, 'and he likes to tease the crowd with a little flesh now and then. You watch – they'll all be wearing their trousers like this soon.'

Liz squeezes her eyes shut and scrunches her face.

Norman reaches the top of his walk, pauses, and spins theatrically on one foot before slowly sashaying to the back of the stage.

Paul continues his commentary. 'This warm and stylish piece is a timeless classic. The ensemble will flow effortlessly from rice field to formal function. A wardrobe must-have this season for the truly refined gentleman.'

Norman disappears behind the curtains to tumultuous applause. Even the locals smile and clap with passion at his performance. It's clear they appreciate our clumsy attempts to embrace their complex culture.

Louise arrives on stage. She's also wearing traditional Nepalese dress.

'Our next model is Louise. She is looking dazzling tonight in this glistening *gunyou* dress – a broadcloth cotton variation of the wonderfully versatile sari. This daring and savvy creation highlights the shapely profile of the midriff.'

There is polite applause as Louise proceeds along the catwalk. She walks in time to the ready rhythms of the lilting music. I can see her face more clearly now, and it's a study of concentration. With her dark hair and olive skin she could easily pass for a local Nepali.

'The fabric of this indulgent cotton blouse features local hand-embroidered motifs from the House of Hema. And we are delighted to announce that *Didi* Hema is in our audience tonight. Please give us all a wave, *Didi*.'

Hema stands awkwardly and looks sorely embarrassed as the crowd acknowledges her with added applause. Louise seems to relax as the attention is briefly drawn away from her and she turns at the top of her walk.

'Louise features canvas burlap platform wedges that highlight her shapely ankles and feet. This stylistic mélange makes a powerful, provocative statement in our steadily changing times.'

What? Stylistic mélange? Are you kidding me? And among those who *have* footwear in this part of Nepal, I'm yet to see anyone with anything but flat shoes. I'd love to know what's going through the minds of the locals in the audience here.

Louise completes her catwalk and disappears behind the borrowed curtains. The lights go out once more, and I wonder what our team have in store next.

A change in the music now; an upbeat, driving tempo of electric guitar and drums – it's Western rock music, and it's very loud. I wait for the softer Nepalese sounds to return – this is surely another of Binod's blended remix medleys – but no such change arrives; this music is pure, powerful rock.

The lights return to reveal an empty stage. Vocals now from Binod's blaring speakers. Female vocals. It's the animated rapping of a singer I don't recognise. Suddenly, to *ooh*s from the crowd, a young girl jumps onto the back of the stage. Her face is obscured by a large, wide-brimmed hat.

I know this hat. I know this girl. This is Poppy.

Poppy is dressed in clothes that are very much Western, and the audience are hushed as she begins her runway walk. She marches down the long table with a classic model cross-over step. In time to each pulsating blow of backbeat, her strides are long and confident. Her face seems charged with authority as she stares directly ahead. I find it difficult to believe the girl we watch is yet to reach 13 years. Glancing at the faces of the audience, it seems they have the same sense of bewilderment.

'And Ladies and gentlemen, we have our final model for the evening.' It's really difficult to hear Paul's voice over the dark-edged riffs of guitar. 'Poppy is wearing a shimmering black jersey wrap dress. This classic A-line design delivers a flattering silhouette.'

The lights begin to flash to the brutal beat, and Poppy begins to exaggerate the swing of her arms. The bright blue of her bangle sparkles in the reflected light. She reaches the end of the runway and pauses, hand on hip. With one extravagant movement, she whisks off her large hat, and we see for the first time her preened hair and makeup. The girls on our team have obviously spent time preparing for her performance. Over the past few weeks we've become used to Poppy's conversations and demeanour that are very much beyond her years, but this display tonight is in another league. We could be watching an 18-year old up there on stage.

Steph, Jayne, and Norman appear next to the stage with cameras flashing. With extravagant movements, they twist and contort their bodies to mimic paparazzi as they scramble for the best photo shots of Poppy on the runway.

Have we gone too far? I can see the humour in this as we swap cultures in this extraordinary fashion show, and I even laugh along with the rest of the crowd. But something feels wrong. As mature as she looks right now, that girl up there is a child. This is meant to be harmless fun, and the audience clearly appreciate that. They move their heads and shoulders in time to the pulse of the pounding beat. Even the locals in the room are smiling and clapping as one. I guess they are the barometer of our behaviour. I guess they would show their displeasure if they felt we were exploiting a child, or insulting their culture. I guess.

The music blasts build to a near deafening pitch, and the room begins to shudder to the thumping rhythmic bass. The lights flash harshly as Poppy pivots and turns and resumes her brazen walk.

Frenzied guitars scream in torment with each emphatic stride. Gazing around the room, I can see the crowd clapping, but I can no longer hear them. Somehow, time seems to slow. The scene is surreal, and the effect is hypnotic.

Slowly, I become aware of movement at the side of the room. I look across to see someone striding towards Binod. It's a man – a local, it seems – and even though I can only see his back, it's clear there is belligerence in his step. As he reaches Binod, an argument appears to break out between the two men. Their arms flail in wild, hostile moves, and as their dispute progresses, they move toward the blaring speakers. As they turn in my direction, I suddenly see the face of the man who argues with such fervour. With horror, and an overwhelming sense of dread, I realise it is Uttam.

I close my eyes in trepidation and try to imagine how repulsive this all must look through Uttam's eyes. *Of course* this is wrong, particularly if there's been no consent from Poppy's father. How could we be so stupid? How far back have we set our already strained relations?

I open my eyes to see Uttam reach for the power lead to the Binod's blaring speakers. He grabs the lead and violently yanks it from the socket in the wall. The music stops, and bright light floods the makeshift stage. Poppy freezes mid-stride as confused murmurs ripple from the crowd. It's like we've suddenly been jolted out of a distorted dream. A ripcord of reality.

Uttam jumps onto the stage and races towards his daughter. He grabs her arm and pulls her violently from the stage and towards the Dining Hall door. My stomach churns as I dash through the crowd to front them before they leave. The three of us reach the door at the same time. Uttam stops and scowls.

'*Pradusana, pradusana.*' He spits the words at me, and I know their shameful meaning: Pollution. Western culture pollution.

'I am so sorry, Uttam.' I bow my head and join my palms in some sort of desperate apology.

Uttam's face screws into a savage look of disgust. He turns, and with a heavy shove, pushes Poppy through the open door. In silence, they both disappear into the hostile cold night air.

Cleaning Up the Mess

'Oh my God, Ray. What have we done?' Steph has joined me at the door.

'I guess we've stuffed this up big time,' I reply. 'I didn't even know Uttam was here. We should have run this by him.'

I look past Steph to the rest of the audience. They appear perplexed with the dramatic end to the performance as they mutter amongst themselves. 'We've got to speak to the people here, Steph. Right now.'

Mack and Paul approach me as I storm back through the crowd. Their faces are full of fear. 'Later,' I bark at them as I spring up onto the stage. I look around at the faces that stare up at me, and try to think of something appropriate to say. Nabin sits in the second row looking awkward and confused.

'Nabin,' I shout, 'please come up here on the table with me.'

Nabin stands uncertainly. Slowly, he approaches the table and climbs up to join me.

'Thank you, Nabin. I want you to translate my words so everyone in the audience understands what I am saying.'

Nabin stares at the floor and runs his hand through his messy hair. He nods slowly.

'Ladies and gentlemen,' I say, 'I want your attention please.' The room is silent now as the audience appear transfixed. 'As many of you know, most of our team will be leaving tomorrow morning and returning to their homes.' I pause while Nabin translates. 'You all need to know that you have made every one of us feel very welcome here. We understand the importance of family in your country; it is a critical part of your culture. So it means a great deal to all of us that we can say: we have been treated like family.'

I'm a little encouraged by gentle applause from the audience.

'We … all of us – have been overwhelmed with the beauty of your culture. Our team wanted to show you how we've embraced this culture. We also wanted to show you some of our own culture. But it was wrong to parade our culture through a child so young.

'Paul told you earlier that tonight's presentations were our efforts to show our gratitude to all you who have helped us on this camp. But if we have offended any of you with the performances here, we apologise wholeheartedly.'

There is polite applause from our team and Liz and a few of the others, but nothing from the locals. Nabin completes the translation, but still they give no response. Are they offended by tonight, but too polite to complain? But in the heat of Poppy's act they were clapping along with the rest of the audience. Was my apology lost in Nabin's translation? It's too hard to tell.

As the local men and women begin to leave the Dining Hall, I address Nabin once more. 'Can you wander down to these people and ask some of them what their thoughts were tonight? Can you ask them if they were insulted by any of the performances?'

'I will do this,' Nabin replies. 'And, Dr Ray?'

'Yes, Nabin?'

'I want to say to you that everything tonight was very good. I think Uttam does not want his daughter to be like woman from West. But he does not understand tonight is only fun.'

'Thank you, Nabin. But we are guests in your country. The very least we could have done was to ask Uttam for his permission.'

*

The numbers in the room slowly filter out and without speaking, the team begin to return the furniture to the usual positions. As Liz approaches me I shake my head and throw out my hands.

'It was going so well there for a while,' I say to Liz with a sigh, 'but we overcooked it, didn't we'

'You poor bastard,' Liz replies. 'Most of the night was fabulous, it really was. Yeah, that act with Poppy was on the edge all right. I guess that was her dad who dragged her off? I don't think you won a friend there.'

'I can't believe I allowed that to go on. Her act, I mean. Liz, I was actually laughing while she was up there. I had mixed feelings, but I've got to be honest – I sort of enjoyed it.'

'Hey, don't beat yourself up. You know Ray, I was laughing and clapping along, too. I think the whole audience were. Her dad was pretty upset, but did you somehow violate or corrupt Poppy? Absolutely not.'

'Thanks so much for saying that, Liz, but it was still wrong. There I was just now, talking about how important family is in this country – and we've just driven a wedge through a really fragile home.'

'What will you do now?'

'I guess I'll let the dust settle, and then I'll go and meet with Poppy's dad and try to make peace.'

'You want me to speak to him?'

'That's a lovely offer, but let me see how I go … Oh – and on another matter – do you know you really have inspired Poppy? Because of you, she even wants to become a teacher.'

'You're kidding me. That's so touching. I love that kid. I would so love her to succeed somehow. She would be a brilliant teacher. What do you make of her future?'

'A lot less secure after tonight, I'm afraid.'

'I wouldn't be so negative, Ray. Things have a way of working themselves out. Now, if you don't mind, I'm going up to bed. Your gracious team organised me another room for the night when they were planning this whole thing.'

As Liz disappears up the stairs, I look around to see that all of the visitors have left the room. The only people remaining are our team of volunteers. They stand around the potbelly, silent and shamefaced.

'Who wants to start?' I ask as I approach them.

'Ray,' says Mack. 'I think I can speak for everyone here. We feel so foolish. Yes, we planned all of this. Yes, it included Poppy's catwalk. But we had no idea it would look so … so … raunchy.'

'I'm so sorry, Ray,' Louise says. 'We feel like we've let you down big time. When we practised this with Poppy through the week, it all seemed so funny and cute. And harmless. But up there tonight – well, the music was blaring, the lights were flashing. We weren't expecting that. And we didn't do her hair or the makeup. She must have done that herself, or gotten someone else to do it for her.'

'Okay,' I say, 'I understand. It got out of hand. It's clear we've offended Poppy's father, and almost certainly pushed him further away from giving Poppy any sort of freedoms in her life. I doubt we've caused any *direct* harm to Poppy tonight – it's the threat to her education and her career that concerns me most.'

'Oh, man!' says Jayne. 'I hadn't even thought of that. She was already struggling to get a decent sort of education. This is terrible. Ray, you must think we're all, like idiots.'

'Well, if you're all idiots, I'm one, too. I was laughing along to Poppy's routine, as well. It was funny, and like you guys, I got carried away. I didn't consider the bigger picture. I think we've all learned a tough lesson tonight.'

'Is there any way back from here?' Mack asks. 'Is there anything we can do to repair this?'

'I'll go and smoke the peace pipe with Uttam tomorrow. Dipak leaves us in the morning, as will most of you. But before he leaves, if I can convince him to speak to Uttam, I think we'll have a better chance of smoothing this over.'

The Mothers and Babies Hospital – I realise that I haven't even mentioned the idea to any of the volunteers yet. Do I bring this up now? Earlier tonight I was exhilarated with the possibilities of the project, and I was so desperately eager to share the plans with my team. With all the frenzy and upheaval over the three or four hours since then, the thought of telling them has lost a lot of its buzz. I'm still really excited about the hospital proposal, but decide that tomorrow morning will be a better time to share this with them. Instead, I start another tack.

'Let's put all of this business about Poppy and her father behind us for now. Let's talk about the rest of the entertainment you all put on tonight. Guys – I've gotta tell you, I was blown away. While I was out all week, running around with my little secret, you guys were busily preparing your own. I loved the surprise, even though I hated the lead-up, and apart from the final act, the evening was superb. Well done for a sensational production, and more importantly, well done for an outstanding camp. Thank you, all of you. I know you all must be exhausted right now, and some of you have a long day of travel tomorrow, but let me say one more thing – I would be honoured to work with every single one of you again.'

There is a procession of hugs, with Steph first, and then Jayne. Jayne has tears in her eyes as she embraces me.

'You old softie,' I tease. 'Just promise me you'll come on another camp with us.'

'Just try and stop me,' she sniffles.

Paul and Norman approach now.

'Okay,' Paul says. 'Man hug.'

We pat each other's shoulder during our embrace, in that classic man-on-man way. I look up to see Norman waiting with his teddy bear grin.

'Now, Norman,' I say, 'promise you won't crush me like one of your soft drink cans.'

I'm surprised to see that this gentle giant also has tears in his eyes. His hug is long and frighteningly firm, and when he finally finishes, he stares at the ground and walks away.

Louise and Mack walk up to me now, with arms poised.

'You guys?' I say with some surprise. 'You're not leaving tomorrow. We don't say goodbye for a few days, yet.'

'Yeah, well,' Louise replies, 'we know that. But we need a practice hug.'

Transforming People and Places

Day #25. 7:15am, Dining Hall

Jayne seems downcast at breakfast this morning. While the rest of the team chat freely amongst themselves, she sits alone at one of the smaller side tables. I sit down opposite her.

'You're going to miss all of this, aren't you?' I say.

Her voice is quieter than usual. 'Well, yeah, of course I will. But right now, I feel a bit stirred up, to be honest.'

'Because of last night?'

'I loved so much of last night. I just wish we hadn't been so stupid with Poppy's catwalk thing.' Jayne gives a shallow sigh before she continues. 'I was so miserable when I went to up bed last night. But since I got up this morning, I've been thinking about the whole camp – you know, not just last night, but all of the last three weeks here. This camp has been such an amazing experience. There've been so many ups, with a few horrible downs. But, can I tell you? I feel like these last few weeks have changed my life. They've changed my life, Dr Ray. For the better, I mean. I've never experienced anything like this before.'

'That's great, Jayne,' I say, 'but you still seem so ... detached.'

'I'm sorry. My head's still kind of jumbled. We've seen so much misery, and so many, like destitute people. It's fantastic to be able to help a lot of them, but I can't help feeling rotten that we can't help a lot more.'

'I'm guilty of that myself, Jayne. Louise keeps reminding me that I dwell too much on the negatives. We've got to acknowledge that

327

we have helped a lot of women. But at the same time, there's nothing wrong with dreaming for bigger and better things.'

'I know. Lu's right, of course. And, I've been thinking about stuff at home, too.' She looks down at the table and takes a long, slow breath.

After a few moments she looks up sadly and says, 'You know, I've got this little car at home, and sometimes when I'm driving along it makes this rattling noise. It's not a loud noise or anything, but it's still kind of annoying. I take it to the mechanic and he checks it out, but he can't find the rattle. I drive away and there it is again – that damn rattle. That sort of thing used to make me scream with fury. Well, I feel like such a jerk now when I think about how I used to carry on like that. There must be a hundred little things that my friends and I whinge about all the time. *Problems*, we call them – *problems*. Well, that's rubbish, Dr Ray. People over here – *they* have problems. When I think of the stuff I used to grumble about … I'll tell you this, I'm gonna appreciate things from now on. When I get back home, I'm not gonna complain about any of the petty little things anymore.'

'I know exactly what you mean, Jayne. A place like this really puts things into perspective.'

'And another thing,' Jayne says, 'it doesn't seem fair that you and Lu and Mack have to stay here at the camp after the rest of us leave today. You guys have worked as hard as anybody. You should be able to rest up now, too.'

'We'll be fine, Jayne. Without any more surgery here, it'll be pretty cruisy for us. I'm sure the three of us will be able to get lots of rest. And you know that some of us need to be here for a few more days in case there are any post-op complications. It'd be crazy for the whole team to stay on.'

As I look around the room, I realise that this will probably be the last time the whole of our group will be together. Suitcases and backpacks sit impatiently by the door to remind us of the looming departure.

Breakfast plates are being cleared by kitchen hands I haven't seen here before; it's no surprise that Poppy is not with us today. It's so disappointing she won't be able to say goodbye to those in our team who are leaving this morning. Sadly, I wonder if *any* of us will see Poppy again.

Liz is still here. She's in lively conversation with Steph at the other end of the main table. Dipak and Binod haven't arrived yet. They'll join us shortly before they begin their trip back to Dhulikhel. I'm so hoping Dipak will agree to delay his trip home to help me confront Poppy's father later this morning.

Uttam ... I sigh uneasily and try to block out the unsettling thoughts of the showdown to come.

I stand up and clink my glass to grab the team's attention. 'Okay, guys, most of you have to leave in a few minutes. There's something I need to say before you go.'

'Is this the last Sixty-Second Summary?' Paul asks with a grin.

'This will take a bit more than sixty seconds,' I reply soberly. 'What I have to say is really important to everyone here.'

The team are quiet now. Even Liz and Steph stop their noisy banter, and smile curiously as they wait for me to continue.

'Amongst all of the emotional ups and downs of these last few days, I've had a chance to think about our camps and our future here. And I'm sorry to say our model of medical care here in Nepal is not working. We cannot continue these camps.'

The smiling faces fall as the volunteers lean in towards me. Louise stares, eyes huge, and mouth agape.

'Early on in this camp I asked you all how we could make a major difference to the scourge of genital prolapse in this country. It was Norman who explained to me that in order to fix a problem, we need to get to its source – what's causing the prolapse in the first place? We all saw firsthand that there was another major problem with women's health here, too – the chilling loss of life of mothers and babies. And Louise helped me believe that we should tackle maternal issues as well.

'Well, we have identified a number of causes for both prolapse, and for the deaths of mothers and babies. We've found a number of factors – cultural attitudes, poor education, scarce medical staff, limited training of doctors, and nurses and midwives; poor hospital facilities. Jyoti, Dipak, and Liz have helped me understand these issues.

'What we've done until now is move our camps around the country. Like this camp we've just finished, we spend a few weeks at a time in one place, and then just move on. We've been using band-aids to patch up one problem at a time, without getting to the real cause of that problem. If we continue in this fashion, we're not going to make a major difference in this country. This is not going to work.'

I pause now, expecting some protests from the group. But everyone in the room remains silent. The team simply stare with looks of confusion and concern.

'This next part is really important. I want you all to think about this on your way home, or on your trek through Annapurna, or wherever you are over the next few days. It's an idea that Binod raised, and Dipak has developed. And I believe we can do this ... Let's change our model. Let's turn it on its head.'

The door to the outside opens and Binod and Dipak enter the room. But none of the volunteers appear to notice their arrival; every pair of eyes, fixed and uneasy.

I motion to Binod and Dipak to take a seat at one of the smaller tables. Once they're settled I continue my spiel.

'Let's take this collection of ramshackle buildings here that we loosely call our "hospital" and turn them into a real hospital. When we get home, let's campaign for funds to restore these buildings into a hospital that we can feel proud of. In fact, let's knock down these crumbling buildings, and build a proper hospital. A Mothers and Babies Hospital. Let's train up more local doctors, and nurses and midwives so that this place can run 24 hours a day, 365 days a year, even when we're not here. A full-time labour ward, a full-time surgical ward, with a really well-equipped operating theatre. Let's do this. Are you with me?'

I watch the looks of apprehension change to unsettled smiles of wonder. After a moment of silence, the team all begin talking at once, to each other, and to me.

'Whoa. One at a time,' I shout.

'But, Ray,' says Mack, 'how on earth could we do this? How do we fund the running of a hospital all year round? You said yourself – the organisation only just gets by with funding our trips a few times a year!'

'It's a crucial question, Mack,' I reply. 'There's no doubt we'll need to find some sizeable donations to build the hospital here, but the ongoing costs are another matter. Dipak has some ideas about this ... Dipak, would you mind sharing them with the group?'

'Of course, Dr Ray.' Dipak stands. 'As most of you know, I work with Dhulikhel Hospital. This is not a government hospital. It is an independent, not-for-profit hospital in Eastern Nepal. Those of us who work at Dhulikhel Hospital share the same principles as all of you do here – social equity and compassion. Over the last 15 years the hospital has grown substantially, and we are now a very large centre.

'One of our philosophies is to provide health care to remote areas of Nepal, and we have a number of successful outreach centres in rural regions of the country. We are aware of the profound difficulties with women's health in these parts of Nepal, and while I cannot give you any firm promises, I am quite confident that the authorities in my hospital would be very interested in supporting a Mothers and Babies Hospital here. As Dr Ray pointed out, in order to provide high standards of care for larger numbers of patients, the buildings here would need to be substantially upgraded. It may be more sensible to replace them all together. Dhulikhel Hospital would not be able to renovate or construct hospital buildings, but if somehow you – your organisation – were able to provide this development here, we are likely to be able to provide all of the funding for the operational costs of the hospital.'

Mack smiles. 'Ray, if we could pull this off, this could be sensational.'

'What about … what about our other camps in other parts of Nepal?' Louise asks. 'Do we stop these now?'

'No,' I say firmly, 'we've given our commitment to run these camps later this year, and we won't back down from that. I know it sounds like we're tackling more than we should, but we'll need to keep raising funds for these camps as well. I know some of you won't necessarily be coming back for other medical camps, but can I get your pledge to at least help out raising awareness, and to help with fundraising when we get back?'

'Well, *I'm* in,' yells Jayne. 'I don't know about the rest of you guys, but I love the sound of all of this. Imagine turning this place into a fully-fledged Mothers and Babies Hospital. Do you know what? We should call it the *Arpan Hospital*. She has inspired us. It would be a great tribute.'

'Did her little baby get a name?' Steph asks. 'We could name the hospital after the two of them.'

'I'm *absolutely* in,' says Louise, grinning broadly.

'I'm in,' says Norman.

'Paul?' I ask.

'Let me count the ways ...'

'Steph?'

'Well,' she says, 'you know this was my first camp. When we arrived here three weeks ago, I was really excited to start working here. I'm just about to leave now, and right now I'm even more excited than on that first day!'

I look across to Liz. 'As Liz knows, we're not leaving out the education side of this venture. Public health education and community-based programs are a crucial part of the whole package to improve things here. If we can get this hospital off the ground, if we can do this, we'll include a really active Community Health Department. This team will coordinate the work here with the families and teachers and schools in the region. As you know, there are so many forces that crush the health of the mums and their babies here. We're not going to tackle just one or two of these forces – we're going for an all-out assault on every factor we've found.'

I look around and fix on the eyes of each of the volunteers in turn. 'We *are* going to make a major difference.'

Farewell to Four

There are hugs and backslaps, and a few more tears as Jayne, Steph, Paul, and Norman prepare to leave the camp. The local porters have arrived to carry the luggage to the local village where our four volunteers will catch their bus. The first part of their journey will be a grueling nine-hour bus ride to Pokhara.

'Strange, isn't it?' says Norman as we watch the porters lift all of the luggage onto their backs. 'Every one of our porters is male. They can carry *these* loads, but they get their wives and daughters to carry everything else.'

'That's a start, I guess,' says Paul. 'We just have to convince the men to branch out and start carrying other heavy things.'

'You and Binod are catching the same bus?' I ask Dipak.

Dipak nods and smiles.

'You have been extremely helpful to us, Dipak, but I wonder – is it possible for you to help me one more time? It would mean you would need to delay your departure this morning ... what time is the next bus to Pokhara?'

Dipak gives a soft chuckle. 'I do not mean to be disrespectful when I laugh, Dr Ray, but there is only one bus to this village in a day. And even that bus does not always come.'

Of course – it's not as if we're at the centre of a major transport hub here. My spirit slumps as I realise I'll need to confront Uttam today without the valuable help of Dipak.

'Dr Ray,' Dipak continues, 'last night – the incident with the child and her father – that was a very difficult situation. After I left here, I continued to think about the conflict and its implications. And so, today, I have taken the liberty of arranging an interview with the child's father. I would be very happy if you wished to come with me, so that we could see him together.'

'Dipak – that is fantastic! But… I don't understand – the bus leaves from the village in only 30 minutes – barely enough time for you to walk there from here. There is no time for you to conduct an interview.'

Dipak expands his warm smile. 'I am catching the same bus as Binod and your team members, but I do not catch this bus until it travels the same route to Pokhara *tomorrow*. I have delayed my departure by one day in order to see the child's father.'

'Dipak, you continue to amaze me.' I shake my head and grin. 'You asked me if I wished to join you to see Poppy's father together? Right now, there is nothing more I would rather do.'

We step outside as the departing group begin their final goodbyes. The biting chill has returned, and once again a heavy frost coats the path and surrounding cypress trees. Binod is the only one among us who doesn't appear cold. He comes over and shakes my hand firmly.

'It has been a great pleasure to be working with you and your team. I have learned more surgery here in one week than before in one year.'

'I want this to be the start of much more to come, Binod. And it has been a joy to have you with us.'

Binod walks up to one of the porters who carries a number of backpacks on his shoulders. After a brief conversation, the porter lifts off one of the packs and hands it to Binod. It's clear that Binod intends to carry his own luggage.

Paul hugs his coat in close as he approaches me. 'Dr Ray – these three weeks have been spectacular. We've all decided we absolutely want to do this again.'

'Thanks, Paul. You know I'd be delighted to have every one of you back for another camp. Right now, you all need to recharge, and then you've all got some serious fundraising to do. Our dream has suddenly expanded.'

'And we'll all be doing everything we can to get there. Thanks for this wonderful opportunity, Ray. Oh – and I've got a farewell present for you.' Paul reaches into the inside pocket of his coat and pulls out a large plastic bag. 'I finally managed to get hold of some more coffee pods.'

'Okay,' I say with a smile, 'it's official then – we're not doing any more of these trips unless you come too.'

Jayne walks over slowly, and looks up at me with puffy eyes. She opens her mouth to speak, but no words come out. Instead she gives Louise and Mack, and me one final heavy hug before she turns away.

'I'll take care of her,' says Steph. She puts her arm around Jayne's slumping shoulders. And as I watch them slowly walk away together, I'm suddenly struck by the haunting image from last week when the two were so crushed at the loss of Arpan and her baby.

I walk over to address the departing group. 'Okay. Thanks, guys. For everything you've done. You've been a magnificent team. Safe travels now. We'll see you all again in Oz.'

With their bulky loads on their backs, Binod and the porters join the volunteers, and they all begin their slow and wistful walk along the frosty mountain path to the village. Even though our departing four volunteers carry none of the cumbersome luggage, somehow it is their footsteps that seem the heaviest.

A Crucial Confrontation

Mack, Louise, Dipak, and I sit around the potbelly planning our day. It's quieter than it should be with the loss of only four of the team.

'Not a good day to be outside,' says Mack. 'Thinking I might be staying in today. I seriously need to catch up on my crime fiction.'

'I think I'll be joining you,' says Louise, 'but they've only got one or two crime novels here. I might be fighting you to get my hands on them.'

Mack smiles softly. 'If you and I get into a fight, Louise, the crime might not be fiction.'

'Now, now, you two,' I say. 'See if you two can avoid this turning into a murder mystery, would you?'

'You'll be seeing Poppy's father this morning?' asks Mack.

'Dipak has very kindly decided to see Uttam this morning, too. We'll go together.' I turn to Dipak. 'I really do appreciate this.'

'Leaving one day late is no problem,' says Dipak. 'It is more important to try to calm this father.'

*

Dipak leads the way on our walk to Uttam's home.

'How do you know where Uttam lives?' I ask.

'Last night, when Uttam became angry, I asked some people from the village who this man was and where he lived.'

'You're sure Uttam will be at home? What if he's out working for the day?'

'This morning I left a message with some village farmers. I said I have important business with Uttam. He will wait for me.'

There is a quiet confidence about this man that I find endearing.

'Tell me a little more about the girl you call Poppy,' Dipak says.

'Well, as you saw last night, she breaks the mould of young girls in this part of the world. She's a child from remote Nepal, but often she's more like an adult from the West. She intrigues all of us with her poise and her spirit. We would so love the other girls in the region to somehow tap into that. But as you know, most girls here are shy and subdued. Most of the women are the same, and this is one of the big reasons for their massive health problems.'

'And you are concerned that Poppy's father will suppress her spirit and deny her opportunity?'

'Exactly. And last night will only reinforce Uttam's constraints. Even before last night he didn't want Poppy to continue her schooling, or go on to tertiary education. She's such an intelligent child, and she *wants* to learn more; she *wants* a career. If her education is blocked, it will be such a waste of a really promising life.'

Dipak stops walking, and looks at the ground in front of him. He seems to be processing what I've said. 'I don't know this girl, Poppy,' he says eventually, 'but I do know this situation – a strict father who is set in his ways, and very dominant over his wife and his daughters.'

'Uttam has no wife; she died in childbirth. Poppy is the only daughter.'

'I see,' Dipak says. He sighs. 'These things are likely to make this man even more protective of his daughter. Dr Ray, you must understand – this inflexible behaviour, these rigid constraints you see in Uttam that frustrate you so much – they come from a place of fear. Fear of change, fear of ridicule among his friends. It is difficult to change this behaviour, but if we have any chance of change, we must first remove this fear.'

As we continue our walk, Dipak's wise words dance disorderly steps in my head. What he says makes so much sense, but how do we remove Uttam's fear?

There is no one in sight as we arrive at the entrance to Uttam's home. We're about to call out to him when Uttam greets us at the door. His face is dirt-stained, and his eyes tired and resentful. I introduce him to Dipak, and immediately they strike up a conversation. Uttam directs us inside where the air is warm from the fire that flickers in the open stove. The room's murky fog is deeper today, and I struggle more than usual to breathe the bitter fumes. I look around in the dim, smoky light, and note there is no one else in the room.

Dipak addresses me. 'Uttam asks if you know where Poppy slept last night. She did not sleep here.'

'I have not seen Poppy since she left the Dining Hall last night with Uttam.'

Uttam scowls before he and Dipak resume their exchange at a lively pace. I pick up very few of their words, and eventually give up trying to understand their meaning. I accept that I'll need to wait for Dipak's translation. While I wait, my mind wanders to the others who usually share this small home. Where is Gorham? Is she safe from Suntil? Nerum is probably at school. But where is Poppy? And was she punished for last night's 'performance'? This would be grossly unfair.

Several minutes pass with Dipak and Uttam still deep in discussion. My eyes have adjusted somewhat to the light, and I can now see the faces of the two men more clearly. Now and then Uttam appears intense, at times fierce, but Dipak remains calm and centered throughout.

Finally there is a pause in conversation between the two men. They both stare at me with faces that are fixed and firm. Dipak addresses me.

'We have just talked of last night and Uttam's anger at the portrayal of his daughter. I asked Uttam to explain exactly why he was so furious. Uttam said, "This dancing, this makeup on face – this is for *bad* women, *bad* girls. Bad girls do not find husband. You, Dipak – you are Nepali. You must understand this."

'I explained that I am indeed Nepali, and that in fact I have come from a village in this same region. I have two daughters of my own, and I also want the best for them. I explained that the purpose of last night was to exchange cultures – cultural dance and cultural dress. The evening was your team's expression of thanks to the people of this village. It was never your intention to display lewd or corrupt behaviour in anyone, and especially not in his daughter.

'"This cannot be truth," Uttam said, "Wild music happen. Makeup happen. You people make this happen."

'I explained to Uttam that the 'wild music' was in fact selected and played by Binod, another local Nepali, and it had nothing to do with your team. No one is sure where Poppy got the makeup and hairstyle. The performance last night simply got out of hand, and you and your team are deeply sorry for offending him.'

I look across to Uttam and nod solemnly. 'I want to be open with Uttam. Can you please translate this next sentence?' I take a breath, then continue. 'I must be honest with you, Uttam – there was brief time during your daughter's performance where I laughed. Even though I knew it was wrong, I laughed. It is not meant to add your offence, but I laughed.'

Dipak's jaw tightens. 'Dr Ray, are you sure you want me to translate this?'

'No, I am not sure. But please translate this anyway.'

Dipak pauses, and with a deeply troubled expression, begins another discussion in Nepali. As I wait for Uttam's response, this morning's breakfast churns queasily in the pit of my stomach.

Uttam's eyes flash to me, back to Dipak, and then to me again. Dipak translates once more.

'There was no need to be telling this,' Uttam replies. 'You could keep this secret from me. But, Dr Ray, you do not know this – last night I watch you during show. I see you laugh. And now you tell me truth … I respect honesty from you.'

A win. A big win, I think. And a big sigh of relief from me. Dipak has a quiet smile on his face now as he continues to translate.

'Uttam,' I say, 'there are good things and bad things in both our cultures.' I decide to launch into another delicate area. 'You know we lost a mother and her baby in our hospital last week?'

'Yes. But you do the best you can to stop this.'

'This mother tried to deliver her baby at home. This is a tradition in many parts of your country. If this mother had come to the hospital for care, she and her baby would almost certainly be alive. I believe care of mothers at home, without trained midwives, is a bad part of your culture.'

Uttam does not respond to this. He simply stares into the dwindling flames of his open fire.

'Twelve years ago, your wife may have survived if she had delivered in a hospital.' I reach out and put my hand firmly on his. He looks to my hand, and then to my face. 'No one can be blamed for her death,' I continue. 'Twelve years ago we did not know as much as we know today.'

After a long stretch of silence, Uttam speaks again. 'What other things bad in our culture?'

'I am a foreigner here, a visitor to your country, and I have no right to interfere with your culture. But I am also a doctor who sees many women suffer with conditions that are preventable, or at least treatable before they reach severe stages. You know we spend most days here performing surgery on women. These women suffer with conditions that are due to 'bad' things in your culture – heavy lifting, poor care during the pregnancy, poor diet, barriers to medical care ... and poor education.'

I search Uttam's eyes to weigh his reaction, but I see nothing. He remains silent and stone-faced. Suddenly, he stands and stares back into the fire. I sense that he's going to demand Dipak and I leave his home. Instead, he moves closer to the stove, picks up the heavy kettle, and proceeds to make us all a large pot of tea.

*

There is silence among the three of us as Uttam gathers three teacups and places them before us. He pours the brew into each cup, and then looks across to Dipak and me in turn. After some time he begins to speak.

'Your country, Dr Ray,' he says, 'it is rich country. My children learn this from school. Your country have big homes, big cars, much food.' He squats down now, wraps his hands around his teacup, and stares ahead. 'My country not have these things. My country poor for money, poor for food.' He turns now and looks directly at me. 'But my country has *parampara*.'

I'm confused as Dipak translates this last sentence. '*Parampara*?' I say to him, 'Dipak, I don't understand this word.'

'I'm sorry, Dr Ray. The closest meaning to *parampara*, I think would be *tradition*. Nepal has much tradition.'

Uttam nods sternly. '*Parampara,*' he repeats, and Dipak continues to translate. 'Tradition. You have rich, we only have tradition. And you wish to take this away?'

I pause to collect my thoughts. 'Tradition is crucial for your country, Uttam. It's a big part of your identity, your soul. It is the backbone of your culture. And when we foreigners visit Nepal, this is something that we admire profoundly. But some of your traditions are cruel. They are responsible for many deaths and a great deal of suffering, particularly of women and babies.'

Uttam flinches, but says nothing.

'When humane people choose to reform their harmful traditions, they do not surrender their culture or their soul. On the contrary, they *strengthen* these things. I believe that strength of culture cannot be measured by repeating practices from the past. If values and traditions are simply frozen in time, the culture weakens. A strong culture recognises its past mistakes and makes crucial changes. In this way, it must evolve through the generations.'

I stop and wait as Dipak translates my last sentences, and I wonder if my thoughts might be lost in their translation. There is no way somebody like Nabin would be able to get across these more complex ideas, but with a more educated interpreter like Dipak, I think I'm in with a chance.

After a lengthy translation, Uttam nods tersely a few times before beginning another long conversation with Dipak. I sip my tea with uncertainty and watch the two men's faces as they continue their sober exchange.

After a time Uttam stands again and begins to pace the small room in silence. His face appears darker and more tortured than I've seen it before.

Eventually, it's Dipak who speaks. 'Ray, I told Uttam that even in remote areas such as this, we cannot hide from change. Television and radio have already arrived. Soon internet and social media will follow. New ideas will be introduced to tempt the people in his village, and especially the children. I have confronted these challenges with my own children. I told Uttam that instead of chastising our children, we must guide them.'

Uttam squats down again next to me, puts his open hand to his chin, and stares directly into my eyes. He looks utterly miserable.

'Uttam,' I say, 'it takes courage to rise above the cruelty of deep-rooted traditions. My team and I make mistakes, too, but we are all compelled to overcome these. The force that drives our organisation is compassion. Let compassion be your guiding force, too.'

Uttam continues to stare in silence. Wearily, he stands once more and looks into the dying flames of his stove. As if in a dream, he walks to the corner of the room and stops. Slowly, he lowers his head to face the floor. I follow his eyes and see the collection of centuries-old rhododendron wood by his feet. He stares at the small pile for some time.

Finally, he stoops down uneasily and picks up the solid, gnarled branches. And with a look of biting defeat, he heaves the ancient logs into the smoldering fire.

A Confusing Encounter

1:00pm, Dining Hall

'You know, Lu Lu,' I say, 'I really think we've started making inroads. Uttam is as stubborn as a mule, but this morning was the first time he's really looked like budging from his misogynist ways.'

Louise looks amazed. 'Wow! But that doesn't make sense. He looked so angry last night with the Poppy thing. How on earth did you calm him down – let alone get him to change his beliefs?'

'I'm sure he hasn't suddenly changed his beliefs, but now he's entertaining the idea that there may be a better way to treat women and girls in this country. And to be honest, I think Dipak had a lot to do with that.'

'And what will that mean for Poppy?'

'Well, before we left, I said to Uttam that if he allowed Poppy to continue at school and then to go on to university or some other tertiary studies, we would pay for her education. I said that we would arrange a scholarship for her that would cover all her school fees and an allowance for the amount she would have earned if she'd been working here in the village.'

'I *love* the idea. He agreed to that?'

'He's considering it. And I'm quietly confident he'll accept. When we leave here, Dipak will follow through with this and set up everything.'

'When you say "we" will pay this, does that mean *Australians for Women's Health*?'

'No. I think we've got more than enough on our plate right now. It's not a lot of money, Lu Lu. I'm sure we'll get a sponsor for this. I'll pay out of my own pocket if I have to.'

'You won't need to do that, Ray. I'm sure every one of our group would put in for a scholarship for Poppy. Things really are coming together finally, aren't they?'

'It's just amazing when I think of how miserable it all looked a few days ago. There's still a fair way to go, but I really feel we're getting somewhere.'

'After lunch, will you come with me to see Laxmi?'

'The shy girl you've been coaxing out of her shell?'

'You certainly wouldn't call her shy any more, Ray. I can't wait to show you how she's blossomed.'

3:30pm, Hospital Path

'Look at that, Ray,' Louise says. She points to the high naked branches on the poplar trees. 'Finally, all the leaves have gone. I thought those last few might hang on forever.'

We continue along the winding path until it eventually opens into the broad grasslands.

'There she is,' Louise says. 'Come and see how much she's changed.'

Laxmi stands in the rice paddy behind her family's small home. Her shoulders are hunched, her arms firmly by her side. It's three weeks now since we first met her, but from here her pose seems no different to the one I remember on that day.

'Laxmi!' Louise shouts as she beckons the child to join us. But Laxmi does not move. Louise turns to me. 'This is not like her, Ray. Honestly, she's so changed.'

We walk towards Laxmi, but she cowers as we approach. When we're quite close, she speaks softly. 'No more. Please. It is wrong.'

'Lu, this must be me. I'm making her uncomfortable. I'll go and leave you two together.'

But as I turn to leave, I hear Laxmi's gentle voice once more. 'No, Dr Ray. It is not you.'

I turn back to face Laxmi. 'What do you mean?'

She doesn't answer me, but as I study her features I see that there *is* a change to the demeanour we saw earlier in the camp. She no longer looks to the ground; today she looks into our eyes. But her face is deeply flushed, and she holds her tiny hands to her cheeks as if to cool them. Today, her look is not of shyness, but instead suggests shame.

Louise reaches out to her. 'What is it, Laxmi? What is wrong?' As she gently touches the young girl's hand, Laxmi recoils with a look of terror. It's as if she's just been slapped.

'*No!*' Laxmi shouts. 'I am sorry.'

Louise and I look at each other again, confused.

'Please tell us what's wrong,' Louise repeats.

But Laxmi turns and walks away. We watch her as she heads through the stubbly rice paddy towards the small toilet hut that sits at the edge of the field. She stops there, and leans uneasily on the wall of the low mud brick structure.

'I don't think we should push this, Lu,' I say. 'She seems to want her space.'

'I just don't understand,' Louise says, shaking her head.

Behind us now, we hear shouting. The words are in Nepali. We turn to see a middle-aged woman running towards us from the direction of Laxmi's home. I don't recognise the woman, and I don't understand her words.

'*Phohora!*' she screams, as she approaches us. As she reaches us, she directs her frantic words to Louise. '*Phohora!*'

The woman carries a small stone jug in her right hand. She hurriedly grabs Louise's right arm and throws the fluid contents of her container over her hand. Louise looks horrified as she stares at her hand, and then at the woman. The woman continues to mutter in Nepali while she walks off in the direction of the home. Louise lifts her sodden hand to her nose and immediately screws up her face.

'Oh, gross!' she cries. 'That is revolting.'

I let out a light chuckle. 'Hey Lu – welcome to the club. I've been screamed at in Nepali while my arm is pulled, too. Haven't had any foul fluid thrown on me yet though. You probably have to be really special for that.'

'Just when I think I'm starting to understand this country,' Louise sighs, 'and then something crazy like this happens.'

7:15pm, Dining Hall

It's still difficult to get used to the quietness of the room. I already miss the laughter from Jayne and Steph, and the wisecracks from Norman and Paul. Louise and I join Mack, who sits by the stove reading his crime novel.

'It was so bizarre, Mack,' Louise says. 'This young girl, Laxmi – she'd become so friendly, almost confident. And today she ran away from us. And then this woman came from nowhere, screaming, and threw this stinking liquid all over my hand. Like, what the …?'

Mack puts down his book and strokes his chin. 'Perhaps she's a Shaman. Ray and I had a fun time with one early in the camp. Is there such a thing as a female Shaman? A Sha-woman? She could have told your young girl that is was dangerous for her soul to speak to strangers from the West. Your stinking fluid might be some form of spiritual cleanser.'

'Nabin might be able to enlighten us,' I say. 'It's his last night with us so I asked him to join us for dinner.'

'Anyone seen Poppy recently?' Louise asks.

'Not since the catwalk incident,' I reply.

'Will her father punish her, do you think?'

'I think Dipak managed to convince Uttam that guidance is better than strict punishment.' But as I say these words, I realise they are more hope than belief.

Nabin enters the room and walks over to our table to join us.

'*Namaste*, Nabin,' Mack says. 'Do you mind me telling you? You look exhausted.'

'*Namaste*, everybody. Yes, I feel very much tired. I enjoy work with everybody here, but normally I do not work so long hours. Soon I need big rest.' He smiles wearily.

Poor Nabin. We've worked him hard. Our other official interpreter, Gamika, has only been available on limited days, and as a result Nabin's workload has been heavy. On top of this, I've asked him to help me after hours a number of times with all sorts of other activities.

'I hope you understand that we really appreciate everything you've done for us,' I say. 'You've gone above and beyond.'

Nabin looks to the ceiling as if to find 'above and beyond'.

'Hey, Nabin,' Louise says, 'why would someone throw foul-smelling fluid on me?'

Nabin looks confused. 'A Nepali person put this on you?'

'Yes. A woman, today.'

'You are sick, Miss Lu Lu?'

'No, but I sure felt sick when I smelled it. It was putrid.'

'Miss Lu Lu, this fluid is probably urine from cow. Cow urine take away sickness.'

'Whoa!' Mack says. 'Cow urine cures disease?'

'Yes, Dr Mack. Many believe cow urine fix infection, abdominal problem, even cancer.'

'But why would the woman think I was … wait – I touched Laxmi. Perhaps she is sick.'

The four of us look up as the kitchen hands enter the room carrying tonight's dinner. Sadly, Poppy is not among them.

As our food is placed before us, Louise turns to me. 'Ray, I'm going to get to the bottom of this. If Laxmi is sick, maybe we can help her.'

'You want to visit her again tomorrow?'

'Absolutely.'

We all begin our meal and I turn to Nabin. 'You spoke to some of the audience from last night? What was their reaction to Poppy's dance routine?'

'I spoke to a few persons, Dr Ray. Most not seem to understand this dance. They say they laugh because their friends laugh. I think last night not such a problem for them.'

We're all finishing our meal when the Dining Hall door opens. Uttam walks inside. A white smear of frost covers Uttam's hat and shoulders. He looks over to our table with a frown and walks quickly towards us.

'Ganuradha,' he says. 'Ganuradha?' Poppy – he's looking for Poppy. Clearly, she's still missing.

I ask Nabin to explain that we still haven't seen Poppy since the concert. Uttam looks troubled, as he sits down with a jolt. Nabin translates as Uttam continues to speak.

'Child not come home since yesterday night. I try home of relatives. No good.'

'Has this happened before, Uttam?' I ask.

'Child always comes home. Sometimes late with working here. I told no more working here … That before I speak to you today, Dr Ray.'

'And she was upset with this?'

'Yes. Angry. Not respect for father.'

'She has definitely not been here, Uttam. Is there somewhere else you could try? A friend's place?'

'Not at friends' places.' Uttam scowls once more.

I'm at a loss to offer any other advice. What do you do in these parts when a person goes missing? Call the Nepali police? The nearest police would be several hours from here.

'Uttam?' It's Mack who speaks. 'Would you like us to help you look for her?' Nabin translates once more.

'No. Thank you. I will get friends to look. I go now.'

And with that, Uttam storms out through the Dining Hall door.

'What do you make of all that, Ray?' asks Mack.

'Well, she's a strong-minded thing. I wonder if she went to school today. If she did, there's a decent chance she's with a school friend, or maybe even Liz.'

'Should we do something?' asks Louise.

'Why don't we ring Liz to see if she knows anything?' I say. 'She left her mobile number with us. Hopefully we'll get reception tonight; it's so hit and miss up here.'

But when we try to make a call, there is no reception. Mack curses in frustration. 'One thing I've learnt this trip,' he says, 'the mobile network is right up there with the electricity system.'

'I don't think there's anything else we can do tonight. If she's still not back in the morning we'll ask some of the school kids if they saw her at school today.'

Imparting and Departing of Wisdom

Day #26. 7:55am, Dining Hall

After a fitful night's sleep, I wander downstairs for breakfast. Mack and Louise are already here, warming themselves next to the fire.

'Morning, Ray,' says Mack. 'You know the best thing about those other four of our team leaving us?'

'What's that?'

'I don't have to compete for a spot next to this damn fire.'

'Good for you. I would have thought you Scots would be used to the cold.'

'There's cold, and then there's the Himalayas, Ray.'

'You two sleep okay?' I ask.

'I tossed and turned,' Louise says. 'I was really worried about Poppy. I kept thinking we should have done something else to help last night.'

'I know, Lu. I was the same. But I kept thinking – what could we do? Wander around in the dark calling out her name? I tried Liz's mobile again this morning, but there's still no reception. I'll chase up Milu, or one of her other friends, before they head off to school this morning.'

The Dining Hall door opens again, and we look up to see Dipak. He greets us as he removes his hat and coat.

'*Namaste*, Dipak,' I say as I glance at my watch. 'The bus leaves the same time as yesterday? You'll need to get to the village fairly soon.'

'Yes, you're right,' he says. 'I won't have much time to chat, I'm afraid.'

'Can we quickly ask you about a strange incident we were involved in yesterday?' Louise asks. And after she describes yesterday's encounter with Laxmi, Dipak nods his head.

'*Chaupadi*,' he says. 'I'm afraid this practice is still very common in this part of the country. Women and girls are banished from their home during the time of their menstruation.[145]

'Oh my God,' Louise exclaims. 'I thought she must have had some horrible disease, like leprosy. It was just a period? I don't know whether to be happy or sad.'

'*Chaupadi*?' I say. 'It's a disgusting practice. But I thought that was outlawed here. How? How can it still go on?'

'There is now legislation in Nepal that bans this practice[146], but I'm afraid this law is rarely applied in these parts. During the time of menstruation women cannot enter the home. They must live and sleep in a separate area to the rest of the family. Usually this is within a *goth* – a very small dwelling away from the home.'

The tiny hut that Laxmi retreated to yesterday morning – I realise now that this was no outside toilet. I feel foolish as it hits me that this crude structure was obviously a *goth*. And the many other huts dotted around this village and surrounds – it's likely these are also *goths*.

'Dipak,' I say, 'these *goths* – they have no doors or windows?'

'No, Dr Ray. The women and girls who are exiled to these small sheds are very much exposed to the elements – the cold, the wild animals, and sometimes men who are looking for vulnerable females. I am sorry to say there have been many deaths in *goths* – some from hypothermia, a number from snake bite.[147] And many girls suffer rape.[148] We don't know the full number of rape victims because families will usually not report the assault for fear their daughter would then be unable to be married.[149]

I feel sick as I hear these words; even more torture for the women of this region.

'And what about the offensive fluid that was thrown over Louise's hand?' Mack asks.

'Yes, that will be urine of cow, sir. Cow is holy, and cow urine is felt by some to purify a person who is sick or accidentally touched by a menstruating woman.'

'They can't *touch* anyone while they're having their periods?' Louise asks, astonished.

'That is the rule. They are told they are impure during this time. If they touch cattle, the cattle will die; if they cross a water source, it will dry up; if they enter the home, it will infuriate the gods, and as a result their whole family will suffer.[150] They must try to survive on rice, and some cereals or dry foods. It is forbidden to eat nutritious foods like milk and meat and vegetables.[145]

Mack and Louise and I stare at Dipak in disbelief as he describes the appalling life that women and girls must endure for up to five days each month.

'We've been here for nearly a month now. Why are we only hearing about this now?' I ask.

'It is not something that is spoken about. Because it is now illegal, families usually keep these things to themselves.' There is so little emotion in his voice. Dipak is a compassionate man; I have seen this so often in the short time I've known him. Why is he not disturbed as we are at this brutal, inhumane practice?

'And after birth, Dipak?' I say. 'There is more seclusion while the mother continues to pass blood?'

'In many cases, yes, Dr Ray. She and her baby must try to survive in the *goth* with these terrible conditions and a most unhealthy diet.'

As I try to absorb this alarming information, I wonder how many others have suffered like this during the few weeks we've been here. Surely this must contribute to the numbers of deaths of mothers and babies in this region.[149]

'I am happy to discuss this further with you all,' Dipak says, 'but I'm afraid that if I don't soon leave to catch my bus, I'll be spending another unscheduled night here.'

Dipak stands and says his goodbyes to Mack and Louise, but they still seem numb to his dreadful revelations. As Dipak turns to me I say, 'May I come with you while you walk to the village? I need to see some school children, and I'm keen to explore this more on the way.'

'I would be most happy for you to join me.'

I grab my jacket and head off with Dipak along the winding path that leads to the local village.

'A lot of this doesn't make sense, Dipak. As you know, ten days ago here, a dying mother lost a great deal of blood. Many of the locals were touching her. Some were even stained with her blood. It didn't seem to hold back any of these people.'

'Yes, it seems irrational. A woman menstruating or losing small amounts of blood after birth is considered untouchable. But with heavy bleeding – life-threatening bleeding, whatever the source – the gods seem to overlook contact with blood.'

'That's very generous of them,' I reply as we continue our walk. 'Please don't be offended by my next question.'

'I think that is most unlikely, Dr Ray.'

'You don't seem to be upset with the whole practice of *chaupadi*. I'm not suggesting you support the tradition, but I guess I'm surprised you're not outraged like we are.'

Dipak stops and gives me a gentle smile. 'Please believe me, Dr Ray, I am very disturbed by the practice of *chaupadi*. I deeply believe this most harmful tradition needs to be stamped out. But outraged? No. I have found that outrage rarely helps overcome adversity. What I have found is that the most effective way to tackle difficult problems is to methodically work through them and then carefully execute a well-planned strategy. *Chaupadi* occupies a considerable part of our Community Health program.'

'What can we do, Dipak? How do we overcome this disgusting tradition?'

'People must want change, Dr Ray. You will find that many of the women in these parts do not want to stop chaupadi. It is not just the men who push for it to continue.'

'But it's so obviously bad for them. You said yourself that there have been rapes and deaths because of the girls' isolation. How do we make them *want* to change?'

Dipak looks at me with his blazing cobalt eyes. 'Dr Ray, yesterday we seemed to have a win with Uttam. We managed to influence an individual. But these individual battles are so rarely won. I know you understand that this society is a collectivist one. People do things as a group – work, play, religious ceremonies – so many things. They rely on each other. To risk going against the norm in regions like this means risking being ostracised. And in a society where people are so dependent upon each other, being excluded can make living nearly impossible.'

I think back to Jyoti's shrewd thoughts about the education of women. *Together they have better chance to make change.*

'But there are some individuals who break this mould?' I ask.

'Yes. We must throw most of our efforts into educating groups, but if there can be a few brave individuals who can pioneer healthy change, we have an even greater chance of success.'

'The banished girl Louise described – Laxmi. I want to see her parents and reason with them. And if they won't listen, I'll remind them of the law against *chaupadi*.'

'Dr Ray, I strongly suggest you do not do this. There are better ways to tackle this problem, and it will require a community approach.'

It's obvious Dipak has far more experience in this area than I do, but I struggle to hide my frustration that we can't do much right now to battle this repugnant practice. I make a promise to myself that we will promote Dipak's Community Health programs to stamp out this miserable scourge.

Dipak and I continue a little further until we reach the trail that divides the village.

'And here I must leave you, Dipak. I need to head in the other direction to meet some of the children.'

'Well, Dr Ray, it has been an enormous pleasure working with you and your team. I must say I have been extremely impressed with your passion and your commitment in what you do. Your team are already changing so many lives, and with the plans for a hospital here, we can improve many thousands more.'

'Dipak, I've learned so much from you. You've managed to guide me through all sorts of challenging situations here, and I'll never forget that. I totally look forward to a really successful working relationship together.'

We give each other a warm *Namaste*, and a Western handshake, and walk our separate ways.

Mounting Distress

As I continue along the first part of the school trail, I think to myself how fortunate we are to have come across this wonderfully wise man. Dipak has opened my eyes to so many things in this underprivileged part of Nepal. But I begin to feel a little disappointed that I didn't really thank him enough for all his help.

My thoughts are broken with the shouting of children.

'Dr Ray! Dr Ray!'

I turn to see several children running along the path towards me.

'You come with us to school again today?' a tall boy shouts.

'Not today,' I reply when they reach me. I don't recognise anyone in the small group, but I ask, 'Do any of you know Poppy? That's Ganuradha. Anyone know her?'

Every child laughs, and the tall boy speaks again. 'Dr Ray, everybody knows Poppy.'

'Okay,' I say, 'was she at school yesterday?'

There is mumbling in the group, as each child looks from one to another. While they discuss my question, three more children run up to join them.

'Nobody sees Poppy yesterday, Dr Ray,' the tall boy replies.

'Thank you,' I say as I try to hide my concern. 'Now, you should all continue on to school.'

As I turn to leave, I see another child in the distance. This child is small and thin, and walks without purpose. I quickly catch up to the child and say, '*Namaste*, Milu.'

Milu turns and looks shocked to see me. '*Namaste*, Dr Ray.'

'Milu, I need to speak to you. Can you talk?'

'Yes, sir, Dr Ray.' He nods extravagantly with his reply.

'I need to know when you last saw Poppy.'

'Sir. Not for two days now. She promised she will be walking with me to school yesterday, but she not come. She said she will come because I do things for her. She not come to school. I worry for her.'

'Okay. What things did you do for her?'

'Sir ...' But Milu looks down and says nothing more.

'Milu, it is important you are honest with me. This is very important for Poppy. If she is in danger, we need to help her.'

Milu does not lift his head and merely looks from one foot to the other.

'She make me promise, but now I am scared for her.'

'We can help her if you tell me what is going on. I will not tell anyone else your secret.'

Milu looks up slowly and sighs. 'Sir, Dr Ray – I do anything for Poppy if she is nice to me. Poppy say, "If you like me you will help me with my plan."'

'Yes, Milu. What is Poppy's plan?'

'You will not punish me, sir?' Milu's chin trembles with his plea.

'No, Milu. Tell me what you did.'

'Sir ... I steal things for Poppy to help her. I steal ladies' makeup for face and hair. I steal these from guests. Poppy say she want to be looking like grown up. I give these things to her, and now she is gone. It is my fault, sir. I am so sorry.'

At least an explanation for Poppy's appearance on the catwalk, but I still don't see a connection with her disappearance.

'I understand why you want to help Poppy, Milu, and it is wrong to steal. But if Poppy is missing, why do you blame yourself?'

'Sir, I cannot be in Dining Hall for your concert. I wait outside in cold to see Poppy after concert. But I see bad men, sir, *bad men*. I know these bad men from photos they show at school. These men take children, take girls for India. Make girls do bad things.' Milu is more agitated now, and his whole body shakes as he speaks. I hold my breath and wait for him to continue.

'I see these men go into concert. I know they see Poppy with makeup. I hear much laughter from concert. Then I see Poppy leave with father. Father is very angry. Then I see bad men leave, too. Two men. They watch Poppy with father and follow them. Bad men not see me. I follow them. They go all way to Poppy's home. Now they know Poppy's home. I should say to Poppy and father, "Beware".' Milu hangs his head low once more. 'Poppy's father is so angry. I am too scared to say, "Beware". Milu is weak. I am so sorry.'

Child trafficking. I can't be hearing this. I try to be calm, to somehow reassure little Milu, but now I feel my own hands start to shake in alarm. Oh my God – what next?

Child sex trafficking from Nepal to India is rampant. With the 1850km open border between the two countries, up to 10,000 women and girls are trafficked to India each year.[151] Most trafficked girls of Poppy's age are sold to brothels, where they become the property of the brothel owners. They are forced to work as young prostitutes until they can pay back their purchase price.[152] The very thought is repulsively nauseating.

Poppy is far too smart to be coerced or deceived into trafficking. If she has been abducted, this will most likely have been by force. But when? Perhaps on the night of the catwalk, after some verbal abuse from Uttam. It's easy to imagine her storming out of her home after a violent outburst from her father. The image of two 'bad men' seizing her by force is bone chilling, let alone the unspeakable violations that would follow.

Milu has tears streaming down his cheeks. I put a hand on each of his shoulders. 'Milu, look at me. You must try to be brave. I promise you, we will do everything in our power to find Poppy and bring her home safely.'

Milu merely nods in response.

'You must go to school now. I want you to speak to one of your teachers, Miss Beeyan. You need to find her and ask her to telephone me immediately, do you understand?'

Milu nods again and moves in the direction of the school. I walk away in a daze. I have no idea where to go or what to do.

Dipak – I need advice from Dipak. I walk quickly towards the village. I pick up my speed and start to run. Faster now, like a maniac. I need to get to the pick-up point for the bus that runs to Pokhara. Perhaps the bus is yet to arrive, and Dipak is still waiting.

Out of breath, I arrive at the bus stop. I look around in hope, but the area is deserted. It's clear the bus has already left. I squat down and dial Dipak's mobile number. What a surprise – there is no reception.

I remain in my squatted pose and cover my face with my hands. There must be authorities who deal with these sorts of things. Whoever they are, I need to find them and alert them. The photos of the 'bad men' will help. They'll also need a good description of Poppy – will there be a photo of her somewhere? I'll ask Liz when she calls me. And Uttam – what do I tell Uttam? God, what a mess.

10:30am, Dining Hall

'Thank God you're both still here,' I say to Mack and Louise as I walk back inside. 'We've got a potential disaster.'

Mack and Louise put down their books.

'It's Poppy,' I say. 'I think she's been abducted.'

I explain my meeting with Milu and his terror when he described the 'bad men' who followed Poppy and her father home after the concert.

'You should have seen poor Milu's face – he was distraught.'

'Ray,' says Mack, 'your own face looks distraught.'

'Is there another possible explanation?' asks Louise. 'Maybe she's just upset with her dad and she's run away from home.'

'I'd love to believe that,' I reply, 'but you heard Uttam say he's tried her friends' homes. And with the freezing conditions here, she wouldn't survive a night outside.'

Mack and Louise are silent now as they realise the gravity of Poppy's situation. I hear the sounds of a mobile phone and realise that it is mine. It's Liz.

'Ray,' she says, 'I have Milu with me. He's sobbing. He won't tell me what is wrong, but he says I must call you. Is everything okay?'

'I'm afraid not, Liz. I hate to tell you this, but Poppy may have been abducted.'

'Oh my God!'

'You show the school children pictures of men associated with child trafficking?' I ask.

'Yes, as a warning to stay away from them. Oh my God, these men have taken Poppy?'

'Well, we're not sure. Milu saw two of these men follow Poppy home last night. She's been missing since then. Her father is really worried.'

'I don't blame him. Ray, this is awful. *3 Angels* – I'll get in touch with *3 Angels*. They're the group who brought us the photos. They're an NGO who do some wonderful work with child trafficking. Not just with rescue, they rehabilitate the children, too.'

'Child trafficking' – the sound of those words sends chills down my spine. 'They might find her, Liz? Bring her home safely?'

'Ray, I just don't know. This happened two nights ago? They may already have crossed the border. We've got school photos of all the children. I'll get Poppy's photo and the photos of the men Milu spotted, and I'll send them to *3 Angels*' office. It's our best hope.'

'Is there anything we can do down here?'

'I doubt it. Does Poppy's father know?'

'I think he may be suspicious, but I don't expect he knows.'

'The best thing you can do right now is to see him and explain everything. Try your best to calm him.'

'Liz?'

'Yes?'

'Be easy on Milu. He feels it's all his fault for this because he didn't warn Poppy.'

'Of course, Ray. I'll let you know if I hear anything.'

As I outline Liz's ideas to Mack and Louise, Nabin arrives at the Dining Hall to say goodbye.

'*Namaste*, Nabin,' I say. 'You're walking back to your village from here?'

'Yes, Dr Ray. I come to say thank you for everything. I very much love the work your team doing.'

'It's we who must thank you, Nabin. We have worked you so hard. But now I am going to ask for one final thing.' My tone becomes urgent. 'We think Poppy may have been abducted. I need you to help me explain this to her father.'

Nabin's face blanches in horror. 'Abducted? Stolen? Please not to India – please no. This very, very bad, sir.'

'We must tell Uttam. Do you know where he is now?'

'I will try home, sir. And in fields. You will come? Or I can bring Uttam here?'

'I'll wait here where the phone reception is better. I'll make some calls to the police at the Indian border. It would be very kind of you to bring Uttam here.'

'This very important, Dr Ray.'

'Thank you, Nabin. And please do not tell Uttam anything. It is probably best if he hears this from me.'

As Nabin sets off to find Uttam, Louise says to me, 'Ray, I can't tell you how gutted I feel. She's such a gorgeous, gorgeous creature.'

'I'm struggling to compute any of this, Lu.'

'You'll ring the Dhangadhi police, Ray?' asks Mack.

'Yeah. Dhangardhi is the closest border town to here. I guess this is the most likely place they'll try to cross into India – if they haven't already done so.'

There are a number of brochures and magazines in the Dining Hall advertising various hostels and hotels in Dhangardhi, and after a series of unsuccessful calls I finally get through to *Hotel Saathi*, where the staff give me the phone number for the Dhangardhi Police Office.

The officer I speak to understands English, but shows a disturbing lack of concern.

'Very many children go missing every day. We cannot be expected to look for every child.'

'I will send pictures of the child and, also the two men who are likely to have abducted her. This will give you a better chance.'

'We have many pictures of children missing. Send your pictures, but we are very busy.'

'Please, this is very important.'

'Yes, yes, every case important.'

I end the call and shake my head in frustration. Mack, Louise, and I sit in silence as the potbelly fire grumbles in support.

'I feel so helpless, Ray,' Mack says eventually. 'Surely there's something else we can do. Why don't we walk around the village and ask people if they've seen her?'

'I know how you feel, Mack. It's too hard just sitting here, waiting. But with the language barrier, asking if people have spotted her would be really difficult. I'll text Liz and ask her to send us a photo of Poppy. We could show that around the village.'

Within minutes Liz sends an SMS of Poppy's cheeky face. It's an old photo, and as I stare at her younger, playful image, I begin to feel overwhelmed with a sense of fear. The photo will serve our purpose, and I forward it on to both Mack and Louise. At my request, Liz also sends pictures of the two child traffickers, and with little more than feeble hope I forward all three photos and Liz's details on to the Dhangardhi Police Office.

'One of us should stay here in case Nabin comes back with Uttam. Lu Lu?'

'That's okay, Ray. I understand.'

'I appreciate this. Mack and I will probably be out of phone reception, but try to call us the moment you hear anything.'

Mack and I grab our coats, and head off in separate directions. I choose the path to the village. Every person I see, I stop and point to the impish photo on my phone. 'Ganuradha? Poppy?'

The response is the standard head wobble.

'Yes? No?' I ask. 'What are you saying?' And then a demoralising shrug of their shoulders and a gentle smile as they move on. *Don't you understand? We might be losing this magnificent child. Forever.*

Closer to the village, the trail is busy with people walking in both directions. 'Hoy!' I yell, and grab the attention of 10 or 12 of the villagers. I show them Poppy's face, but their response suggests polite interest, but nothing more. I try again with another group, and a middle-aged woman seems to recognise the photo. She walks forward and makes a circle with her middle finger and thumb, and places the circle around her other wrist.

'Her bracelet. Yes, she has a special bracelet! That is her! Have you seen her lately? *Kaha* – where?' But the woman simply smiles and walks away.

It's exasperating, but I remind myself that at least I'm occupied. Poor Louise sits alone in the Dining Hall, simply waiting.

In the village my pleas become desperate. 'Poppy? Somebody? Please!' I shout to anyone who can hear.

A very old man approaches me, and nods more clearly as he focusses on the face on my phone. 'Uttam,' he says.

'Yes, she is the daughter of Uttam,' I reply, 'but, *kahah* – where? Where is she?'

Another hopeless shoulder shrug, and another infuriating grin.

I've been questioning for over an hour now with not even a hint of a lead. I suspect Mack will have had the same frustrations, and I begin to realise the futility of our search. I should probably return to the Dining Hall. I look at my phone again, and wonder if Louise has been trying get through to me. I'm about to call her to check, when the phone rings. It's Liz.

'Hi, Liz. Any news?'

Rapid fire words – incomprehensible words, drowning in the sounds of sobbing.

'Liz? What's going on? Liz?'

I can hear her laboured breathing between each urgent sob. And finally, the words that will haunt me forever.

'Ray. It's horrible. I'm so sorry … it's Poppy. She … she's dead.'

I'm not hearing this – it's a dream. I'm not hearing this – it's a dream. I'm not hearing this – it's a dream … But I am hearing this, and it is not a dream. My body shakes ferociously as Liz's words penetrate to the depths of my being. I fight to get air to my lungs, and try to speak.

'Liz … How? How did it happen?'

More sobbing. 'The police – the border police – they've identified her. Oh, Ray. I can't believe this.'

'But there could be a mistake. It could be someone else. Maybe someone who looks like Poppy?' I'm so desperate to hear some words of doubt. Give me some hope. A glimmer of something.

'No, Ray. She was wearing her bracelet. They … They killed her.'

Sharing and Shredding of Grief

In the numbness that follows calamitous news, time seems to stand still. I have no idea how long I have staggered around the paths of this village, or even where I am right now. But as the numbness slowly fades, I begin to feel a freezing pain in my chest. It's as if some of the Himalayan ice has forced its way inside my body.

I look around me and realise I've taken the narrow forest path that leads to Poppy's special place. An eerie fog fills the spaces between the trees. I must get back to the Dining Hall to tell the others. I must tell Uttam and Nerum. Oh, how utterly abhorrent this is going to be. Probably better to hear it from me rather than some unknown official. But I pause and squat down for a few minutes to find some sort of composure before I can return to break the devastating news.

I make my way back to the main trail, and on to the Dining Hall. When I walk inside, Louise and Nabin are there. They search my face with imploring looks of hope, but all I can do is close my eyes and shake my head grimly.

'You haven't heard?' I ask eventually, but I know they clearly haven't.

'What's happened?' Louise asks, obvious fear in her voice.

I walk over to her and embrace her. My nose starts to burn, and my throat tightens as I push out the words, 'She's gone, Lu. We've lost her.'

Louise pushes me away. 'You mean she's over the border now? She's in India? They saw her go through?'

I look at Louise and shake my head slowly. I can feel tears stream down my already wet cheeks. 'They found her body, Lu.'

The look of horror on Louise's face is heart-breaking. She hugs me again, and I hear her ragged breathing turn into gasps. I seem to be holding all of her weight as her knees slowly give way. Another pair of arms wrap around us as Nabin joins our delirious embrace.

We stand there for several minutes in an awkward huddle until the Dining Hall door opens, and Mack walks inside.

'Oh dear,' he says. 'It's bad news?'

I explain to Mack that it's the worst news possible. He closes his fists tightly, and sits down quickly on the nearest chair.

'How? Who?'

'We don't know much yet, Mack,' I reply. 'The Nepalese police found her body near the Indian border. They've confirmed the ID with her photo and her bracelet.'

Mack puts his hand to his forehead and sighs deeply. 'What on earth is this world coming to?'

I turn to Nabin. 'Uttam? You couldn't find him?'

'Yes, Dr Ray. He is in home. He not want to come here. He not want to leave in case Poppy come home.'

'Nabin, we must see him now. Will you come with me?'

'Of course, Dr Ray.'

*

Today, the path to Uttam's home is a miserable walk of dread. It was only yesterday – and yet it seems like days ago – that Dipak and I walked this same path to confront Uttam over the catwalk incident. As unpleasant as the journey was yesterday, I would prefer that an infinite number of times over this walk we take now.

Nabin will translate the news to Uttam. As charming a person as Nabin is, it's clear that Dipak would provide a far better intermediary for this most painful duty. Uttam's last contact with Poppy was one of fury. It possibly led to her storming out of their home, and into the clutches of the child traffickers. This will lead to overwhelming guilt that could consume Uttam.

Then there's Nerum. How will he cope with the loss of his only sister? And Gorham – as the only two females in the home, I suspect she and Poppy had a close relationship. I'm guessing that Poppy is the person who taught her basic English.

As Nabin and I approach the home, Uttam waits in the open doorway. He ushers us inside and we sit by his open fire. There is no one else in the room.

'Nabin,' I say, 'I want you to translate my words as precisely as you can.'

'Yes, Dr Ray.'

Uttam stares at me intensely, and I grimace at the pain to come.

'Uttam,' I say, 'I have terrible news.'

A slight flinch in Uttam's fierce face as Nabin translates.

'Your daughter's body has been found by the Nepal police.'

A more perceptible flinch, but Uttam's eyes remain fixed on mine.

'I'm afraid she is dead.' My voice croaks on the final word.

Uttam breathes deeply but says nothing. Our eyes remain locked as he bares his stained teeth. His breathing quickens and I wait for his response. 'No!' he says through Nabin. 'How can police know this my daughter? Which police?'

'The police near the Indian border at Dhangadhi.'

'These police not know my daughter.' Uttam stands. He is almost shouting now. 'No true. Ganuradha alive. I wait for her come home.'

Denial – the first phase of grief – I should have anticipated this.

'Uttam, the police had a photograph of Poppy – of Ganuradha. And they found her bracelet.'

Uttam's head jolts when Nabin translates the word 'bracelet', and his defiance seems to soften. I feel my gut twist another turn as I realise Poppy's mother would have been wearing this same bracelet at the time of her own death.

'No!' Uttam repeats. 'Ganuradha not dead!' He paces the small room.

I'm not sure what to say or do next. 'Nabin,' I say, 'what do you suggest?'

'Uttam not believe before he sees body.'

How does this happen, I wonder. I doubt the authorities will transport the body here. We will have to convince Uttam to travel to Dhangadhi for a viewing there. But it won't be sensible to attempt this now. Perhaps in the next day or two Uttam may be persuaded. In the meantime, how should I approach Nerum and Gorham?

Despite Uttam's adamant denial, it doesn't seem right to leave him alone right now. I turn to Nabin once more. 'I should get back to

Louise and Mack. Nabin, do you mind waiting here with Uttam for a while? When Nerum returns from school, could you ask him to come to the Dining Hall?'

I stand, and stare into Uttam's troubled eyes. I join my palms and bow my head solemnly. 'I am sorry,' I say. And walk out the door.

*

A thousand tortured thoughts tumble savagely through my mind once more as I walk slowly without purpose. How do I tell Nerum when I see him? How tormented will Gorham be when she hears this agonising news? Oh, God – and then there's little Milu. How could he ever recover from this? Milu will be scarred for the rest of his life.

Why? I know it's futile to question, but why did this happen to one so innocent and full of such beautiful promise? Where is the sense and reason in this? Dipak – what would you be saying right now? Will you still have no 'outrage'? I'd like to see you crush that impulse this time.

As I stumble along the forest path, I'm only vaguely aware of people and places I pass. My eyes are fixed on the trail I tread, but they don't seem to register the view. On and on, and then slowly, fitfully, a perception of fog. The people have gone, and the path is now narrow. I stop and shake my head to realise that, once again, I have wandered on to the trail that leads to Poppy's special place.

I look up to take in the magnificent rhododendron forest that Poppy and I savoured in silence only a week ago. But today the trees are ghosts, wrapped in a spectral mist. Their ancient twisted roots writhe in a silent scream. In the deathly silence I walk on further to where the path weaves its way among the waist-high crumbling rocks. Weathered gravestones shrinking into the soft, damp earth.

I reach the cliff face of massive granite boulders and pause. I should head back. After the death of Arpan and her baby I spent too long wallowing alone. I will not make the same mistake again. It's time to go.

But not yet.

I begin to climb the steep rock face. I can still hear Poppy's words at this very place last week. *But I will not lose you, Dr Ray.*

Oh, Poppy, but we have lost you.

Over the escarpment and through the dense scrub and woodland trees. Onward, and somehow with focus now, until I reach the narrow fissure that splits the imposing granite masses. I turn my body sideways and edge through the fearsome crevice until I reach Poppy's cliff face cave. Poppy, dear Poppy – could you please be here? Be alive and hiding in here your special place with your cheeky, sparkling smile.

As I did on my first visit here, I close my eyes for a few moments, and slowly open them … But now the cave is empty. I sit down on the rock floor and stare out at the river and forest, and distant Himalayan peaks. There is no charm, no fascination in the view today. Instead, heavy tears well in my searing eyes.

I've come to honour you, Poppy. I have no idea why this had to happen to you, but one day, one day I will learn the full horrors of the despicable torture that is child prostitution. And only then I will realise that you were better off dead.

I should get back. As I emerge through the tiny rock fissure, I hear a noise in the scrub of the forest floor that surrounds me. I've startled an animal, but as I look to see the source of the noise, it's difficult to make out anything clearly. The scattered sunlight causes tangled shadows in the wild canopy undergrowth. I move on, but hear the rustling noise once more. I stop once again and look around. Nothing.

And then …

'Dr Ray. I knew you would come to find me.'

I close my eyes tightly and freeze. This time, I don't want to open them. My mind is playing tricks. It is a cruel dream of unfulfilled hope.

'Dr Ray? What is wrong?'

I turn, and very slowly open my eyes. Standing in front of me, a beaming, and very much alive, Poppy.

I fall to my knees hopelessly and begin to sob. My shoulders shake in heaving waves as I try to absorb what I see.

Poppy walks forward and embraces me. Her head is at the same level as mine. 'Why do you be so sad, Dr Ray?'

I struggle to get the words out, 'Poppy – you're alive! You're alive!'

'Of course. What do you think I am – ghost?'

'No, Poppy. Everybody thought you were dead. You're alive! Your bracelet – where is your bracelet?' I look down through and see that both her hands and wrists are cut and bruised.

'Bracelet broken in fight. But I escape.'

I shake my head in some sort of effort to make sense of this. After several more deep breaths I ask Poppy to explain everything.

'After concert in eating room, I go home with my father. Father is yelling at me. He does not like concert. I do not want more yelling, so I go outside. But strange man grab me and pull me away. I kick him in balls, just like Miss Beeyan shows me. Very hard kick. I pull away but my bracelet breaks and falls. I want bracelet, but I don't care. I run and run and run. I come here. Nobody find me here except Dr Ray.'

'Poppy, why did you stay here so long? You've been missing for nearly two days. We've been worried sick. And it's freezing at night. How on earth did you keep warm?'

'Well, you think Poppy's special place is only cave in these rocks? I know other caves. Small caves that have not so much cold. And ...' she says with a guilty grin, 'I take blankets from laundry in case woman's time comes.'

'Woman's time? Menstruation? You planned to come here during your period?'

Poppy looks a little awkward now, and I feel mean that I've made her feel uncomfortable. 'It's okay, Poppy. I'm a gynaecology doctor – we talk about these things all the time. And besides, when we do surgery, there is always some bleeding.'

Poppy sighs and gives me a bashful smile. 'I knew my first menstruation is coming soon. I take blankets and food to prepare for *chaupadi* in caves. First period comes on day of concert. I do not tell anyone. I do not tell my father because he will make me go to goth. Goth is horrible, Dr Ray. But I know my father will find out I have menstruation. And he is already angry about concert. I want *chaupadi* in caves, not in goth.'

My senses are still too overwhelmed with relief that Poppy is alive to be saddened by this. 'Do you believe in *chaupadi*, Poppy?'

'Of course not, Dr Ray. Is stupid tradition. No spirit will punish girl for having menstruation. She can work, play, do anything with menstruation. Miss Beeyan tells us this. But father and uncle are very strong. Gorham goes to goth with menstruation.'

'Poppy, your father and I have had a number of conversations lately. I can't promise you anything, but I think you might find his views are changing on a number of things.'

Poppy looks puzzled and she tilts her head to the side.

'We may even have worked out a way for you to continue your education.'

A shimmering smile now, tinged with uncertainty.

'Now, please come with me, Poppy. Your father is so worried about you. Not to mention Miss Beeyan, and Louise and Dr Mack, and so many others!'

Breaking News

5:50pm

I can't contain a triumphant grin as Poppy and I approach her home, and I can't wait to see the expression on Uttam's face. Poppy slowly opens the door to her home, but does not to go inside. I knock and call out to Uttam and Nabin, and I enter the small home myself, but I'm surprised and disappointed to find there is no one inside.

'That doesn't make sense,' I say to Poppy as I walk back outside, 'I was sure they'd still be here.'

'But my father is normally working in this time.'

'Yes, Poppy, but this is not a normal day. Will you come with me to the Dining Hall? Maybe he and Nabin have gone there.'

As we make our way to the Dining Hall once more, I consider phoning Louise and Mack to let them know the spectacular news before we arrive. But I choose instead to wait, to take a more dramatic approach, and show them Poppy in person. But Liz – poor Liz. I must put her out of her misery now. I phone her number and hope for reception.

'Liz!'

'Ray – how the fuck can you sound so happy?'

'There could only be one reason, Liz – she's alive! Poppy's alive!'

'No. No way. Don't say that. How can you know that?'

I smile furiously. 'Have a listen to this,' I say as I hand Poppy the phone.

'Hello, Miss Beeyan.'

369

Even though the phone is at least a metre from me now, the yelling and screaming at the other end are impossible to miss. Poppy holds the phone away from her ear. Once the screeching settles, I take back the phone.

'I don't know who the other child was, Liz, but somehow she's ended up with Poppy's bangle. This is still a tragedy, but thank God it wasn't Poppy.'

'Oh my God. Oh my God. Yes, it's awful for the other child. Is it wrong to feel so happy?'

'Of course not. Liz – come here now. Come to the Dining Hall tonight. Come and see Poppy yourself.'

'I'm on my way.'

*

The light is fading, and the air is noticeably colder as Poppy and I reach the Dining Hall. But beneath my skin I feel an easy warmth; it's as if the chilling air can no longer penetrate my outer shell.

I enter the Dining Hall alone, and Louise and Mack look up quickly. As I catch their eyes, they shake their heads despondently.

'No news?' I call from the doorway.

'Nothing, Ray,' Mack replies.

'I did find something,' I say. 'Okay – now!' And in walks Poppy.

Louise screams and jumps up from her seat. She runs to Poppy and sweeps her off her feet as she engulfs her in a smothering bear hug. 'Poppy – I can't believe this! You're okay? You're okay? My God – look at your arms. But you're alive!'

Poppy looks bemused as Louise finally sets her down. Mack comes over and kneels before Poppy. He puts his hands on her shoulders and says, 'Dear child, you can't know what you've put us through. I don't often pray, but I was praying today. Thank God you're alive.'

'But how?' Louise says as we all walk over to the main table and the fire. 'How can this be?'

'It's still a bit of a mystery, Lu,' I reply. 'Poppy was accosted by a man two nights ago.' I glance across to Poppy who gives me an indifferent look. 'It sounds like she put up an impressive fight. In the scuffle her bangle was broken. Somehow, another child ...' I begin to explain that another girl must have been the victim in the murder, but decide not to mention this right now in front of Poppy. 'I'm sure we'll find out more in due course.'

Louise hugs her again, but Poppy breaks away, grinning. 'It is dinner time now,' she says. 'I will get food for everyone.' She continues to smile as walks to the kitchen.

'I'm sure she doesn't realise how close she came to disaster,' Mack says.

'It's important she knows this,' I say, 'but not tonight. I'll sit down with her tomorrow.'

'You spoke to Poppy's father?' asks Louise.

'He doesn't know she's alive. I told him that we thought Poppy's body was found, but he refused to believe she was dead. I thought he was in denial, but maybe he knew something we didn't. When we returned to his home to tell him the good news, he and Nabin were gone.'

The Dining Hall door opens once more. In walk Nabin and Uttam, and following them, a very small middle-aged man – it is the Shaman, Lhapa.

'Dr Ray, Dr Ray,' Nabin says. 'Uttam find Shaman. Shaman say Poppy's spirit has no change. Spirit does not leave body. Poppy cannot be dead.'

I stand. 'Come with me,' I say. As we reach the kitchen doors I ask Nabin to explain that we found Poppy this afternoon alive and well in the forest. Nabin beams as he translates, and I push open the doors to usher Uttam inside. Uttam looks uncertain at first, but once he spots his daughter, his face becomes a magnificent mixture of wonder and relief.

Poppy looks up as we enter. Louise and Mack join us in the doorway as we watch the scene unfold. Poppy's head sinks to her shoulders as Uttam approaches. He stops before her and simply stares. I glance across to Louise, who bites down hard on her lower lip.

Slowly, Uttam opens his arms and walks forward to envelop Poppy in a loving, desperate embrace.

'We should leave these two alone for a while,' I say, as I let the kitchen doors swing closed in front of us. 'Nabin – I do believe you're crying.'

Mystical Moments

7:30pm, Dining Hall

Liz has just arrived. She runs up to Poppy and hugs her furiously. She speaks at breakneck speed.

'Oh, my child! Thank God! I can't tell you the torture I've gone through. It was total agony. I've never felt this horrible. But then to hear your voice on the phone – oh my God! But I had to see you in the flesh. Let me look at you.' She steps back and scans Poppy's face. 'You're okay? Yes? All the way over here tonight I kept thinking this was some cruel mistake and we'd still lost you. But you're here! You're here!' She launches another extravagant hug.

'Yes, Miss Beeyan.' Poppy glances over Liz's shoulder, and throws me a crazy look of confusion.

Liz's frenzy gradually settles as our meal arrives. Uttam and the Shaman have left the Dining Hall. We've managed to convince Nabin to stay one more night, and he's joined Liz and the rest of us for dinner.

'You and Liz may as well stay upstairs, Nabin,' Mack says. 'There are lots of spare rooms now the others have left.'

Poppy returns to the kitchen and we begin to go over the disturbing events of the last two days.

'I spoke to the police from Dhangardhi,' Liz says in a loud whisper. 'They've caught the two men who murdered the child. It seems they were the same men who tried to abduct Poppy. They've confessed the whole thing.'

'Poppy claims there was only one man who attacked her,' I say.

'Yes, they took shifts watching Poppy's home. Only one of the men was there when she came outside.'

'Did he admit that he was beaten in a fight with a 12-year old girl?'

'Huh. Strange that. The one who attacked Poppy says he decided to let her go. Obviously too much pride to admit he lost a fight.'

'It seems Poppy has you to thank for that, Liz. You gave self-defence instructions? Kicks to the groin?'

Liz smiles. 'I'm sure you know that technique doesn't always work. But she did this? Good on her.'

'What about the bangle?' asks Louise.

'The guy who attacked Poppy says he just found it. He and his colleague in crime – they used Poppy's bangle to lure another girl away with them.' Liz gives an agitated sigh. 'This is the girl who they eventually murdered. The police are not sure who she is, but the two men say they picked her up from a town about 5km south of here.'

'But why on earth did they murder the poor child?' Mack asks.

'Both men had been drinking a lot of *Rakshi*. It seems the girl started screaming when they approached the Indian border. The men had drugged her, but it obviously didn't work. They couldn't settle her and they panicked. They didn't want to attract attention with the authorities. They took her out into a field … Oh, God. It's just horrible … And I keep thinking – this could so easily have been Poppy.'

We're all silent now as we ponder what might have been. The only noise in the room is the crackling of the raw timber of the fire.

After some time, Liz says, 'She doesn't know, does she?'

'About the murder? I'm sure she doesn't,' I reply. 'I don't think Uttam would have told her. She's had so much to cope with, I'm not sure she *needs* to know. What do you think, Liz?'

'I know what you're saying, Ray. She's had so much on her plate lately, it feels wrong to add to her burden and tell her she could easily have been the victim of a murder. But in time she might find out from others anyway. Maybe it's better she hears it from us.'

I nod slowly. 'I'll sit down with her when I think the time is right.'

After a few minutes of silent contemplation, I turn to Nabin. 'We really do appreciate you staying with us for the extra day. You've been magnificent.'

Nabin lowers his head and gives an awkward shrug of his shoulders.

'Tell me more about Lhapa,' I say.

Nabin gives thoughtful smile. 'This is strange man, Dr Ray. Uttam sees him yesterday when Poppy first go missing, and then again today. Both times Shaman say spirit is no change, Poppy alive.'

'How did he know that, Nabin? Was it just a lucky guess?'

'I am not sure, Dr Ray. But Shaman was very much sure.'

'What do you think of the Shaman, Nabin? Do you think he is genuine?'

Nabin doesn't seem to understand my question, and I rephrase. 'Is the Shaman an honest person? Does he really see spirits?'

Nabin's face takes on a strange, heavy look. 'I think this Shaman is like many other Shaman. Sometimes he make some tricks. But most times he is honest. He very much want to help people. He does not charge money.'

Nabin pauses and stares into the crackling fire. 'Dr Ray, this Shaman is very much like you and your team. Except you do not make tricks. Most important thing for Shaman is to help people. This is only way he knows. Some people have sickness. After see Shaman, some people no longer have sickness.'

I look over to Louise, and then to Mack and Liz. Their faces are glued to Nabin in deep inquiry.

'And the spirits?' Liz asks.

'I think Shaman has belief that he see spirits. When people have problem, Shaman see spirits and ask them to fix problem. Shaman does not believe he is healer; he only believe he crosses fence between person and spirit.' Nabin smiles softly now. 'Shaman is like translator for people and spirit.'

'I've been thinking about this business of Shamanism,' says Mack. 'It's not just an alternative medicine – it's an alternative reality.'

And as this strange and stressful day draws to a hazy end I think, are we really very different from those who believe in the world of Shamanic journeys and spirit channelling? It was Mack himself who, only hours ago, found himself praying to his own God, his own 'alternative reality'. Many would consider priests and other religious leaders as mediators between the lay and the spiritual world.

As a student and a practitioner of conventional medicine, it's natural to be sceptical of the mystique of Shamanism and its lofty claims. I understand there is no 'evidence base' to the proposed healing powers of Shamanism, but I also understand the placebo effect and the potent consequences of the powers of suggestion. In this corner of the world many continue their deep faith in spirits and the healing powers of the Shaman, and there are thousands who swear their sickness – physical or mental – has been cured with Shamanic treatment. Whether these healing effects are psychological or spiritual, or both – in many ways is not important. Shamans remain prominent in rural Nepal. They are highly valued, but not simply for their perceived healing abilities. They are advisers and mediators in their society, they are diviners and protectors. In many villages they are the centre of society. Shamanism is woven into the intricate fabric of Nepalese tradition.

And yet there are times where Shamans are clearly harmful. They have often been the source of life-threatening delays in the presentation of sick children and adults to hospital.[153,154] It's quite likely that the death of Poppy's mother would have been avoided when she first commenced bleeding if she had sought help from a hospital post, rather than a Shaman.

So how do we play this? How do we respond to these mystical beings?

I believe our best way to improve the health of the people of rural Nepal is not to work against the Shamans and their traditional methods of healing. It is to accept that many people in Nepal who suffer a medical disorder will continue to seek out a Shaman before a conventional health worker. It is to accept that Shamanic healing does not have all of the answers to illness and disease, and that neither does conventional medicine. Rather than competing with these Shamanic healers, we must collaborate. As with other forms of traditional medicine, we must avoid mistrust between providers of Shamanic and Western healthcare.

Through the Community Medicine program to be based at our Mothers and Babies Hospital, we must work together using the best features of each system, and compensating for the weaknesses of the other.[155]

The Other Side of Solace

Day #27. 3:15pm, Dining Hall

'Ferin,' Liz says as she puts down her phone. 'Her name was Ferin.'

'Her family knows, then?' asks Mack.

'The Dhangardhi border police just told me the father identified the body this morning.' Liz sighs heavily once more. 'God – it's gotta be a parent's worst nightmare.'

Liz, Mack, Louise, and I sit around the fire, each with a novel open in front of us. But no one seems very interested in reading. There is no school today, and Liz has decided to spend another day here with us.

'Liz,' I say, 'I know there are thousands of children in Nepal who are victims of trafficking each year. But there can't be too many who are found murdered like this?'

'No, thank God. Although most of the children are never seen again, so we don't really know the true numbers.'

'This girl, Ferin – she wasn't from your school?'

'I don't recognise the name. It's a salient message for the children at our school, though. This whole episode drives home just how dangerous it is for young girls here. This area of Nepal – it's so poverty-ridden. It makes children more vulnerable to child traffickers. They promise food, and jobs, and a better life – and bangles, too, it seems.'

'What do you do then, Liz?' asks Mack. 'How do you overcome this?'

'We're not going to improve poverty very soon. I think the answer is education. We've been doing a bit of this at our school, but when I get back there tomorrow, I'm going to make sure we ramp it up. And if those other teachers even think about standing in my way – well, I'll be using Poppy's assault techniques on them.'

It seems that it's not only children who need more education in the perils of child trafficking. Parents often fall for the false promises of a better future for their child. We need to expand community-based programs to fight this exploitation of children. Another essential project for our hospital's rapidly expanding Community Medicine program.

Liz soon stands and begins to say her goodbyes. 'Better start making my way back. I'm so glad I got to see you all again. I feel such relief for Poppy, but it's still kind of a kind guilty relief.'

'I'm sure we all share that,' I say, 'but I can see this has inspired you. You've got a few more weeks left of your teaching appointment here? When you educate the children about trafficking, don't just teach them for those few weeks. Start some compelling programs that will continue when you're gone.' I look across to Mack and Louise. 'Sometimes a tragedy can lead to all sorts of positive outcomes.'

Liz smiles and gives me a warm hug. 'I've only known you for such a short time, but I'll totally miss you. I won't see you again this trip, but I feel certain we'll meet again. I'd love to think we could work together one day.'

Mack and Louise stand now, and wish Liz well. She grabs her small overnight bag and turns to leave.

'Keep a close eye on Poppy,' I say.

Liz looks back and smiles again. 'It will be impossible not to!'

7:20pm, Dining Hall

'It's our last full day here tomorrow, Lu Lu,' I say. 'If our post-op patients are all still stable, you feel like going for a long walk in the morning?'

Louise seems to be enjoying her vegetable momos. 'I think I'm up to it,' she replies. 'Where'd you have in mind?'

'A little village … 5km south of here.'

Louise stops mid-mouthful. 'You want to visit the dead girl's parents?' she splutters.

'Does that sound weird? Something inside is telling me it's the right thing to do.'

'But … what could we do? We don't know them. It's so unlikely that they'll speak English. We've got no interpreters left. And even if we did …'

'After our ward round in the morning, I'll ask one of the nurses if she can join us to interpret. I know it doesn't make a lot of sense to see the girl's parents, Lu. I'm not sure why I need to do this. Maybe I'm just trying to flush out some of this guilt that Liz touched on.'

Louise says nothing, and simply puts her fingers to her forehead. After a few moments she reaches out and puts her hand over mine. She raises her chin and looks me in the eye. 'Yeah. I would love to come, Ray.'

I look across the table to Mack. 'Are you in, Mack?'

'I admire your sentiment, Ray. But I think too many visitors may be a wee overwhelming for the parents. I'll stay here, if it's all the same to you.'

*

The plates are all cleared, and Mack and Louise have gone up to bed. I sit alone and reflect on the powerful events of the last couple of days. The cold is not so harsh tonight, and for once the pot belly seems to be winning its headstrong battle against the evening chill.

The doors to the kitchen swing open, and I look up to see Poppy walking towards me. 'Hello, Dr Ray,' she says gently.

'Poppy,' I reply. 'I had no idea you were still here.'

'Which dead girl's parents do you see tomorrow?'

'Where on earth did you hear this?'

'I am sorry, Dr Ray. Please do not be thinking I am rude. But I hear you talking tonight with Sister Louise.'

I shake my head slowly and give a sad smile. 'Poppy. Sit down while I tell you what's been happening.'

As I describe the tragic events that led to a young girl's death, Poppy stares ahead, emotionless. I explain that the man she bravely fought off joined another, and together they abducted a young girl. I watch Poppy's impassive face as I tell her our horror when we thought she was the dead child. Slowly she nods with new understanding. 'This is why everybody so happy,' she says.

'Yes, Poppy. We are very sad for the child who died, but we are very happy that you are alive.'

Poppy looks at me for a long time and says, 'Dr Ray, I wish to visit girl's parents, too.'

I've lost count of the times that Poppy has surprised me. 'Of course,' I say. 'Do you think your father will be okay with that?'

Poppy smiles. 'My father very much happy now, Dr Ray. Just like you said, he is different. He say it is okay for me to go to school, to finish school. This makes me very much happy, too. I know if I am with you and Sister Louise, my father will be okay if I go to see parents of dead girl.'

'We will walk to the parents' village tomorrow morning. If you come, you will miss the day at school. Are you sure you want to do that?'

'I know school is very important, Dr Ray. But seeing dead girl's parents is more important.'

I smile again, but this time with pride. 'In that case, Poppy, I would like you to be our official translator for the day.'

Ferin's Parents

Day #28. 9:40am, Village Trail

It's an overcast day as Louise, Poppy, and I begin our descent along the trail that heads south from our camp. The first part of our walk follows the same route I took to Jyoti's Health Post two weeks ago. Today the path is noticeably damp, no doubt from the thawing of a recent frost. Icy puddles litter our winding trail as we slowly make our way past the crumbling terrace walls and the scattered clay huts.

'Ray,' Louise says, 'when we meet the family of the girl who died, what are we going to say to them?'

'To be honest, Lu, I've got no idea. I'm kind of hoping something will come to me.'

'Do you think we could make things worse for them? You know, upset them more than they already are?'

'It's crossed my mind. I think we should be ready for that. When we do meet them, if it looks like they're really uncomfortable with us there and we're distressing them, we should make a quick exit.'

The ground is sodden here, and we begin to slip and slide as we continue our wary descent. Syrupy, swamp-like mud squelches beneath our tentative feet.

Louise looks down at her boots that are now caked with heavy, dark mud. 'Ray, remind me again why I haven't gone trekking before now?'

'Delayed gratification, Lu,' I reply. 'It's obvious you wanted to save the most fun for your last days here.'

Louise gives an exaggerated roll of her eyes as we all continue our walk.

'Hey,' I say, 'you remind me of Jayne on our trek to Poppy's school. I think you and Jayne would have been brilliant trekking partners.'

We reach the solid ground of Jyoti's village and continue to her Health Post, but the building appears deserted. There is no answer when I knock on the door and call out, so we continue our walk to the outskirts of the small village. I pull out my phone and stare at the photo of hand-drawn map. 'I got the Dhangardi police to text me this map yesterday,' I say. 'According to this, we've got another few kilometres to go in this direction.' We turn on to an undulating path that winds through scattered evergreen forest.

'Poppy,' Louise says as we continue our journey, 'are you concerned that we might make the dead girl's family uncomfortable?'

'Sister Louise, Dr Ray,' Poppy replies. 'I think you do not understand Nepali people. When people lose relative or friend, Nepali people are happy for very many people to come to their home. It is not important that family does not know us.'

This makes sense when I think back to Puru and the loss of his wife and stillborn son. It seemed I had almost insulted Puru when I did not spend more time in the operating theatre when he mourned for the loss of his family.

But Louise's face remains contorted in concern. 'What will you say to the parents, Poppy?' she asks.

'Even though they will be sad they have lost their daughter, I will remind parents that spirit of the child cannot be destroyed.' Louise gives little more than a fleeting grin at Poppy's response before resuming her troubled glare.

As we press on further towards the next village, the winter sun appears fitfully as the clouds sporadically clear. Weak puddles of light spill onto our woodland trail, but within minutes the sunshine is lost. Louise look up in hope, but it seems the clouds can't fully withdraw.

After another 30 minutes, we finally reach the village of the fated child, Ferin. The shabby buildings here are in an even worse state than the dilapidated structures of our own village. I pull out my map once more and study its coarse features. 'It's up here on the left.'

Our step slows as we approach the small home. The dismal dwelling is more of a shelter than a house. Stacks of collapsing clay blocks form floundering outer walls. Rusted iron sheets serve as a sagging roof that is secured, not by bolts or screws, but by randomly placed rocks.

A young woman with bare feet squats at the front of the decaying hovel. She looks up as we approach. Suddenly she stands and shrieks with a piercing cry. She puts her hand to her mouth and stares at Poppy with wild, frightened eyes.

Poppy turns to me, clearly confused, and it takes me a moment to realise that there must be a striking similarity between Poppy and the murdered child, the cause of the tragic confusion yesterday.

'Poppy,' I say, 'tell this woman that you are not Ferin. You are simply somebody who looks like her.'

Poppy speaks to the startled woman, but there is no reply. Her trembling fingers are curled into fists, and her eyes remain wide and bewildered. Poppy continues to speak to her in reassuring tones, but the woman holds up her arms and begins to back away towards the open door of the home.

Louise whispers in my ear, 'This is going really well so far, Ray.'

Before the woman can retreat to the home, a man appears at the doorway. He is bald, with a dome so pale it looks to have been very recently shaved. He speaks to the woman in Nepali with words that are calm and measured. When he looks across to us he stares at Poppy briefly, and then attends to the woman once more. Poppy speaks to the bald man now, and a short conversation begins between them.

'Dr Ray, Sister Louise,' Poppy says, 'this is mother and father of the child who is dead. I tell them we are here for respect. We do not wish to make them upset. Mother think I am spirit of daughter. I tell her, "No – I am just girl from different village".'

Poppy and the father continue their conversation for a few more minutes before the father beckons us to enter their home. Louise and I give a silent *Namaste* and bow our heads as we walk through the low doorway.

The tiny home seems even smaller inside. Scattered light enters from the multiple gaps in the exposed clay walls. Louise and Poppy and I are guided to sit on three plastic chairs. Once seated, I realise there are no seats for the parents, as they squat before us. But when I stand and offer my seat to the mother, Poppy says, 'No, Dr Ray. If you do not to take these seats, it is insult.'

We learn from the father that Ferin was ten years old, and their only child. She had gone missing from the village a few days earlier.

Her father is thankful we are all here to pay our respects, but he is confused as to why strangers would travel from another village to do this. I ask Poppy to translate my explanation.

'I sincerely hope that what we say does not give you any more pain than you both must already be suffering. Three nights ago, the men who took your daughter also tried to take Poppy, but somehow she managed to escape. I am not sure if it is simply chance or not, but Poppy and your daughter must have quite similar looks. Poppy is two years older than your daughter, but the photo given to the police was taken two or three years ago. The police also found a bracelet that belonged to Poppy. The men took this from her and gave it to your daughter.'

I watch the parent's faces as Poppy translates. Ferin's mother's expression is no longer frozen in fear, but she now sobs softly. Ferin's father's face is rigid as he stares straight ahead. When Poppy completes the translation, I continue.

'We realise that it could easily have been Poppy who had died. I don't know if you can understand this or not, but even though we don't know you both, we felt it was our duty to come here and give you our respect.'

After Poppy translates this these latest words, an awkward silence fills the room. The gentle sobbing has stopped, and helpless tears stream down the mother's face. I'm not sure what to do or say next, and I glance across to Louise for some sort of suggestion. She looks uneasy and says nothing.

Slowly, Ferin's father stands and helps his wife to her feet. He walks to a corner of the room and then returns to face Poppy. He looks directly into her face as he reaches down, and picks up her hand. Gently, he opens each of her fingers, and places into her hand a bright blue sparkling bangle.

Poppy's face lights up with excitement, but instantly changes to one of torment. For the second time since I met her, her face gushes with free-flowing tears. She speaks rapidly in Nepali and kneels down before both parents. And with a passion I have not seen from her before, she hugs the knees of the father and the mother in turn.

*

Over a pot of hot chai tea, the five of us spend the next hour talking and learning from each other. Ferin's father explains that Ferin's body will be brought to the village within the next couple of days following further forensic tests. Her parents plan to bury her body in an area of arid land just outside their village.

'This is very important,' Ferin's father says through Poppy. 'We must keep soul of our daughter close to our home. Otherwise soul can stop mother having more children.' I had no idea of this custom, but find some comfort in the idea that Ferin's parents wish to one day have more children.

We also learn of another tradition in this region of Nepal. The male relatives of a deceased family member shave their heads as a mark of respect. If Ferin had a brother, he would have undergone the same ritual.

'Shaving head is custom when person in family die, but also important because funeral rite is performed by male. If head is not shaved, sickness can come to this male.'

Ferin's parents enquire about Poppy's own family. Poppy explains the loss of her own mother during childbirth, and that the bangle is her only memento. And as I study the bangle now, I see that it has been broken in two places, and crudely repaired with wire.

As Poppy continues the conversation with the parents, Louise whispers to me. 'I just wasn't sure at all about coming here today, but I'm so glad we came now. Thank you.'

'I'm sure my doubts were as strong as yours, Lu Lu.' I wink and give her a tight smile.

It's time to go, and we all give Ferin's parents a long and heartfelt *Namaste*. Poppy promises to return in a few days for the funeral rites. Louise and I apologise that we won't be able to attend because we'll be returning home tomorrow.

We wave goodbye and begin our walk back to our camp, satisfied that we've made a small difference to this shattering time in these pitiful people's lives. But after only two or three minutes, Poppy stops.

'What is it, Poppy?' Louise says. 'Forget something?'

'Yes, I forget something. Please wait for me for just a few minutes.'

Poppy turns and walks back the way we came. Despite her request, Louise and I follow closely behind her, curious as to what she's forgotten. Both parents are outside and appear confused when Poppy returns. She stops in front of Ferin's father, and reaches down to grasp his hand. Slowly, she opens each of his fingers. And staring directly at his puzzled face, she places the blue bangle into his outstretched hand.

*

We walk in silence on our return to the camp. Louise is about to speak, but I hold up my hand and shake my head. I sense that Poppy prefers a quiet time right now to reflect on this morning's moving interaction.

After quite some time, Poppy speaks. 'Sister Jayne teach me this, Dr Ray.'

We all continue walking as I look across to her. 'You and Jayne are both amazing people,' I say.

'Sister Jayne – Miss Piggy – she talk about Puru. Sister Jayne says, "This man has so little; I have so much." Well, Dr Ray, this mother and this father have so little, too. But now they have something. Just like Sister Jayne, now I have some good feeling inside.'

I stop and look to Louise, who gives me a radiant smile. We both hug Poppy fiercely before we continue on our way.

Louise whispers in my ear once more. 'Are you *sure* we can't take her home with us?'

The Last Round

Day #29. 7:15am, Postoperative Ward

It's our final round on our final day of the camp. Fazi and Laya have returned from Pokhara to take over the postoperative care of our remaining patients. There are eight patients here, in various stages of recovery following their surgery. All of the women continue to progress well.

'Thank you for coming back,' I say to Fazi and Laya. 'I expect the patients here will be able to be discharged over the next few days. And we appreciate you both coming in early today for this handover. Our bus leaves in a couple of hours.'

'Dr Ray,' Fazi replies, 'I wish we could have stayed for the whole camp. We have so much pleasure to see these women become well again.'

'Laya,' Louise says, 'do you enjoy your time here, too?'

'Oh yes,' Laya replies softly, 'and I tell my doctor friends in Pokhara. Many wish to come to see the work you do here.' She looks across to catch Fazi's eyes. They both nod briskly, as if to encourage each other.

'Dr Ray,' Fazi says, 'we hear about the Mothers and Babies Hospital you will build here. Is this true story?'

I give a gentle smile. 'Yes, Fazi. This is our plan. It will depend on funding and the commitment of a larger hospital in eastern Nepal, but we are determined to do our best to make this happen.'

She looks across to Laya again, and then back to me. 'We are not surgeons, Dr Ray, and we do not wish to be surgeons. But we both have very much interest in women's health. When hospital is built, we wish to be considered to work here.'

'That is fantastic! You've both been very reliable doctors, and we've all loved working with you. I can guarantee that, if we can build our hospital, we will do everything we can to welcome you back.'

We all complete the postoperative round and then walk up to the final patient in the ward, Jumari. Once again I try to imagine how distressing it must be each day to watch so many other women as they're cured of the same horrible problem you're now compelled to suffer yourself.

Jumari stands and allows Louise to give her one more hug. She pushes out a sad smile before she lies back down on her bed to allow us to assess her prolapse once more. The ulcers have almost cleared again, and I feel she's well enough to return home. Fazi translates as I speak to her.

'When we return to this hospital, you will be the first woman on our operating list.'

Jumari nods cheerlessly now, and says, 'Yes, one year.'

'No, Jumari. I can't promise you *when* we will return here, but it will be much less than one year. Hopefully less than six months.'

The sad smile returns, and Jumari stands again and hugs me, and then Mack, and then Louise once more before we turn to leave the ward. But I'm surprised to see our door to the outside is blocked by several of the local nursing staff. It's unusual to see so many nurses here at any one time. Guna and Mani are among the large group and they smile broadly as we approach. Sangina steps out from behind them and begins to address us.

'We come to wish goodbye, Dr Ray. Your team teach us many things. Sister Jayne teach us in operating theatre. Sister Louise teaching us in ward. We wish you all come back very soon.'

And with that, all of the nurses come forward with bright orange leis that they've been concealing behind their backs. They place the garlands of fresh marigolds over our heads, and give us an enthusiastic *Namaste*.

'Fresh flowers,' Mack says with surprise,' in the Himalayan winter? How on earth?'

There is no response to Mack's question, so Fazi converts it to her native tongue. Sangina replies in Nepali, and we wait for Fazi's translation.

'Sangina say that to get these flowers is special secret, Dr Mack. She also say that life in hospital is very dull and very cold. Hospital here is like winter. But when your team came here there is suddenly much life. Everybody is happy. She says your team in hospital is just like colourful flowers coming in winter.'

We laugh at the lovely analogy and thank the nurses for their very kind words and for their valuable work over the past four weeks.

Mack shakes his head and smiles as he speaks again. 'And you people of Nepal add even more colour to our lives.'

The gratitude from the nurses has caught me off guard. Throughout the past four weeks they've worked solidly and almost silently, but until today we've had no idea of the positive effects the camp has had on them. We promise them that we'll return to the hospital as soon as it's possible. We're swamped by a rush of hearty goodbyes and *Namastes*, and with a delightful sense of optimism we leave the ward for our final walk to the Dining Hall. But the sparkle in our step is short-lived.

When we open the ward door to the outside we're confronted by a large group of distressed women. They surround us as they press their palms together and deeply bow their heads. Despite our notifications that medical care can no longer be provided on this camp, it's clear these women are imploring us to treat them. With no further surgery and only few medications left, our small hospital is now little more than a basic Health Post.

A few of the women call out to us in Nepali. I look around to Fazi, who translates for us again. 'These women say they travel for days to reach here. They say they have bad women's problems. They ask us to help them.'

'Fazi,' I reply, 'please tell them that we cannot help them at this camp. We will provide another camp in the spring or the summer. We will try very hard to help them then.'

Fazi translates my response, but the women simply protest and continue their pleading poses. It's precisely the painful the scene I've been dreading since we arrived here four weeks ago.

'It makes you more determined than ever, doesn't it,' Louise says, 'to fix this problem, I mean.'

'Not that we really needed motivation, Lu Lu,' I reply, 'but we should keep this image in our mind. Let's draw from it whenever our fundraising gets to be more of a challenge.'

We push past the forlorn group of women, and with the ache of added burden, we make our way to the Dining Hall.

A Grateful Goodbye

8:30am, Dining Hall

Quite a crowd have assembled here as we make our final preparations
to leave. The kitchen staff have kindly prepared some breakfast for
Fazi and Laya, who have joined a number of the locals to see us off. As
I look around the room, I'm moved to see so many people have come
to say goodbye. Many of the domestic workers who have helped us
over the last four weeks are here, and several have brought along their
young children, who squeal and cavort as young children do.

A large man walks up to me. 'Riken!' I say. 'So good of you to see
us off.'

Riken gives me one of his hearty laughs and slaps my shoulder
firmly. '*Namaste*, Dr Ray.' He continues in Nepali, but the only words I
can make out are 'Riken *Rakshi*'. He hands me a bottle of his famous
brew, no doubt as a farewell gift, and slaps me once again.

'*Danyavad* – thank you,' I say, and I give Riken an equally firm slap
on his own shoulder. Badal approaches me now, and begins to speak in
Nepali. I grab his arm and steer him over to the table where Fazi and
Laya have begun their breakfast. Once again, Fazi translates for me.

'Dr Ray,' Badal says through Fazi, 'before I am not giving proper
thanks for your helping me.'

'Nonsense, Badal,' I reply. 'You have been more than thankful.'

'I was rude at my home when you look for Suntil. This man no
longer my friend, but I should not be rude to you. I say properly now
– thank you for being Badal's friend.'

I smile and join my palms. 'Badal, we will be coming to this village many times. I hope to see you again and again. It's possible we can become long-term friends.'

Badal's scarred face lights up. '*Namaste*, Dr Ray. *Namaste*. *Namaste*.'

I walk over to Mack and Louise who are in conversation with some farmers I recognise from the village. I check my watch. 'Ten minutes, guys. You nearly ready?'

'All packed, Ray,' replies Mack. 'Just give us the word.'

I feel a tap on my elbow and turn around to see little Milu looking up at me. 'Milu!' I shout. How wonderful to see you!'

'*Namaste*, sir. I will miss you, and I will miss your friends.'

'And we will miss you, Milu.' I study his tiny features. 'You must have been overjoyed when you heard Poppy was safe.'

'Yes, sir. I pray to Lord Shiva. He makes this happen. From now, I make sure Poppy is always safe.'

'Good, Milu.' I bend down and speak quietly into his ear. 'But you must always ask Poppy if she wants your protection. She may not want a bodyguard – or a boyfriend. This may be difficult for you to accept, but if Poppy asks you to give her space, all you should do is say, "Okay, Poppy, but I am always available if you want me".'

Milu nods slowly and solemnly. 'Thank you, Dr Ray. I will be trying at my best.'

I look around the room again and realise that Poppy is not here. Uttam is standing alone in a corner of the room. I return to Fazi and Laya's table and address them. 'I'm so sorry to do this when you haven't finished your meal, but would one of you be kind enough to come with me to translate another conversation?'

Both young doctors stand immediately, but Fazi gestures to Laya to sit back down. She utters a few words in Nepali to Laya and then follows me to the corner where Uttam stares at me soberly.

'*Namaste*, Dr Ray,' he says, and then through Fazi, 'I have respect for you. I come to see you before you leave.'

'*Namaste*, Uttam. Thank you for coming. I am very glad to know you. I have not agreed with all of your beliefs, but I have enormous respect for you, too.'

'I am becoming old man, Dr Ray.' Old man? *He can't be any older than mid-forties*. 'It is very difficult for me to change beliefs. I understand from our talking and from talking with Dipak that some things must change. Most important thing in this world is good family. I ask what is best for family? I answer – best for family is good health, good education.' He breathes in deeply. 'Not just for men – for women, too.'

I beam, and do everything I can to avoid reaching out and embracing Uttam. Instead, I simply bring my palms together, bow my exultant head, and kneel down at the feet of this remarkable man.

I scan the crowded room for Poppy again, but I still can't see her. My eyes catch Gorham, and she looks over expectantly. As I walk over to her, she smiles softly and bows her head.

'*Namaste*, Gorham. It is very good of you to come to say goodbye this morning.'

'*Namaste*, doctor.' Her voice barely louder than a whisper. She looks from side, as if to make sure no one else is in earshot. 'I am not good with speaking. I want thank you for what you do.'

'We all get enormous pleasure from our work here.'

Gorham wobbles her head. 'Yes, but I thank you for what you do for me, doctor. You fix my sickness, and you make my husband stop. I think my husband not come back. This is good thing.'

'I was very happy and very honoured to help you, Gorham. When we return here we will need to give you one more blood test. I hope that will be soon.'

As Gorham lowers her head once more, the doors to the kitchen open and finally I see Poppy. She enters the Dining Hall with her mischievous grin and a large bowl of poppadoms. She walks up to me and says, 'This is going away present for you and your team, Dr Ray.'

'And what a lovely present this is. My favourite Nepalese snack. Thank you, Poppy.'

'No, Dr Ray. Thank *you*, and thank your team. Even though there is much sadness sometimes, this is still best month of my life.'

'Poppy – that's a wonderful thing to hear you say.'

'I remember English word you teach me when we go to special place. This word is *inspire*.'

'Yes. And Miss Beeyan inspires you. She makes you feel like you wish to be a teacher.'

'Yes, Dr Ray. But I am thinking there is more. I watch you, I watch your team. Your team help many people, but also you all have very much fun. Very much laughter. Miss Beeyan inspires me, but your team inspires me, too, Dr Ray. I want to help people, and I want laughter.'

I laugh myself now, but it's somehow mixed with sadness. It's been a very long month, and I'm keen to get home to my family and friends, but there is a part of me that doesn't want to leave these endearing people and this extraordinary child. I look at Poppy once more. There is a heart-stirring joy we get from guiding this wonderful creature, and from having her continually surprise us with her antics and her maturity that is so beyond her years.

'Well, Poppy – you are going to be able to inspire people yourself. We're going to make sure you can continue your schooling and your higher education. We're going to do everything we can so you can use your very special gifts.'

The door to the outside opens, and our three porters enter the room.

'Time to go!' Mack shouts. 'Poppy – it's been an absolute honour spending time with you.'

'Thank you, Dr Mack. I have very much enjoyed being with you.'

Louise appears and gives Poppy another long hug. 'Look after yourself, Little One,' she says. 'Please be careful. You are too precious for anything to happen to you.'

'Goodbye, Sister Louise. We have so much fun together. I hope I can see you again.'

'Oh, you will. Nothing will stop me from coming back here.'

The porters begin to collect our main luggage while Louise and Mack grab their smaller bags and walk outside. I follow them, and Poppy joins me. While the porters load our suitcases onto their backs, Poppy looks up at me. This time, there is a sadness in her smile. She points to her upper arm. '*Bala*,' she says.

'*Bala*,' I repeat. 'Arm?'

'No, Dr Ray. *Bala*.' She points more precisely now to the area of her biceps.

'Muscle? *Bala* means *muscle*?'

'No.' Mock disgust now. '*Bala* means strength. Dr Ray – you, your team – you give Poppy strength … I will not let you down.'

'*Bhitra pracura*,' I say with a proud smile.

Poppy's face lights up. 'Yes, Dr Ray. You remember. *Bhitra pracura* – inside body we feel rich.'

And now, a faint quiver of her bottom lip, before she walks towards me and slumps her head on my chest. I hug her shoulders and feel their gentle quake. And as Poppy and I continue our heavy embrace, I feel another pair of arms envelop the two of us. It seems so appropriate that Louise has joined us for our farewell hug.

But as I open my eyes, I'm surprised to see Louise standing several metres away from us, simply smiling and watching on. Who, then, has joined our final sad embrace?

Slowly, curiously, I step back to take in the extra party, and to my astonishment, I see the unruffled face of Uttam.

*

Our final walk along the village mountain path is a silent one. I look across to Mack and Louise, who both appear to be in careful contemplation.

We're jaded. We're *all* jaded. It's been a massive four weeks, and at times, we've all been close to the edge. The cultural battles have been as challenging and exhausting as the medical ones. But I can see through this tiredness, and I want to believe that Lu and Mack can see through it, too. As I reflect on this extraordinary camp with its assortment of extraordinary human beings, a cinema of images run relentlessly through my mind. The sights and sounds of this consuming month will continue to play out for a long time to come.

I think to myself how lucky we really are. Yes, we come from a wealthy part of the world where opportunity and health and education are so readily available, but it's so much more than that. We've been able to make a difference to the lives of so many people who aren't as fortunate as we are, and more – we've come to know a group of people who have taught us all some priceless lessons in life.

Despite the hurdles, and despite the countless painful struggles along the way, the reward from all of this has been sublime.

I look again at my companions. At some stage on our long journey home I will ask them their thoughts on all of this, but not right now.

As Poppy would say, 'Sometimes it is nice to have no words'.

About the Author

Dr Ray Hodgson is an Associate Professor in Obstetrics & Gynaecology. He is a specialist gynaecology surgeon and obstetrician based in Australia.

After discovering the appalling state of women's health in Nepal in 2010, he founded the humanitarian organisation *Australians for Women's Health*. Several times each year he organises teams of volunteers to join him on medical camps to remote regions of Nepal where they provide surgical care to underprivileged women in need. Throughout their camps, the team provide extensive teaching to local doctors, nurses, and midwives.

Dr Ray's latest project is to construct a Mothers and Babies Hospital in remote Nepal where they can base their life-changing work.

All profits from the sale of *Heartbreak in the Himalayas* will fund the construction of the hospital.

For more information or donations to the hospital project, see: www. A4WH.org.

Want to Help us Build our Hospital?

Our Mothers and Babies Hospital will be constructed in the district of Dolakha, eastern Nepal. Even the smallest donation will help us achieve our dream to transform the lives of countless thousands of mothers and babies.
If you feel you can help, please contact us on **admin@A4wh.org** or visit the web site at **www.A4Wh.org**
All donations are tax deductable.

References

1. Beatriz A E, Ridgeway B, and Barber MD. Complications of neglected vaginal pessaries: case presentation and literature review. Int Urogynecol J19, 2008;8:1173-1178.

2. Nepal Safer Motherhood Project: Cultural issues. 1997 (Online) Available at: http://www.nsmp.org/publications_reports/documents/InfoSheet10CulturalIssues.pdf

3. Shrestha B, Onta S, Choulagai B, Poudyal A, Pahari DP, Uprety A, et al. Women's experiences and health care-seeking practices in relation to uterine prolapse in a hill district of Nepal. BMC Women's Health 2014;14:20. DOI: 10.1186/1472-6874-14-20)

4. Shrestha B, Onta S, Choulagai B, Paudel R, Petzold M, and Krettek A. Uterine prolapse and its impact on quality of life in the Jhaukhel–Duwakot Health Demographic Surveillance Site, Bhaktapur, Nepal. Glob Health Action 2015; 8: 10.3402/gha.v8.28771. doi: 10.3402/gha.v8.28771

5. Pradhan,S. Unheeded agonies: a study of uterine prolapse prevalence and its causes in Siraha and Saptari Districts, Nepal. Kathmandu: Center for Agro-Ecology and Development (2007).

6. Subedi M: Uterine prolapse, mobile camp approach and body politics in Nepal. Dhaulagiri J Sociol Anthropol. 2010;4: 21-40

7. Bonetti TR, Erpelding A, Pathak LR: Listening to "felt needs": investigating genital prolapse in Western Nepal. Reprod Health Matter. 2004;12(23): 166-175. 10.1016/S0968-8080(04)23110-X

8. Unnecessary Burden. Gender Discrimination and Uterine Prolapse in Nepal 2014 Amnesty International Ltd. (Online) Available at: https://www.amnesty.org/download/Documents/8000/asa310012014en.pdf

9. Department of Health Service. (2014). Annual report: Department of health service 2012/2013. Kathmandu, Nepal (Online) Available at: http://ghdx.healthdata.org/record/nepal-department-health-services-annual-report-2012-2013

10. Campo M & Tayton S. Domestic and family violence in regional, rural and remote communities. An overview of key issues. CFCA Practitioner Resource— December 2015. (Online) Available at: https://aifs.gov.au/cfca/publications/domestic-and-family-violence-regional-rural-and-remote-communities

11. UNFPA Report: Status of Reproductive Morbidities in Nepal. 17 March 2009. (Online) Available at: http://un.org.np/node/10576

12. Muluki Ain (National Code) Regarding Rape, Chapter 14 (Online) Available at: http://www.asianlii.org/np/legis/laws/marrc14276/

13. A study on gender-based violence conducted in selected rural districts of Nepal, OPMCM, Nov 2012 p34. (Online) Available at: https://asiafoundation.org/resources/pdfs/OPMCMGECUGBVResearchFinal.pdf

14. Focus group discussion with Amnesty International, 11 May 2013, Mugu district. Ref 97. (Online) Available at: https://www.amnesty.org/download/Documents/8000/asa310012014en.pdf

15. Amnesty International, Nepal: The search for justice (Index: ASA 31/001/2013), p15 (Online) Available at:https://www2.ohchr.org/english/bodies/hrc/docs/ngos/AI_Nepal_HRC108.pdf

16. Fitchett JR, Bhatta S, Sherpa TY, Malla BS, A Fitchett EJ, Samen A, Kristensen S. Non-surgical interventions for pelvic organ prolapse in rural Nepal: a prospective monitoring and evaluation study. JRSM Open. 2015;6(12):2054270415608117. doi: 10.1177/2054270415608117.

17. Dangal G. Utero-vaginal prolapse in Nepal: gravity and challenges. Lancet Jan 2008. (Online) Available at: https://www.researchgate.net/publication/260796512_Utero-vaginal_Prolapse_in_Nepal_Gravity_and_Challenges

18. Rai OA. Government lowers uterine prolapse treatment target. Republica, Jan 2010. (Online) Available at: http:/www.myrepublica.com/.portal/index.php?action=news_details&news_id=515

19. MacLennan AH, Taylor AW, Wilson DH, Wilson D. The prevalence of pelvic floor disorders and their relationship to gender, age, parity and mode of delivery. BROG 107(12)December 2000:1460–1470 DOI: 10.1111/j.1471-0528.2000.tb11669

20. Nepal Demographic annd Health Survey (2006) Population Division, Ministry of Helath and Population, Government of Nepal, Kathmandu, Nepal.

21. Ghetti C, Skoczylas LC, Oliphant SS, Nikolajski C, Lowder JL. The emotional burden of pelvic organ prolapse in women seeking treatment: a qualitative study. Female Pelvic Med Re. 2015;21(6):332-338. doi:10.1097/SPV.0000000000000190.

22. Omics International. Pelvic Organ Prolapse (Online) Available at: https://www.omicsonline.org/poland/pelvic-organ-prolapse-peer-reviewed-pdf-ppt-articles/

23. Bonetti T R, Erpelding A, Pathak L R. Listening to the 'felt needs': investigating genital prolapsed in Western Nepal. Reprod Health Matter12 2004; 23:166-175

24. A Reproductive. Morbidity Report on Clinic-Based Survey: Status of Reprod. Morbidities in Nepal 76 (2006). Institute of Medicine Tribhuvan University. (Online) Available at: http:/www.advocacynet.org/modules/fck/upload/file/upa/Status%200f%20Morbidities%20in%20Nepal_august%202%202006_UN.doc

25. Budhathoki, S.S., Shrestha, G., Bhattachan, M. et al. Latrine coverage and its utilisation in a rural village of Eastern Nepal: a community-based cross-sectional study BMC Res Notes (2017) 10: 209. https://doi.org/10.1186/s13104-017-2539-3

26. Ministry of Health and Population (MOHP) Nepal. Nepal demographic and health survey 2011. Kathmandu; 2012. (Online) Available at: https://dhsprogram.com/pubs/pdf/FR257/FR257[13April2012].pdf

27. UNICEF: Without toilets, childhood is even riskier due to malnutrition. Nov 2015. (Online) Available at: https://www.unicef.org/media/media_86283.html

28. McMichael, C. Toilet Talk: Eliminating open defecation and improved sanitation in Nepal. Medical Anthropology. Cross-Cultural Studies in Health and Illness. Volume 37, 2018 - Issue 4. pp: 294-310

29. Zutt J. Nepal aims to be 'open defecation free'. The World Bank Dec 2013. (Online) Available at: http://blogs.worldbank.org/endpovertyinsouthasia/nepal-aims-be-open-defecation-free

30. Stout JH. Myths-Dreams-Symbols. The importance of myth. Sept 2018 (Online) Available at: http://mythsdreamssymbols.com/importanceofmyth.html

31. Australian Charities and Not-for-profits Commission. (Online) Available at: https://www.acnc.gov.au/

32. Gurung G, Rana A, Amatya A, Bista KD, Joshi AB, Sayami J. Pelvic organ prolapse in rural Nepalese women of reproductive age groups: what makes it so common? N.J.Obstet.Gynaecol 2007;2(2):35-41.

33. Ravindran TK, Savitri R, Bhavani A (1999) Women's experiences of utero-vaginal prolapse: a qualitative study from Tamil Nadu, India. In: Berer M, Sundari TK (eds) Safe motherhood initiatives: critical issues. Blackwell Science, Oxford, pp 166–172

34. Aryl TR. Age at menarche. Differentials and determinants. J Nepal Med Assoc 2004; 43: 1-5.

35. Sunuwar L, Saha CG, Anupa KC, and Dhungel KU. Age at menarche of subpopulation of Nepalese girls. Nepal Med Coll J 2010:12(3):1883-6.

36. UNFPA, Health related qualtity of life of women suffering from pelvic organ prolapse. 2013. p. 20 (Online) Available at: https://nepal.unfpa.org/sites/default/files/pub-pdf/UNFPA-QualityBook-Final-ALL.pdf

37. UNFPA Nepal. Study on selected reproductive health morbidities among women attending reproductive health camps in Nepal 2016. (Online) Available at: https://nepal.unfpa.org/sites/default/files/pub-pdf/RH%20Morbidity%20study_0.pdf

38. Child Marriage in Nepal. Research Report 2102. World Vision International Nepal. (Online) Available at: https://www.wvi.org/sites/default/files/Child%20Marriage%20in%20Nepal-%20Report.pdf

39. WHO (2008). Why is giving special attention to adolescent important for achieving Millennium Development Goal? Fact sheet. (Online). Available at: http://aecid.lac.unfpa.org/webdav/site/AECID/shared/files/Adolescent%20pr egnancy%20fact%20sheet.pdf

References

40. Human Rights Watch. (2016) "Our time to sing and pray" (Online) Available at: https://www.hrw.org/sites/default/files/report_pdf/nepal0816_web.pdf

41. *Sharma, A.* Reasons why no rush to end child marriage in Nepal with history. (Undated) (Online) Available at: http://www.imnepal.com/child-marriage-nepal/

42. Girls not Brides Nepal. (2017) (Online) Available at: https://www.girlsnotbrides.org/child-marriage/nepal/

43. Nepal Multiple Indicator Cluster Survey 2014. UNICEF (Online) Available at: http://unicef.org.np/uploads/files/597341286609672028-final-report-nmics-2014-english.pdf

44. 44. World Health Organization (2016). Nepal sexual and reproductive health. Adolescent contraceptive use. (Online) Available at: http://apps.who.int/iris/bitstream/10665/252419/1/WHO-RHR-16.64-eng.pdf?ua=1

45. Early pregnancy in Nepal: barriers and facilitator factors for its prevention. Restless development 2015 (Online) Available at: http://restlessdevelopment.org/file/early-pregnancy-in-nepal-barriers-and-facilitator-factors-for-its-prevention-pdf

46. Sharma AK, Verma K, Khatri S, Annan AT. Determinants of pregnancy in adolescents in Nepal. Indian J Paediatr 2002;69(1):19-22.

47. Nepal: The hidden costs of early marriage. Safe World for Women (undated) (online). Available at: http://www.asafeworldforwomen.org/about/403-asia/nepal/2686-nepal-hidden-costs-of-early-marriage.html

48. Percynska A. Nepali Times 11 - 24 October 2013 #677. Let's talk about girls. Nepal has laws that prohibit child marriages, but not the enforcement mechanisms. (Online) Available at: http://archive.nepalitimes.com/article/nation/nation-child-marriage-young-brides,829

49. Sapana P and Others v. Prime Minister & Council of Ministers and Others, decision no. 7659, N.K.P 2063, Vol 3 at 289 (2006).

50. Adolescent girls' access to secondary education in rural Nepal. Working Paper 2012. (Online) Available at: https://www.brookings.edu/wp-content/uploads/2012/06/adolescent-girls-access-to-secondary-education-in-rural-nepal.pdf

51. Shrestha S. Socio-cultural factors influencing adolescent pregnancy in rural Nepal. Int J Adolesc Med Health. 2002 Apr-Jun;14(2):101-9.

52. Teenage Pregnancies: Growing Challenge. New Spotlight Magazine. Vol 7. Jan 12 2017 (Online) Available at: www.spotlightnepal.com/News/.../Teenage-Pregnancies-Growing-Challenge

53. Slater JJ. Teen Life in Asia. (Online) Available at: http://www.ios.sinica.edu.tw/ios/people/personal/wupaper/2004e1.pdf

54. Nepal. Department of Health Services (2011). Annual Report. Ministry of Health and Population, Government of Nepal. (Online) Available at:

http://www.bibalex.org/Search4Dev/files/428878/455706.pdf

55. Tripathi M, Sherchan A. Outcome of teenage pregnancy. J Univ College of Medical Sciences. 2014; 12 (2) issue 6.

56. Shrestha S. Socio-cultural factors influencing adolescent pregnancy in rural Nepal. Int J Adolescent Medicine & Health. 2002;14:101-109.

57. WHO (2008). Why is giving special attention to adolescent important for achieving Millennium Development Goal? Fact sheet. [Online]. Available at: http://aecid.lac.unfpa.org/webdav/site/AECID/shared/files/Adolescent%20pregnancy%20fact%20sheet.pdf

58. Gubhaju BB. Adolescent reproductive health in Asia. Asia –Pacific Population Journal. 2002;17(4). (Online). Available at: http://www.iussp.org/Bangkok2002/S30Gubhaju.pdf

59. Birech J. 2013 Child Health: A cultural Health Phenomenon International Journal on Humanities and Social Science. Vol 3. No.17 University of Nairobi.

60. United Nations Department of Economic and Social Affairs. Population Division. (Online) Available at: http://www.un.org/en/development/desa/population/theme/rights/

61. Pokharel S, Kulozycki A, Shaky, S. School-based sex education in western Nepal: uncomfortable for both teachers and students. Reprod Health Matter 2006;14(28):151-161.

62. Reproductive Health Education Projects for Adolescents in School (RHEPAS) (2009). (online). Available at: www.youthfornepal.org/system/files/rhepasreport.doc

63. School Textbooks, Grades 6-9. Text on file with Amnesty International Nepal. (Online) Available at: https://www.amnesty.org/download/Documents/8000/asa310012014en.pdf

64. WHO (2007). Adolescent Health Fact Sheet Nepal. Adolescent health and Development (AHD) Unit, Department of Family and Community Health, Regional Office for South East Asia. World Health House. India. (Online) Available at: http://apps.searo.who.int/PDS_DOCS/B0419.pdf?ua=1

65. Jha AK, Shah RK. Our Environment, Health, and Population Class X 4th ed. Kathmandu: Ekta Books 2008.

67. Department of Health Service, Annual Report 2010/2011. Ministry of Health and Population, pp. 86-88.

68. Osotimehin B (New SpotLight News Magazine Sunday, January 08, 2017 (Online) Available at: http://www.spotlightnepal.com/News/Article/Teenage-Pregnancies-Growing-Challenge

69. International Center for research on Women 2013. Asia child marriage initiative: summary of research from Bangladesh, India and Nepal. (Online) Available at: https://www.icrw.org/publications/asia-child-marriage-initiative-summary-of-research-findings-in-bangladesh-india-and-nepal/

70. Marshall E and Jones N. 2012 Charting the future: Empowering girls to prevent early pregnancy. Overseas Development Institute UK. (Online) Available at: https://www.popline.org/node/564101

71. UNICEF, State of the World's Children, 2016. A fair chance for every child (Online) Available at: https://www.unicef.org/publications/files/UNICEF_SOWC_2016.pdf

72. Narang S. Snapshot: behind the walls of Nepal's women. PRI's The World. Aug 14, 2013. (Online) Available at: https://www.pri.org/stories/2013-08-14/snapshot-behind-walls-nepals-women

73. Food and Agriculture Organization of the United Nations

Rome, 2011. (Online) Available at: http://www.fao.org/docrep/013/i2050e/i2050e.pdf

74. Norlha. Background research on gender issues in Nepal. June 2015 (Online) Available at: http://norlha.org/wp-content/uploads/2015/04/Background_Research_on_Gender_Issues_in_Nepal_Norlha_June_2015.pdf

75. Palm S. The value of sustainable protocol to address uterine prolapse in Nepal: health camp, awareness, and employment strategy. Eighth Annual Himalayan Policy Research Conference (HPRC 2013) (Online) Available at: https://static1.squarespace.com/static/52a626cfe4b0e076e263cf7c/t/52c5b3dbe-4b0dfd4db4a5f1a/1388688347663/The+Value+of+Sustainable+Protocol+to+Address+Uteri+Prolapse+in+Nepal+%281%29.pdf

76. Paudel L N, ter Meulen U, Wollny C, Dahal H and Gauly M Gender aspects in livestock farming: pertinent issues for sustainable livestock development in Nepal. Livestock Research for Rural Development. 2009;21 (40) (Online) Available at: http://www.lrrd.org/lrrd21/3/paud21040.htm

77. World Bank Group. Gender and Food Security. Module 1. (Online) Available at: http://siteresources.worldbank.org/INTGENAGRLIVSOUBOOK/Resources/Module1.pdf

78. Mahat, I. Rural energy planning and policies in Nepal: gender perspectives. J Res En Dev 2004;1(1):19-41.

79. Simkhada B, Porter MA, van Teijlingen ER. The role of mothers-in-law in antenatal care decision-making in Nepal: a qualitative study. BMC Pregnancy and Childbirth 2010;10 (1):1.

80. Shrestha AD, Lakhey B, Sharma J, Singh M, Shrestha B, Singh S. Prevalence of uterine prolapse amongst gynecology OPD patients in Tribhuvan University Teaching Hospital in Nepal and its socio-cultural determinants. Safe Motherhood Network Federation, (SMNF) Beyond Beijing Committee (BBC) Tribhnuvan University Teaching Hospital (TUTH). (Online) Available at:

http://www.who.int/woman_child_accountability/ierg/reports/2012_18N_UPResearch_study_Nepal.pdf

81. Safe Motherhood Network Federation , Beyond Beijing Committee , Tribhuvan UniversityTeaching Hospital (2009) Prevalence of Uterine Prolapse Amongst Gynecology OPD Patients in Tribhuvan University Teaching Hospital in Nepal and its Socio-cultural Determinants.

82. Bodner-Adler B, Shrivastava C, Bodner K. Risk factors for uterine prolapse in Nepal. Int Urogynecol J Pelvic Floor Dysfunct 2007;18:1343–1346.

83. Nepal Energy Situation - energypedia.info. (Online) Available at: https://energypedia.info/wiki/Nepal_Energy_Situation

84. Ekantipur.com editorial (2013, 9/4) Better than Cure (Online) Available at: ekantipur.com/2013/09/04/editorial/better-than-cure/377483.html

85. Strategies to increase facility-based skilled birth attendance in South Asia: a literature review Int. Health 2012 doi: 10.1093/inthealth/ihs001 First published online: December 19, 2012

86. Borghi, T Ensor, BD Neupane et al. Coping with the burden of the costs of maternal health. 2004 At: < Bang AT, Reddy HM, Deshmukh MD, Baitule SB, Bang RA. Neonatal and infant mortality in the ten years (1993 to 2003) of the Gadchiroli field trial: effect of home-based neonatal care. J Perinatol 2005;25 Suppl 1:S92–S107 http://www.sciencedirect.com.wwwproxy0.library.unsw.edu.au/science?_ob=RedirectURL&_method=externObjLink&_locator=url&_issn=09688080&_origin=article&_zone=art_page&_plusSign=%2B&_targetURL=http%253A%252F%252Fwww.nsmp.org%252Fpublications_reports%252Fdocuments%252FCopingwiththeBurdonoftheCostsofMaternalCare.pdf13

87. Sharma S, van Teijlingen ER, M. Belizán JM, Hundley V, Simkhada P, Sicuri E. Measuring what works: an impact evaluation of women's groups on maternal health uptake in rural Nepal. PLOS Published: May 23, 2016 (Online) Available at: http://dx.doi.org/10.1371/journal.pone.0155144

88. Witter S, Khadka S, Nath H, Tiwari S. The national free delivery policy in Nepal: early evidence of its effects on health facilities. Aama Program of Nepal | Dimensions of Public Health. (Online) Available at: https://academic.oup.com/heapol/article/26/suppl_2/ii84/643333/The-national-free-delivery-policy-in-Nepal-early

89. Lagarde M, Haines A, Palmer N. Conditional cash transfers for improving uptake of health interventions in low and middle income countries: a systematic review. JAMA 2007; 298(16):1900–10.

90. Elmushara K, Byrne E, O'Donovan D. BMC Public Health. 2015; 15: 870. Strategies to increase demand for maternal health services in resource-limited settings: challenges to be addressed. doi: 10.1186/s12889-015-2222-3 PMCID: PMC4562346

91. Gyawali K, Paneru DP, Jnawali B, Jnawali K. Knowledge and practices on maternal health care among mothers: A Cross sectional study from rural areas of mid-western development region Nepal. J Scien Soc 2013;40(1):9.

92. Bohara, M. S. Sexually Transmitted Infection among Migrant People and Their Wives in Far Western Nepal. Am J Epidemiol Infect Dis. 2014 2(1), 24-28.

93. When the safety of Nepali migrant workers fails. International Labour Organisation, 2016. (Online) Available at: http://www.ilo.org/wcmsp5/groups/public/---asia/---ro-bangkok/---ilo-kathmandu/documents/publication/wcms_493777.pdf

94. Aryal N, Regmi PR, Van Teijlingen E et al. Injury and mortality in young Nepalese migrant workers: a call for public health action. Asia Pac J Public Health 2016; 28: 703–5.

95. Bam, K, Thapa, R, Newman, M. S, Bhatt, LP. and Bhatta SK. Sexual behavior and condom use among seasonal Dalit migrant laborers to India from Far West, Nepal: a qualitative study. 2013PloS one, 8(9), e74903.

96. Rana MS, Nepali B, Sathian B, Aryal RP, Thapalia M, Bhatta DR. The socio-demographic characteristics of the clients of female sex workers and their perspectives, behaviours and attitude on HIV and AIDS: A Questionnaire based survey from Pokhara, Nepal. J Clin Diag Res 2013;7(1):112-117. doi:10.7860/JCDR/2012/4391.2683.

97. Bohara MS. Sexually transmitted infection among migrant people and their wives in Far Western Nepal. Am J Epid Inf Dis 2014;1:24-28

98. Poudel KC, Okumura J, Sherchand JB, Jimba M, Murakami I. and Wakai S. Mumbai disease in far western Nepal: HIV infection and syphilis among male migrant-returnees and non-migrants. Trop Med Int Health 2013;8:933–939. doi:10.1046/j.1365-3156.2003.01110.x

99. Bam K, Thapa R, Newman MS, Bhatt LP, Bhatta SK. Sexual behavior and condom use among seasonal Dalit migrant laborers to India from Far West Nepal: a qualitative study. Tang JW, ed. PLoS ONE. 2013;8(9):e74903. doi:10.1371/journal.pone.0074903.

100. Population Council (2011) Migration and HIV in India. (Online) Available at: http://www.popcouncil.org/pdfs/2011HIV_IndiaHIVandMigrationReport.pdf

101. Smith-Estelle A, Gruskin S. Vulnerability to HIV/STIs among rural women from migrant communities in Nepal: A health and human rights framework. Reprod Health Matter 2003;11(22): 142-151.10.1016/S0968-8080(03)02292-4 PubMed: 14708405 [PubMed]

102. Care (2004) A pilot initiative on understanding people living with HIV/AIDS and exploring the ways forward for their support in Nepal. Care Nepal. Nepal: Kathmandu.

103. Mahato PK, Bi P, Burgess T. Voluntary counseling and testing (VCT) services and its role in HIV/AIDS prevention and management in Nepal. South East Asia J Pub Health 2013; 3(1): 10-16 DOI: http://dx.doi.org/10.3329/seajph.v3i1.17705.

104. Global information and education on HIV and AIDS. Avert, August 2017. (Online) Available at: https://www.avert.org/professionals/hiv-social-issues/stigma-discrimination.

105. Vaidya NK, Wu J. HIV epidemic in Far-Western Nepal: effect of seasonal labor migration to India. BMC Public Health. 2011;11:310. doi:10.1186/1471-2458-11-310.

106. WHO statement on HIV testing services. WHO, UNAIDS highlight new opportunities and ongoing challenges. 28 August 2017. (Online) Available at: http://www.who.int/hiv/topics/vct/hts-new-opportunities/en/

107. San Francisco AIDS Foundation, 2017. HIV Info. Is there a cure for HIV or AIDS? (Online) Available at: http://www.sfaf.org/hiv-info/basics/is-there-a-cure-for-hiv-aids.html

108. Samji, H, Cescon, A, Hogg, RS et al. Closing the gap: increases in life expectancy among treated HIV-positive individuals in the United States and Canada. PLoS One. 2013 (Online) Available at: https://journals.plos.org/plosone/article?id=10.1371/journal.pone.0081355

109. Australian Federation of AIDS Organisations. (Online) Available at: https://www.afao.org.au/about-hiv

110. Cohen, MS, Ying, QC, McCauley M, Gamble T, Hosseinipour MC, Kumarasamy N, et al. Antiretroviral therapy for the prevention of HIV-1 transmission. N Engl J Med 2016; 375:830-839. DOI: 10.1056/NEJMoa1600693.

111. UNAIDS Facts Sheet. July 2017. (Online) Available at: http://www.unaids.org/sites/default/files/media_asset/UNAIDS_FactSheet_en.pdf

112. UNAIDS Global HIV and AIDS statistics – fact sheet 2018. (Online) Available at: http://www.unaids.org/en/resources/fact-sheet

113. Thapa S, Bista N, Hannes K, Buve A, Vermandere M & Mathei C. Vulnerability of wives of Nepalese labor migrants to HIV infection: integrating quantitative and qualitative evidence. Women Health 2016; 56(7):745-66. DOI: 10.1080/03630242.2015.1118726. Available at: http://dx.doi.org/10.1080/03630242.2015.1118726

114. HIV/AIDS Country Progress Report Nepal 2017. Government of Nepal Ministry of Health National Centre for AIDS and STD Control. (Online) Available at: http://www.aidsdatahub.org/sites/default/files/publication/Nepal_2018_countryreport.pdf

115. Brown L, Macintyre K, Trujillo L. Interventions to reduce HIV/AIDS stigma: what have we learned? AIDS Educ Prev. 2003 Feb;15(1):49-69

116. Paudel T, Singh N, Raj Banjara M, et al. Epidemiology of HIV, programmatic progress and gaps in last 10 years in Nepal. J Virus Erad 2016;2(Suppl 4):35-40.

117. Pellowski JA. Barriers to care for rural people living with HIV: a review of domestic research and health care models. J Assoc Nurses AIDS Care. 2013;24(5):422–37. PubMed Central PMCID: PMCPMC3640620. pmid:23352771

118. Young, S. D. & Bendavid, E. (2010). The relationship between HIV testing, stigma, and health service usage. AIDS Care, 22, 373–80. doi:10.1080/09540120903193666.

119. Poudel AN, Newlands D, Simkhada P. The economic burden of HIV/AIDS on individuals and households in Nepal: a quantitative study. BMC Health Services Research BMC series 201717:76. (Online) Available at: https://doi.org/10.1186/s12913-017-1976-y

120. Poudel KC, Jimba M, Okumura J, Joshi AB, Wakai S. Migrants' risky sexual behaviours in India and at home in far western Nepal. Trop Med Int Health. 2004;9(8):897-903.

121. Subba T. Women's vulnerability to HIV risk: decision making on condom use among migrant spouses. Master's thesis, Public Health School of Medicine Faculty of Health Sciences University of Eastern Finland April 2017. Available at: http://epublications.uef.fi/pub/urn_nbn_fi_uef-20171010/urn_nbn_fi_uef-20171010.pdf

122. N Aryal et al. Knowing is Not Enough: Migrant Workers' Spouses Vulnerability to HIV, SAARC Journal of Tuberculosis, Lung Diseases and HIV/AIDS (2017). DOI: 10.3126/saarctb.v13i1.16 23

123. Tiemessen CT, Kuhn L. Immune pathogenesis of pediatric HIV-1 infection. Current HIV/AIDS reports. 2006;3(1):13-19.

124. HIV/AIDS in developing countries. Government of Canada activities and initiatives. 8th June 2017 (Online) Available at: http://international.gc.ca/world-monde/issues_development-enjeux_developpement/global_health-sante_mondiale/hiv_aids-vih_sida.aspx?lang=eng

125. Strasser R, Kam SM, Regalado SM. Rural Health care access and policy in developing countries. Annu Rev Publ Health 2016;37:395–412. (Online) Available at: http://www.annualreviews.org/doi/pdf/10.1146/annurev-publhealth-032315-021507

126. Campbell J, Dussault G, Buchan J, Pozo-Martin F, Guerra Arias M, et al. 2013. A universal truth: no health without a workforce. Geneva: WHO, Glob. Health Workforce Alliance. (Online) Available at: http://www.who.int/workforcealliance/knowledge/resources/GHWA-a_universal_truth_report.pdf

126. Health Profile Nepal. United States Agency for International Development (March 2008). (Online) Available at: https://www.usaid.gov/our_work/global_health/aids/Countries/ane/nepal_profile.pdf

127. Zimmerman, M., Shakya, R., Pokhrel, B. M., Eyal, N., Rijal, B. P., Shrestha, R. N., & Sayami, A. Medical students' characteristics as predictors of career practice location: retrospective cohort study tracking graduates of Nepal's first medical college. BMJ;2012;345: e4826.

128. Patan Academy of Health Sciences (2017) Information Brochure (Online) Available at: http://www.pahs.edu.np/about/about-nepal/

129. Hayes BW, Shakya R. Career choices and what influences Nepali medical students and young doctors: a cross-sectional study. Human Resources for Health. 2013;11:5. doi:10.1186/1478-4491-11-5.

130. Nepal Ministry of Health and Population. Nepal Health Sector Programme – Implementation Plan II, 2010–15. Kathmandu, Nepal: Government of Nepal; 2010.

131. The World Health Report. Primary Health Care – Now More Than Ever. Geneva: WHO; 2008. (Online) Available at: http://www.who.int/whr/2008/en/

132. Al-Shamsi M. Addressing the physicians' shortage in developing countries by accelerating and reforming the medical education: Is it possible? Journal of Advances in Medical Education & Professionalism 2017;5(4):210-9.

133. Increasing Access to Health Workers in Remote and Rural Areas Through Improved Retention: Global Policy Recommendations. Geneva: World Health Organization; 2010. (Online) Available at: https://www.ncbi.nlm.nih.gov/books/NBK138618/

134. Krahe L, Mccoll A, Pallant J, Cunningham C, DeWitt D. A multi-university study of which factors medical students consider when deciding to attend a rural clinical school in Australia. Rural Remote Health 2010;10:1477. (Online) Available at: www.rrh.org.au/journal/article/1477

135. Spencer RJ, Cardin AJ, Ranmuthugala G, Sommers GT, Solarsh B. Influences on medical students' decisions to study at a rural clinical school. Aust J Rural Health 2008;16(5): 262-8.

136. Kirk RM, Mansfield AO, Cochrane JPS. Preface in: Kirk RM, Ribbans WJ, editors. Clinical Surgery in General. 4th ed New York, NY: Churchill Livingstone; 1999: p.v.

137. Wired for Sound: Engineering and Technologies in Sonic Cultures ed Paul D. Greene PD, Porcello T. pp211- 17. Wesleyan University Press, Middletown, Connecticut. 2004.

138. Marahatta K et al. Suicide burden and prevention in Nepal: the need for a national strategy. WHO South-East Asia Journal of Public Health | April 2017 | 6(1). (Online) Available at: www.searo.who.int/publications/journals/seajph/issues/seajphv6n1p45.pdf?ua=1

139. Portelli MS, Tenni B, Kounnavong S, Chanthivilay P. Barriers to and facilitators of adherence to antiretroviral therapy among people living with HIV in Lao PDR: a qualitative study. Asia Pac J Public Health. 2015; 27(2):NP778-88.

140. Tarakeshwar N, Srikrishnan AK, Johnson S, Vasu C, Solomon S, Merson M, et al. A social cognitive model of health for HIV-positive adults receiving care in India. AIDS Behav 2007;11(3):491–504.

141. Ware NC, Wyatt MA, Tugenberg T. Social relationships, stigma and adherence to antiretroviral therapy for HIV/AIDS. AIDS Care 2006;18(8):904–10.

142. Rai, B. (2018). HIV and AIDS: related stigma and discrimination in Nepal. (Online) Available at: https://www.researchgate.net/publication/254892309_HIV_and_AIDS_related_stigma_and_discrimination_in_Nepal

143. The importance of social ties in sustaining medication adherence in resource-limited settings. Tsai AC, Bangsberg DR J Gen Intern Med. 2011;26(12):1391-3.

144. Bangsberg DR, Deeks SG. Spending more to save more: interventions to promote adherence. Ann Intern Med. 2010; 152(1):54-6; W-13.

145. Kadariya S, Aro AR. Chaupadi practice in Nepal – analysis of ethical aspects. Dovepress, 2015. DOI https://doi.org/10.2147/MB.S83825

146. UNHR Office of the High Commissioner for Human Rights. Field Bulletin: Chaupadi in the Far-West. United Nations Resident and Humanitarian Coordinator's Office; 2011. (Online) Available from: http://www.ohchr.org/Documents/Issues/Water/ContributionsStigma/others/field_bulletin_-_issue1_april_2011_-_chaupadi_in_far-west.pdf

147. Amgain B. Social Dimension of Chhaupadi System: A Study from Achham District, Far West Nepal. Nepal: Social Inclusion Research Fund (SIRF) SNV Nepal; 2012.

148. Gaelstel A. The New York Times; 2013. Women in Nepal suffer monthly ostracization. (Online) Available at: http://pulitzercenter.org/reporting/nepal-achham-women-chaupadi-menstruation-ostracize-goth-tradition-hindu-rape-violence-segregation

149. PHASE Worldwide [homepage on the Internet]. Chhaupadi: Giving birth in the cow shed; 2013. (Online) Available at: https://phaseworldwide.wordpress.com/2013/10/05/chhaupadi-giving-birth-in-the-cow-shed/

150. Sauve C. 2014. The red huts of Nepal. (Online) Available at: http://mindthis.ca/red-huts-nepal-isolation-due-menstruation/

151. Koirala A, Banskota HK, Khadka BR: Cross border interception – A strategy of prevention of trafficking women from Nepal. Int Conf AIDS :15. 2004, Jul 11–16.

152. Trafficking in girls with special reference to prostitution. United Nations International labour Organization, 2001. (Online) Available at: www.ilo.org/ipec/Informationresources/WCMS_IPEC_PUB_2379/.../index.htm

153. Lama TP, Khatry SK, Katz J, LeClerq SC, Mullany LC. Illness recognition, decision-making, and care-seeking for maternal and newborn complications: a qualitative study in Sarlahi District, Nepal. Journal of Health, Population, and Nutrition. 2017;36(Suppl 1):45. doi:10.1186/s41043-017-0123-z.

154. Bhattar ai S, Par ajuli SB, Rayamajhi RB, P audel IS, J ha N. Clinical Health Seeking Behavior and Utilization of Health Care Services in Eastern Hilly Region of Nepal. JCMS Nepal 2015;11(2):8-16.

155. Address at the WHO Congress on Traditional Medicine. By Dr Margaret Chan, Director-General of the World Health Organization. (Online) Available at: http://www.who.int/dg/speeches/2008/20081107/en/

CPSIA information can be obtained
at www.ICGtesting.com
Printed in the USA
JSHW022039030919
1337JS00006B/7